About the Author: J. Boles, FGA, FRGS

Jules Boles grew up on England's Jurassic Coast and began geology classes aged eight, later gaining the FGA diploma in gemmology. In 1976 he presented evidence of serious faults in nuclear power plants to the Windscale Inquiry into nuclear reprocessing in Cumbria, England. Visiting 60 countries while working in the gem trade for 35 years, he became Director of the British Gemmological Institute (BGI), now Britain's oldest gem research laboratory. He specialises in valuing rare items, and developed a more reliable diamond standard with the BGI Precision Grading System to prevent fraud, and for use in valuations for Lloyds of London insurers. He invented the first patented electronic *Global Anti-Fraud System*, and became a Fellow of the Royal Geographical Society. He set up the BGI molecular analysis unit and founded the BGI's *Department of Earth & Space Science*, reassessing spacetime theories.

Front cover: This cover shows the time cycle with the 'eye of wisdom' symbol, and the descent from a calm world to the current chaos as time moves round each quarter like a clock. Symbol©

Published in association with:

The British Gemmological Institute (BGI),
Department of Earth & Space Science,
London, England.

First Edition 2018

ISBN 978-1-9997120-9-9

FLASH TIME
The Discovery & Meaning of Cyclic Time

JULES BOLES

To each reader...
for considering
the evidence
for cyclic time

Contents

Introduction and Preface

*Do you not know, my son, with how little wisdom the
world is governed?*
COUNT OXENSTIERNA, 1826, letter to his son

An amazing situation has arisen: the greatest ideas in science are impossible. An entire story has been constructed without real evidence. From human history to the existence of earth, the linear answers are failing, precisely because they are linear. *Flash Time* charts the way this view was literally forced into being by this astonishing evidence. It has never been disproved. These new answers form a new world view. Cyclic time seems to be the huge shift in thinking needed to reach the ultimate goal in science: to explain what we see. Cyclic time appears uniquely able to achieve this necessity.

What you are about to read here challenges the usual beliefs, yet will seem entirely obvious to others: a cycle of events that move round like seasons. This flatly disagrees with current thinking, yet it explains how time exists at all, which Einstein called 'the great mystery'. Put simply, only a cycle seems to work as a solution.

If so, it would mean every major idea in current thinking is incorrect, and that researchers have misunderstood reality and life's 'origins'. This is very good news: instead of the dark ending experts predict, it would mean an age of calm is emerging. A cycle would therefore mean an end to the depression some feel, since no such ending occurs.

Science created some very clever inventions, but when experts make mistakes, they often do so on a cosmic scale. Yet there would be little to discuss without the research of science. The need is to separate the solid science from the items of speculation that have crept into mainstream thinking. Time as a cycle seems to work, but it means unpicking 120 years of the most advanced research in history. Could so much theory and experiment be entirely mistaken? It can, yet even finding out is not easy.

The old answers had to be re-checked. Clear errors were found. Here is a quick outline of why current theories need such a total re-think.

As a firm believer in the standard Big Bang world view, finding major errors was a shock. The expanding universe and so much more looked right, yet the fact the galaxies are speeding up remained a problem. It seemed unthinkable that such long accepted research could be flawed; although actually we should *expect* thinking to change. The aim was clear and simple: to prove the 'line of time' obviously right, being so well accepted... piece of cake.

Yet the old 'facts' just did not add up, so the focus fell on the deepest layer: our notion of time itself. Even so, the old prejudices of those 120 years were deeply embedded, so my conditioned mind still began with the 'certainty' that time *must be a long line* as science claimed, and feeling convinced it would be so obvious as to be hardly worth checking. It should be easy, because 2,200 years of tested thinkers could surely not be so deeply mistaken. Or could they?

A day of careful thinking would be plenty, followed by a return to normal life. All the famous thinkers in history *could hardly all be wrong*.

Reality would be spectacularly different. That day became two years, and still cyclic time could not be dented. Four decades later, it still hasn't. The emerging cyclic model defied all attempts to demolish it. Not only could Time not be proven linear, but all the sciences truly had chosen some basic assumptions, *and then taken them as fact*. The logic was flawed, as we will see. The old timeline had no concrete substance.

It felt very bizarre to find mainstream science could have chosen a huge error as its keystone. Yet in each field, including the real giants of human knowledge like geology, astronomy and physics, the old presumptions just refused to stack up at all. Pick any one, and try it. Not a single linear concept stands without a layer of assumptions. As any first year philosophy student knows, presumption is the very definition of uncertainty.

Could science be that mistaken? The idea seemed so unlikely...

Decades of study rolled by, and it became clearer Time just could never be a line as in Big Bang theory. Linear time was indeed heavily laden with such assumptions, which are famously unreliable in science, because they are unable to 'prove' anything.

Instead of being easy to prove wrong, time as a line was literally impossible to prove right; it is possible others might see this research and agree.

If this was true, it would be a revolution. It would mean the whole of science is not only wrong about Time being linear, but about every other idea based upon this foundational concept. This would take in nearly every major theory in science, from earth's origins to well beyond Evolution. The word 'shock' barely describes this realisation, since the radiogenic dating of volcanic rocks would be in error too. This being apparent, it was soon clear the 'cycle revolution' has more factual support than Big Bang.

A cycle is staggeringly different, and the one thing scientists do not expect to find over breakfast is such a shock that their cornflakes end up on the ceiling.

Could the age of earth be misunderstood?

If time is a cycle of events, any 'clock' should 're-set' at regular intervals. It would mean the billions of years claimed for each phase of earth and space history were incorrect. Could there really be such a 'million year myth'? The evidence shows just this.

How could all those generations of earlier scientists be mistaken? The chances of such a large scale error had to be between tiny and zero, or so I thought. Yet it is wrong to dismiss the very idea of a large error being possible. Any answer has to be proved, especially the ones we think seem obvious. They often hide giant errors. As the evidence amounted to 1000's of compelling points against a line of time, it was time to consider the 'impossible' may be true. One way or the other, it had to be resolved.

If so, we would all be needing a new world view.

Where would such change leave us?

The full implications were worrying, with much of modern science based on this pivotal notion of a line; could there really be no substance at all to its major claims?

No scientist would want to say that, unless it appeared true. Yet the question had to be asked, and resolved. Even using great prejudice against a cycle, the old linear version was failing, so I had to admit it may be wrong. Having checked so very carefully, it was still the cyclic time answer that fitted.

The current answers to the very origins of life on earth were also now in question. Such hallowed research ground is treated as sacred by many scientists, who literally cannot imagine any other explanation, in any shape or form at all. Yet those older certainties were produced without this volume of data supporting a cycle. It could also mean there was insufficient time for Darwinian evolution to happen, so that too would have to be reassessed. Could all this implied need for a huge revolution be correct?

Still convinced it must be my fault in some way, I pressed on.

Still sure the usual scientific view had to be right, largely because 99% of all scientists are hardly likely to misinterpret Time itself, the search was on to find my own error. As this hunt researched the key fields of science, it became clear there were serious problems in each one: they could not actually be proven correct, and believe me, I tried very hard to do so. In place of firm facts at the core, I found only misfitting assumptions. Yet were they correctly thought out? Even a supposition may be right by chance, so they all had to be resolved.

Years of fact-checking in 132 fields later, the line theory still could not be proved, so a new world view was required. Where to find one? One obvious answer was to check the current ideas, remove the failures, and then get one's head around a new idea: that whatever was left would compose the only logical world view in sight. Unpicking these concepts all the way back to pre-history, the old presumptions were falling apart, one by one. What was left after this sieving process is here in essence, ready for judging.

Signs of a cycle

A wonderful synchronicity arose from that process. Far from being a giant basket of separate pieces that made no sense, literally every finding slotted into this short period cycle like the parts of a giant clock.

Anyone can try this with instant success. Take any question or strange fact of life or the universe, and try placing it in a cyclic context of time. It will fit. One initial success was the enigma of the curious Easter Island head statues, usually linked to Peru. Yet why did they have the topknot of stone placed above the head? The answer was in the Brahman symbol that had existed before, in ancient India, despite it being so far away. The iconography was unmistakable, as we will see. Ancient human thinking was also a useful source that may offer ideas about a cycle, so over 65 cultures were included.

In space there are clues too. Take Dark Matter, that invented material that cannot be found, needed to explain why 85% of gravity force is 'missing' when searched for. In a cycle it is not missing, because the facts all point to a very recent 're-set' of this cosmic clock, after which the cosmos all makes sense as it is, with no need to invent any hidden matter at all. A simple cycle solves all these issues.

Could Big Bang be a mistake?

In a word, yes; the evidence shows the whole linear edifice of thinking had never worked even slightly. Yet in earlier days it looked so obvious that time was a line.

In those days, they hatched up a world view that looked valid and real to a tiny band of thinkers, but then so did dragons, unicorns and witches. It turns out linear time is completely impossible, unless someone can re-write the laws of Physics and Chemistry.

Until this happens, Big Bang theory is over forever. Yet few have considered if this could be so. If Time is a circle, then linear time has been the single biggest error in the whole of human history. It forced science into inventing a hugely long past story that never existed, purely because people could not imagine how it was continuous, or that Nature had a system...a cyclic event sequence. That would explain why the fossil record is far beyond being merely incomplete: it shows a short cycle.

Have millions of years passed by in a line?

The old choice had been between science or creation, leaving many to go with science. What we missed was the evidence of a third option of a continuum. That seemed too weird to comprehend, so time was extended back as far as anyone needed. No one minded much that deep mysteries remained, because it seemed to beat creation. Few realised that the universe could still be infinitely old, and yet a cyclic process as well.

A million year myth had been invented in science, since if Time were a constant factor with space, then there would be no 'start', but only identical cycles. Time could then be infinite in length, with any figure placed on its 'length' being too short. 13 billion years old? Try forever, and a world with no start or end.

Now the challenge is to 'think the unthinkable'.

We will explore the Munchausen 'trilemma' effect on this, showing total proof is almost impossible. Modern science does not meet these standards in many cases, and we should be amazed at what has been accepted as real. Even Darwin said the fossil record lacked the proof his theory needed, so *this* evidence for a cycle appears to be why it was never found.

No one ever linked a cycle of time to Darwin's theory, or to the dating methods used since 1900 to support it. When we do, they do not offer the support expected. The problems in geology are so serious that the entire timescale has been mistakenly taken to be sequential. Solid facts recently found in space show it cannot be so. The trilobites appear in different eras in various parts of the world, and there are countless other problems examined here that show the errors in the linear time concept. The nine Cambrian to Cretaceous eras are just a construct based on dating methods that never worked.

The evidence collected here shows all those supposed eras can logically fit into 1600 years or less, and no one can prove it is not so. Such a claim remains unthinkable to many in science, yet it is the only conclusion that fits these new facts.

In their biggest things in particular, scientists can be deeply mistaken. At this level, the answers really are made up. The great shock was to learn that science is often not the pristine, objective method of deriving truth as claimed, for the simple reason we may try to prove the unprovable because we favour that idea, and accept our own findings. This process is a famous source of trouble in science, because tedious facts so often ruin a lovely idea.

Strong opinions are a real problem in science. The views about evolution are an example. There are a few 'ultra-Darwinists', as they are called, who have already decided firmly that Darwin's 1859 idea, shared with Wallace, is 'fact' and will always be so, no matter what anyone learns. Fixed views reject change, so that is not science. If it was, we would still think the cosmos revolves around the earth, as in the Ptolemaic system, which Copernicus showed it does not. Even the Church had to switch to that idea.

In science, certainty shuts out development. This book attempts to set all the old bias aside, and start with a fresh sheet of paper or *carte blanche*. Every scientist is taught never to be so rigid, but to allow the evidence to teach us things, and to be flexible forever. We promised ourselves as students we always would be. In theory we try to do this, yet rarely can because we love a certainty, even if we have to invent one.

What we all should want most is true answers that work, but even scientists admit they do not have them; therefore our ideas must currently be deeply wrong. How wrong? More than most of us care to admit.

Now we might agree how a cycle of time turns everything into a coherent cosmos once again. Most pleasantly, it shows how the present extremes of chaos would soon change into the order we all expect to see each day.

This study shows we appear to have inherited a mistake so huge it takes some effort even to see. This book is written for any reader, and the expert, to understand how this mistake arose, and what can replace it. If correct, the outcome is all good, because it means the universe would never 'end' in a fiery disaster...good news if correct.

It is vital to know what reality is, or some efforts in life would be for no purpose.

Another unexpected and fascinating find emerged during this quest for reality... a 'Super Grid' of energy; evidence shows even we human beings are not just a part of it, but a key influence within it, showing that even thoughts affect the delicate balance of order in Nature. None of these details have been combined before, and now we can appreciate that belief is not needed, because the evidence is clear enough.

This cyclic way of seeing the world resolves these issues. Sure, it disagrees with nearly every major theory about earth and space, but it also solves the problems. Since no one can prove it wrong, it can be correct.

This book explains how this new cyclic world view works, and how some consequently earth-shattering results also have to be true, however uncomfortable and inconvenient they may be.

Chief among these is how we saw the earth. Sure, the earth is old all right, but in the rush to put a figure on it, it was never thought possible that *the infinity of space and time* was an answer that worked...not billions of years in a long line, but a series of repeating cycles in which the same sequence of events repeats again into infinity.

The long 'line' could never answer its own key question: what happened before the beginning? Clearly we cannot create spacetime from nothing, so the only remaining option is a continuous process of decay and renewal. This is why biology never found a missing link between man and ape, why bone marrow collagen DNA in an American T-Rex dinosaur was found unfossilised in Montana, in 2005, by Dr Schweitzer of N.Carolina State University. This would be impossible if time were a long line, so the dating methods had to be re-checked from scratch. Faults were found, and they were serious and systemic. The chief error was in assuming time was a long line, and then using that framework to squeeze in all the answers. Even now, this has not been realised.

Are rock ages measured correctly?

Looking yet again at geology, a daring idea was slowly realised as feasible: that the usual 2 mm per year 'standard deposition rate' assumed for many sediments could be a huge error. It can actually be true that earth's axial changes could have been so much faster than we realised, and that strata could therefore be far younger. The cycle began to fit geology.

Some events could happen in months, with a shift in earth's axis.

Even the claimed 540 million years of the fossil record could be accounted for in a matter of millennia, if Time were a cycle. Millions of years were simply not needed, and had been taken as real for lack of a better explanation. Instead, the surface geology can indeed have been re-worked in a series of truly vast 'Overturns', where huge areas of the original supercontinent [Pangea] were churned up and redistributed.

Blake Outer Ridge, as we shall see, is a classic example of this. Yet if this were true, there would be a marked lack of transitional forms for each species. Surprise surprise, this is exactly what we see. Sure, it means a total re-think, yet it solves these puzzles.

If dinosaurs had really lived for 100 million years or so, there should be literally *trillions of fossils* to find, yet only 653 have been found. The old presumption that they had not been preserved may simply be untrue. This is highly controversial to some thinkers, but it had to be checked, and the results showed they may never have existed.

Today's thinking has gone on so long, that many accept the old ideas as truth.

We may be forgiven for thinking Science knows what it is doing in all this, but in fact many disagree with each other for good reason. Everyone agrees Pangea once existed as the old 'supercontinent' an age ago, yet even Pangea's time span is not agreed, with some experts thinking it existed from the beginning of continental formation, while others think it lasted only from the Permian to the Triassic, a difference of about a billion years.

A billion years is a lot to invent, and then lose. Something was not right.

The real history is disputed, and thus not known for sure. This shows that even a whole vast continent can get lost in conflicting theories, because the evidence is not clear what happened. It all depends on interpretation, so the classic zonal idea of a fossil fixing the age of a rock bed can be a crucial error. The Flash Time cycle resolves all this.

To understand why, we need to put the chair down, sit on it, and think carefully for ourselves about what may be the answer. Most of us have never thought afresh about earth science, even those who make it their profession, because it takes over 20 years to revise these theories, and so ironically no one has time, nor funding to do that.

The problem to solve is this. Current thinking relies on assumptions. They have all failed over the last 60 years, but to see why, we would need to absorb all the new finds from 30 separate fields at least, to form a better version. No one is paid to do that.

Seeing all this is one thing, but letting go of the past was quite another. Instead of accepting the findings, the obvious reaction took hold: to reject it as my own error, and restore my worldview to 'normal' by proving Science was right. Hiding under that reaction was the awareness that we could all be in error.[1]

Shocked by this realisation, the aim was to prove cyclic time wrong, not wishing to suggest Planck, Einstein, Hubble, Hawking, Hutton, Holmes, and even Darwin, were all incorrect to treat time as linear.

After some years, it was clear the old science had failed. Cyclic time did offer a valid alternative after all, if a strange one to Western thinking. Here is just the essence of 3000 pages of that research, so we can all decide for ourselves.

Such huge upsets in science are not new, and even Newton was accused of sending science back to the Dark Ages when he published *Principia* in 1687. Not because his work was incorrect, but because it was just so weirdly different, none of his contemporaries could get their heads around it, or even work out how to handle it.

Even one doctorate may not help to study this, since no-one can have 30 PhD's to cover every subject. It might not help even if they had, because each field already accepts time as linear, thus retaining the same framework or bubble with which to view the world. Thus even the highest levels of academic training can so cement old views in the researcher's mind, that original thinking may then be more difficult, not less.

Should we question old ideas?

Even with all the knowledge in the world, there is no guarantee of reaching the right conclusion of what it means, because we still have to interpret the data, and that needs objectivity, which is hard to come by. One Italian scholar was so appalled by the rigidity of the philosophy he was taught at university that he spent years trying to forget it.

The challenge is open to anyone to write a proof that Time cannot be cyclic, without using linear time as 'accepted fact'. So far, no-one has.

1 Actually only a small number of people accept linear time, and many never believed it at all.

This partial analysis of such huge fields of study will never be enough, but perhaps others will improve on the material.

The author also accepts an immense debt of gratitude to the countless workers who have devoted their lives to their own fields, and produced so much excellent information. Some may think science is only focused on central heating and ways to destroy the world, but we know different, and there is much in medicine that is deeply positive. We have science to thank for all the new data, and must treat all scientists, as all people, with great respect and kindness. If there were never people to see the world differently, and present their work for the critical assessment of their peers, then science and general understanding would never have progressed as far they have.

We have to question an assumption, and see it as tentative, as Sir Karl Popper wrote.

It is therefore no negative comment on their superb body of work to draw different conclusions to those of the great pioneers, in fact quite the opposite. If it was not for their combined epochs of such intense study and candle-burning in the pursuit of better understanding, we would have nothing to work with.

Darwin withheld his key work for many years, before being forced into print by Wallace reaching the same conclusions. It is never easy to see years of work countering the conclusions of others, but we must never lose sight of the whole aim of science itself, which is to find the *correct* answers. This may lead us into areas we dislike for some reason, but go we must if our research is to have any value.

What would be the value of holding onto an idea if it were not actually true? When Velikovsky came up with his catastrophism thesis in the 1950's, the attempts to discredit his work are now seen as mistaken decisions. In fact he was right in many ways, yet science felt threatened as a body, so even Asimov was wheeled out, saying that a 'heretic' could be 'deprived of access to the learned journals', and that the 'questioning process' should not be carried out in public.[2]

---

2 *Scientists Confront Velikovsky*, Norton, 1977, pp7-12.

This must amaze us. Should we dare to question the ideas of science thinking? As Dame S.J.Bell Burnell often says, we must if we find reasons to do so.[3]

To call anything a 'fact beyond question' is to forget what science is for, and how it works. Nothing is beyond question, and this is how science began, and how it had the authority to call into question some of the dogmatic statements of religion, which had never been done before, at least not without losing one's life. Velikovsky should have been allowed to question old ideas.

In a way, we all help in this, by too easily accepting what we are told, and life continues. This book is set out in three parts, each chapter opening with the concepts in essence, and ending with greater detail. Any unusual words are defined or re-defined in the glossary or word list, so that literally anyone can read it without any formal training. Just Google any odd words, via Wikipedia often, to make it clearer still.

Here is that new evidence for discussion.

* * *

Having read the book, the reader has a chance to alter the way the world sees Time and our place within it, and your view is valuable. Please cast your vote on **www.Ftim.tv**, and thank you for doing so. It may be time for the reader to change the future.

* * *

Suggestion for reading this book: being written for both experts and interested individuals, each reader will have different interests. The essence of each chapter outlines the substance of the Flash Time world view, so the reader may like to absorb enough to suit and move on to the key final chapters that complete this cyclic world view.

Thanks are also due to the many kind friends and specialists who have helped in many ways towards realising this lengthy task, including the 42 test readers who helpfully commented on the text, and also

3 In 1967 A.Hewish & Dame S.J.Bell discovered pulsars, a key discovery.

to the team at Oxford Designers and Illustrators for their care with the artwork.

[*Student Caution* for text and Glossary: many of these definitions are agreed in textbooks, yet some points are not, and far too controversial to write in any exam, and *many examiners would fail a student who does*. Science can take years for new thinking to be accepted, so do not risk a failure; first one must 'pass' an exam before using these new concepts.]

PART I

Major Myths
about Time

Can a New World View make us happier?

Maybe everything that dies...some day comes back.
BRUCE SPRINGSTEEN, 1984

Life is not just to be alive, but to be well.
MARTIAL, 85AD

The answer is yes, a world view can make us happier. If this one is correct, the future looks very bright indeed. Yet current thinking sees the universe as a place of random events with lots of chaos and no heart, due to end one day. That is hardly encouraging, so many ignore that vision anyway, and live their lives in a happier frame of mind entirely. Which is right? The evidence shows this 'dark future' is a fable created by assuming time is a line, and based on old ideas that were never true.

Many of us would like to know the answer with more certainty than this, and so let's take a look around the world, and see if there is a viable alternative. It seems there is, and it fits the world we actually see: a continuum which never actually ends. Just as there cannot be a start date for matter to 'jump into existence', nor would there be an ending if time is a cycle.

It is astounding to find that the technical version has run off the rails of reason.

A happier vision is all very well, but it has to be real to have meaning. The current mechanical view of the world, and even spacetime, is too restricted to work. It no long has meaning because it fails to take in the latest information set out here. This lack of speedy adjustment has even created a technical vision of reality that fails to pass even the basic laws of physics, so it needs radical change. The old view declares darkness when actually the answer is filled with light.

A small change in thinking would be enough to put this right very easily.

Is it really necessary to see darkness when that may be a mistake? If it is, we all need to know urgently, and to check what can replace the old ideas. As it turns out, the bright future wins because the darkness ran out of all its evidence.

This is the story of how that unlikely result came to be published, and some facts that back it. As Dr Johnson said in 1757: 'The end of writing is to enable the readers better to enjoy life, or better to endure it'.

We all aim for improving the world, and it is nice when research supports a dazzling future, and may replace an earlier version.

As we bounce along the road of life, we often pause to wonder what is really going on, and if the education we received told us the real answers. The old thinking developed over the centuries has become accepted. The pioneers' view is used, but is it right?

Odd as it may seem, the feeling of insecurity about that many of us have shared at times may stem in large measure from the world view we hold, and science has blocked the mental exit from that dilemma by declaring any other view to be invalid and untenable. It turns out, as we shall see, this narrow vision of life on earth can itself be the invalid option, because it relies on theory, not fact.

If time is a cycle, this would be a reason for great happiness, because it would mean the universe does not end in darkness as claimed, but in a continuum that always turns out well, no matter what.

Many who have studied these issues have come to realise there are huge contradictions and unsolved mysteries sitting in libraries, and a big one is how we come to be here at all. At school they teach students this is well known and long solved, period. Later studies show this is not true at all, and more advanced reading shows up a serious flaw that has never gone away, which goes like this: the universe never had a start date, but moves in a constant cycle, not a line at all.

If this is true, then the 'line' of time would be the greatest error in all of human history. Strangely enough, we also have science to thank for a pathway out of that error, by revealing the mistake it has made, albeit unknowingly.

Here is the curious thing about modern theories of time...they can look impressive with computer simulations, but when we dig a bit deeper, the claims of certainty dissolve into more theory. We, as people of earth, have an expectation of rather more than this for a world view. After all, our lives are on the line with this journey between life and death, so it must help if we knew what we were here for. Is there a deeper meaning, and is earth's future any happier and more positive than we were told? Can we find out? Clearly science is not equipped to answer that, but we can at least start by checking the old story of science, and seeing if there are any new answers learned since the days of Lemaitre, Einstein and Bohr, when the current view was born, and set sail with many of us on board.

Over that century of searching, some really major finds have been made, but the top experts realise they taught us little, because they disagreed with the expected results they wanted to see. Over time, the situation just got worse, as the scientists slowly began to realise they had gone down a road that led nowhere, because it was a wrong turn. Yet no one could quite work out which part held the mistake, and still have not found it.

The real question to check was about Time itself. Could it be a line as so many thought? Logic tells us that is impossible, because matter cannot spring out of nowhere, so that leaves time as a constant, existing always; later, the famous thinker Prof. Roger Penrose suggested this answer in his 2005 book 'Cycles of Time'. That seemed more likely, because it did not rely on a parallel universe popping out of nowhere, and the cycle element could not be disproved.

In terms of happiness, this would be good news indeed, because it offers a better fit to the facts. A circle may be logical, but is it true in reality? We need to check.

For us as people, this is very interesting indeed, because if we have chosen the wrong option in taking time as a line, then it could indeed be a cycle. If it is, this would be the biggest news in history, but as yet there are no newsflashes about discovering reasons to be happier, so perhaps we can look forward to that. If time is a circle, this would happen. Let's look at the options and weigh the details carefully.

As Charles Dickens once wrote in Great Expectations: 'Take nothing on appearance, and take everything on the evidence.' When we look at all this afresh, it seems the very opposite of how we took the world to work turns out to be the case. Why has no one proposed an exactly repeating cycle before? Our ancestors simply never imagined nature could be so uniquely strange as to run such a system. They never had the mass of details we have now, and the line of time later became so deeply accepted that no one thought to check this foundation of our thinking.

It is time we did, because we seem to have chosen an idea that cannot explain any of the problems it tries to solve. If so, this really is good news, because a continuum means we would be meeting again long into the future…to infinity indeed.

CHAPTER I

Flash Time: the Concept

*The pendulum of the mind oscillates between sense and nonsense,
not between right and wrong.*
CARL G.JUNG, 1960, psychoanalyst

*I've not so much invented something, as successfully found
10,000 ways it will not work.*
THOMAS EDISON, light bulb inventor

Essence

Welcome to an entirely new world view, and some sample evidence
to test it. If it is true, then nearly every major concept in cosmology
would be incorrect, and many a date in science may have been wrongly
calculated using a mistaken timescale.

Time seems to be a circle of events. Both in earth's rocks, and in the
microwaves of space, amazingly, there appears to be proof this is the
case. The big ideas in science would then be incorrect. A 'spiral' cycle
has been suggested before, but dismissed as unlikely. A great deal has
been learned since then. So much so, indeed, that no other scenario
looks as remotely promising as the uniquely curious concept of a true
cycle, meaning one that repeats exactly. It has proved impossible to
disprove.

One reassuring point in its favour is that it disagrees with nearly
every major idea ever suggested. Some may think this a distinct disadvantage, but that would be an obvious mistake to make in assessing
world views.

As Sir Karl Popper pointed out in 1959: '*In order that a new theory
should constitute a discovery or step forward...it should contradict
its predecessor...in this sense progress in science, or at least striking
progress, is always revolutionary*'. Whatever research discovers, we
should stand by it.

An exact cycle can appear unlikely, but only in 'old thinking'. For many experts in cosmology a cycle may seem impossible, yet it is viable…if we accept some of our old favourite ideas are entirely mistaken. That is not an easy switch for the mind to make, with so many of the most famous names in recent history all seeing time as the exact opposite…a straight line with a start date. Yet when we peer closely at the tangle of notions of the current world view in science, that accepted 'line' of time has all the hallmarks of a flat out impossibility.

When we look at the evidence afresh, we see a huge mass of pointers showing this same pattern of cyclic time. This can be a little disturbing to those who have already fully accepted the line as Reality, and gone on to other things. Yet back to it we must come, because those famous thinkers do indeed appear to have made a small error, and it slipped past their radar all too easily.

How could Einstein and all those pioneers be wrong about something so obvious as time being a line, we may ask? That is just the point right there…it looked too obvious to any human being with a lifespan of 65 years to be anything else. They just ploughed ahead with the line of time, and used it work out everything else, never realising it would not fit into any of the latest findings about space and even the geology of good old planet earth.

What is wrong with that? A great deal. Everything we can see, and much we cannot see, moves in a circle. Many already see time as a seasonal process of order and chaos, after which Order is restored once again. Actually this is not a new idea at all, but the single oldest one we have ever used. When we look back into history, literally all the ancient cultures thought of life in this cyclic way. Modern thinkers knew that, but in the intellectual climate of the Renaissance, and generally 2–300 years ago, it was the fashion to reject old ideas, and create fresh set, which must be, they reckoned, much smarter than any old ones could possibly be. That was the second mistake. In fact the details we now see show clearly that time not only can be cyclic, but must be, for many reasons. Scholars in every age and every country have written about time being orbital, but there is a twist to the story. Even the Stone Age peoples of pre-history, who did not read or write, all drew disc symbols of time with no other meaning we can suggest. This is a pivotal and new find, because there is a secret hidden in their disc symbols, which is this. Those same identical signs are found on rock and cave walls all over the globe.

What does this mean? It turns out to be deeply significant. These cultures lived in pre-history, long before global transport of any kind. There were no ships with which to meet over 3000 years ago, so how did they draw the same symbols, never having met? The only answer that works is one that demands a new world view. Those people had met before, but in the previous cycle of time before this one. This gave them a deeper memory of time that recognised this natural process of spacetime rotating. Since it answered all their questions, as it does for us today if we use it, they painted and carved those shapes before any others. It thus became the central and most prominent feature in all their art, jewellery and sculpture, all around the world, with no apparent reason...besides this one.

From this widespread global detail of ancient life, previously unseen and unrecognised, it can be inferred this round symbol of the cycle, and associated shapes, represented the single most important aspect of their lives, both spiritually and culturally. It explained their vision of life's patterns, and it is very curious that modern science supports that view; a point yet to be accepted by Science in some quarters. For us in the Present era, this poses a riddle. How can we see time as a cycle when convention assumes it is a line? Quite simply, the line requires matter to be created, which is presently impossible. Much more likely is the concept that matter exists all the time, and events are ruled by cause and effect.

There are experts in this field who do regard time to be a cycle of events, because it is now widely recognised that matter does not pop into being. If nature is a cycle, can major cities like London and New York arise again in each successive cycle, as history repeats? The evidence agrees, and this would be very good news, because it means Life continues on, and we would all meet again each cycle, which is a much nicer prospect than the infinite darkness forecast by some thinkers. Either way, we need to know.

Could Einstein and Hawking really be mistaken about time?

As supporters of linear time, it seems they can. Time has long been presumed to be a line, stretching back in vast eons of successive years. Yet there is a problem with this human idea: the facts do not agree. This usual way to see Time clearly does not work, so what exactly went wrong with this old vision of time, and what could replace it? The answers point to a circle that changes like clockwork, from chaos to order. In a flash of time, order returns in a second. As we will see, it has to be this way, because nature has a plan of events, like the seasons in a year. We cannot ignore winter or spring, since each has its place.

Order begins the cycle, and chaos duly follows (see Fig. 1). When the chaos becomes unsustainable, there is a profound change and the universe begins again, hence the name 'Flash Time'. Nature works in cycles. Time too seems to work in this way, with events repeating in an *ideal sequence* that always turns out well, no matter what we do to disrupt it. This would mean Einstein and other Big Bang supporters would be mistaken.

If so, this requires a total re-think of what many took to be rock-solid certainty. Scientists like saying 'facts can change', but rarely reckon it would be any of their own. The Flash Time solution involves some exceptionally radical changes to what many think is 'normal and expected'. Much of science would need dramatic revision, since the big ideas all depend on Time as a line, but luckily there is excellent news hidden in such change. It turns out those areas of science were not as 'fact based' as assumed. This opens up a very interesting possibility: that events are not random or chance situations. If time moves in cycles, Life would have a different range of meanings.

To say this was unexpected is a huge understatement, and probably the greatest revolution in thinking in 2500 years. If so, the largest scale science seems to have been totally misunderstood. Time would then not be the line of billions of years some thought it was, but a cycle... repeating to infinity. If so, this would mean the old age calculations are a 'million year myth', and untrue. This fits the facts, but the old strongly held views are not easily set aside.

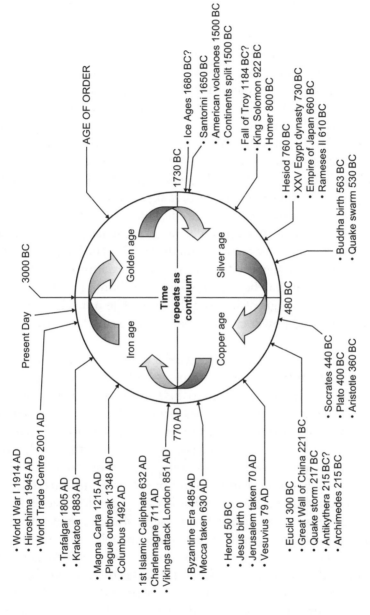

FIGURE 1 *Earth History in a Cycle of Time: short cycle allows all key events and the classic geological eras to occur within 950 years, not billions as claimed.*

Could the core of world thinking be profoundly incorrect? If so, Life itself takes on fresh meaning. Many already think so. No one has ever proved a cycle does not happen.

All of us wonder at some time what life is all about. It looks too crazy to have any pattern behind it, yet there is one. It can be summed up in one word: Rotation. Literally everything is rotating. Not just the obvious matter of the planets around the sun, but there are circles in every part of the earth and the universe. The seasons rotate, our lives rotate, and our daily pattern of sleep-eat-work-rest is also a circle. The oceans circulate in giant circles called gyres, as do the water, carbon and nitrogen cycles. As we walk along, air forms small eddies or vortices around the body's edges. Billowing white clouds can be seen with tips curving over like waves against the blue sky. This is not only impressive to observe, but it also mimics the circular nature of existence.

Life itself is cyclic, but more deeply so than science has realised, because measurement has to focus on the visible. The hidden quantum energy world is forcing scientists to realise there is more to the cyclic pattern of life than has been seen so far. We should not be fooled by its invisibility as a sign of its insignificance. The opposite is true. Its immense scale and power can now be shown to run the world in every detail.

As we will see, there is also strong evidence for the mind being a dot of energy that controls the sub-atomic world...and the larger atomic one we can see. The facts all point to this being true, with human minds holding the balance of power in this orbital dance of Nature. Therein lies a deep secret...the whole of time is a single connected system of events that revolve in a sequence. This is no whim of the mind, but an evidential conclusion we can all see and judge for ourselves.

Oddly enough, our decision to agree or disagree with this statement depends upon who we are, and what lives we have led. We all fit into different groups in our reaction to these profound issues, mainly as materialists or more spiritually orientated people, and whether we are open to new answers or not. We all think we are open as people, but reality tells another story. We prefer things the way we like them. Reality takes a clear second place to that primary wish. This study focuses on setting that old wish aside, with the sole aim of learning the way events actually proceed: the true situation.

Some think there is no truth, but that is not logical. Each large event has one way to exist, and is tied to the physical reality of other events. It has become the fashion to ask if a falling tree in a forest makes a sound if no one is there to hear it. Sound is a consequence of an event, so it would exist whether anyone is there to hear it or not. Anyone who has lived in an old house can hear it creek at night, and there cannot be any change in those sounds it makes, whether we are there or not. The 1908 Tunguska explosion in Russia made a noise so loud it was heard 2000 miles away, and luckily not many people were near the spot in Siberia where the asteroid struck.

As we consider what is real and what has been mistaken with good intentions, we can gradually and gently build a consensus. Bit by bit the image grows, so we can then judge if it is in order, or not, as we wish. If we disagree, it can be because we began with an earlier view we favour firmly, and then have to choose between the two. The key is in the way we perceive the actual world, and to what extent we allow others' theories to influence that perception; a choice often ruled by our wishes rather than facts.

Facts are not as obvious as we tend to think. Thanks to the great efforts of scientists and other thinkers, we can now examine this larger pool of human knowledge as never before. Surely Science could not be so spectacularly off beam as to get the wrong idea about the entire cosmos, could it?

Here is a new approach to this question, with new answers. This is how it works.

Life on earth looks simply obvious to a new generation, but then turns out to be far more complex than they realised. As every human knows, life can be very unpredictable. Even scientists don't know what the mind is, what dreams are, what consciousness is, how memory is even possible, and countless other aspects of human experience.

So what are the answers? To find out, we have to be prepared for some truly unexpected answers to be correct. We are creatures of habit, and often dislike changes to our daily routines, such as meals, let alone entire world views.

After centuries of careful research, many signs now show Time does indeed appear to be rotating. This would mean events are happening

again. We never guessed Time could have happened before, although
déjà vu experiences are common.[4] The Ancient Greeks and others
already knew about this answer, and decided it was true for various
reasons, such as logic. These brilliant thinkers included Socrates and
his pupil Plato, and his pupil Aristotle, who, between them, span an era
from 469–322 BC, and are still hailed as among the greatest philosophers in history, and some say they were the cleverest people to have
lived. There was also the great historian Herodotus, born c484 BC
and known as the father of history, who lived in that famous era.

They took cyclic time as *the chief concept* of all concepts, and with
wisdom.

Hesiod (c750–650 BC), who wrote that the 'the half is greater than
the whole', described cyclic time, and may have meant the first half of
cyclic time on earth when he wrote about a cyclic process of constant
change and renewal.

How else could the cosmos exist now, the Greeks deduced, unless it
was always in existence? Clever stuff, but it was based on the obvious
as well. They could see that objects did not burst into existence by
themselves, such as an apple pie appearing on a table just before lunch,
so it seemed equally unlikely to them that the planets or stars could
do so either. Rabbits and fridges do not tumble out of the sky without
reason, and cannot do so. Our own modern laws declare as much to
be clear fact, such as the Law of Conservation of Matter in Chemistry.
Things do not appear out of nowhere.

Yet here is a very odd thing: science makes a similar claim. We have
logical laws in science, where even gas is weighed and found to be conserved as expected, and yet Big Bang theory claims all this matter came
from another universe. That is conjecture, because there is no evidence
for it. Since the universe cannot appear out of nowhere, or a parallel
place, this is where current theories disagree with Science's own laws.

Science is not knowledge, but rather a study of what knowledge
might be. The mistake of today has been to accept theory as fact. Not
all that glitters is gold. Some ideas are pure fantasy, so let's check if
there is proof either way.

---

4 In an informal survey from 1978–2005 of well over 1400 people, only 2 had never
   had déjà vu (99.8%).

Seeing time as a cycle is the key concept. So far, no other concept can explain what we see. The existence of a cycle of events suggests the old 'line' of time cannot be true. This would mean the whole current concept and calculation of time would be mistaken, because time would never have been the same for a lengthy period. This claim would be a revolution, yet here is the weird thing about there being a 'continuum' that carries on forever...it is strongly supported by a mass of detailed evidence, so how come science never saw it? The answer is they did see it, but only a few gave it emphasis. No one looked at the cycle outside their own special field, let alone many fields.

The secret becomes more obviously seen when we look a little wider.

The simple existence of a cycle of time is clear within Nature as events move between extremes of calm and chaos, and then back again, constantly. The unexpected part is the pivotal role that we human beings may play in these cosmic scale events.

The key is to see the world in its simplest form: as constantly flowing energy. Calm always decays into chaos. All the complexity of what we see then becomes very simple. Gradually an initial period of calm gave way to increasing chaos as time progressed. Today we see that chaos approaching its maximum state, literally a 'Chaos peak'. This is entirely expected, and explains why we are witnessing changes that match the simple principle of Newton's third law, which explains that every action has an equal and opposite reaction. Our actions could be a pivotal factor affecting this state of disorder.

Fortunately for us, the calm period is always restored. When the current state of chaos reaches its peak, that brief loss of order automatically gives way to the calm of a new cycle. The chaos collapses.

Ancient Greeks like Hesiod described this initial calm period as a 'Golden Age at the beginning of time', when the cycle begins again. The chaotic period just before that, which we see present now, would then be the short period in which a decaying Iron Age gives way to an ordered Age of Gold. In this way there can be the 'start' of a new era, like the start of a new day, without having to make every atom afresh all over again (which no one can prove has happened anyway). In this way the world is altered, and then continues.

This concept originated in the more ancient cultures of India and Pakistan, from where DNA and language sciences show the Caucasian branch originated.[5] All those ancient cultures saw Time rather as we see the circular motion of a clock face, with each quarter being related to increasingly reactive metals. They named these Gold, Silver, Copper and Iron to reflect the growing chaos in each age, after the original age of gold, using the analogy of how severely each one oxidises, from zero decay in gold, to total rust in iron.

The oldest culture in the world, from the Indus Valley and Asia, still uses this same 'time disc' or 'swadarshanchakra' in their cultural cosmology. Interestingly, this word translates from Hindi to mean 'the disc to see the self', by which they mean a person may understand their position in a cycle of time and space...a kind of cosmic clock.

We may smile at these ancient distinctions, but they may correctly describe an underlying reality of how the cosmos is restored. Modern science has missed this point by claiming that the world begins with chaos, and then magically becomes so ordered that life forms. Yet this counters entropy, where chaos increases, as we will see.

Modern thermodynamics supports the ancient version, in particular via the second law about entropy. Energy spreads out and becomes chaotic as it degrades, not vice versa. This is why the energy used in boiling water cannot be re-focused to repeat the feat; it is also why claims of 'perpetual motion machines' cannot work, power being lost through friction and heat loss.

Those ancient thinkers in India and Greece were no fools. Indeed they were famously brilliant, and saw time as a constant. They saw how Nature worked in systems that rotated, and that time could be included in 'all that rotates', so their thinking flatly contradicted current thinking today. If they were alive today, they would still find Big Bang theory an impossible idea, because of one key reason: it is logically invalid. It retains a flaw or hole so huge, you could fit the whole galaxy into the hole sideways, and still have room left over for a few Lincoln Continental cars to be popped in as well. It is the same one we have just considered, which is the validity of our law that Matter can neither be created nor destroyed. It just exists. That may seem odd, but not half as odd as claiming that monsters (or matter) pop out of solid objects at random (Big Bang theory).

5 See New Scientist and other articles.

In a cycle, reckoned the ancients, matter just alters; problem solved.

Modern science often dismisses those ancient concerns, reckoning those ancient thinkers could not possibly be given the same credibility that modern physics and astronomy has earned. Yet it seems they should, because our 21st century research suggests the ancients were right. We will cover this later, but the 'Flatness' of space shows this, as do the Josephson Effects, in which Prof. Brian Josephson *et al.* showed how matter can act as one 'super-atom' when super-cooled. Modern thinkers simply never imagined how all these factors point to a cycle of time that repeats, but they may do so now.

Stranger still, every ancient culture around the globe had a version of this same cosmic clock face split into four sections. Some may see this concept as an amusing myth, but nature appears to use it in reality, and the physics agrees.[6] We will see how cyclic time is the only viable way in which these ancient cultures could share the same concept of events 'in rotation', without having met up to discuss it.

How did that happen? The answer is simple, if at first rather perplexing: there must have been an earlier age in which these principles did come to light, and were widely known and shared. When events turned into serious chaos with great loss of life, the memories returned too. In a cycle, it is easily understood as a memory of the last cycle. This explains how they drew the same symbols, never having met [See Fig 4]. Otherwise, that identical thinking and artwork would be an impossible coincidence.

Modern thinking also dismisses the role of people as an influence in all this change, but even that perception is changing nowadays. The interesting and highly significant factor in all this is our own role as human beings in this process. Far from being passive observers of all this chaos, it appears we are its direct architects, and we provide the causes for all these effects. This 'anthropic effect' may be at the hub of all nature, if each human mind is a point source of energy that is directly connected to the world of matter in which we live. So close is this connection, that our very thoughts affect our bodily health every second of our lives, and the atmosphere we sense as well.

---

6 Except in one key respect of how Time switches energy states, which we will cover later.

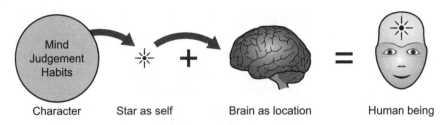

| Character | Star as self | Brain as location | Human being |

FIGURE 2 *Brain & Mind: diagram showing the mind or non-physical 'self' inside the brain yet distinct and separate from the body, explaining dreams, awareness and memories over lives.*

It is unusual to say so, but this human effect could work simultaneously at both the gross external level we can see with our eyes, and at the sub-atomic level of pure energy. We all know the phrase *'it's the thought that counts'*, but we never quite imagined how deeply this may be true. As we shall see, it is possible that human thought energy may drive events both on earth, and in space. This might seem speculative, but there is sound logic to support it, and even the physics, so it is plausible (Bell 1964).

Equally curiously, this mind-matter link is the frontier where science and simple sense can agree about issues once thought irreconcilable.

Science cannot explain human memory, or 1000 other skills of the mind that show the 'self' cannot be reduced to a lump of brain material. For 'point of energy', we can substitute the word 'mind', and it all begins to make sense. Déjà vu then becomes an intriguing insight into how human beings fit into time. We never even imagined that time's events could have happened before, exactly as they do now, and that now and then we can feel and see the identical way in which events repeat.

This is profoundly interesting, because it explains for the first time how life may actually work: a 'perfect sequence of events' that runs its course, and then begins once again, just as the ancient cultures all told us, but we ignored them.

Luckily for us, many superb discoveries in Science provide a wealth of clues to solve all these questions at last, and here is one which is a central key.

Atoms can act as a 'super atom'. When subatomic particles are super-cooled to far below sub-zero temperatures, they begin acting as *one unit*. This doesn't mean they then start to plot out how to take over the world, but they do something very strange indeed that is puzzling physicists: they act together in perfect unison. Push one, and they all move instantly at the same time in the same way, just like dancing dolls on a pole.

The conclusion we can draw from this is the most profound one we may ever draw: that the universe can and does act as one giant unit. If it can happen in one place, it may be possible in every place. Such 'unity of matter' can be seen in literally millions of examples in nature, in our own sports, in flocks of birds or shoals of fish that move as one wave. It works all the way up the size scale, from tiny cells of bacteria, or even electrons, right up to whole galaxies moving at around 830,000 kms an hour. It may all look random and chaotic, but that is an illusion we have imposed on the cosmos. All the effects listed here show just the opposite, which is very good news indeed, because they point to a return of all events to a period of complete order and calm, of which all our lives would also be a part, and help that to happen.

In this way, the calm era that begins each cycle would be like an unlimited form of Day, followed by an era of chaos or Night. We may not like this chaotic night of course, but it has to happen, so we are pleased to know that the day has to follow shortly, and last for millennia. Not only is this possible, but it appears to be what actually happens. This is why a cycle is such a big deal to understand, and check if the clues agree. In linear thinking, none of this positive outcome could ever happen, so we do need to know which version of reality is actually at work to affect us. Such a real process may explain why every ancient culture thought this way, and used the symbol of the four part disc to express such a supremely valuable concept.

This could really be the case, unknown to science, where Nature has a way of sorting out the mess we make, and restoring order so the cycle of good events can begin again. The real action is hidden in the sub-atomic levels, and it works by existing as a path for all energy to transfer, or balance out.

We may see this as a Super Grid, in which all matter is 'connected' all the time. The concept is simple. If something happens in one place, it would instantly affect the local area, and the entire cosmos.

The Poet Laureate William Wordsworth put this into words in

1795 when he wrote: '*In this universe, where the least things control the greatest, where the faintest breath can move a world*'. Combined human actions can indeed have truly vast effects, both at the obvious physical level, but also at the quantum level, as this research suggests.

Reason tells us this would apply to all energy, even to human thoughts, which we feel as force. This would disagree with Einstein's version of Relativity, in which he predicted nothing can cast an influence faster than light's speed, but that may be incorrect.

Now we can apply logic to explain the increasing chaos we see around us, both physically and in human minds. If chaos increases over time, as entropy tells us it has to, then if all particles are connected, there must be a 'cosmic effect' that permeates the entire cosmos, not just that local part where it happened.

When we consider this potential carefully, each life on earth may be far more significant than scientific thinking ever dared imagine. It may work like this: Put things 'right' on earth, even though tiny in physical atomic mass terms, and the entire 'body' of the cosmos, galaxies and all, could instantly alter as it follows suit. If the sub-atomic or 'quantum' world is as intricately connected as this research suggests it is, then there could be no other outcome to each event, but a constant state of change.

The good news is that the evidence also shows something else that defies modern science to explain, which is proof of a very recent reversal of this trend, whereby both matter and 'life' return to order, and continue once again as they did before. This 'perfect cycle of events' therefore contains one complete cycle, each one being based on the contents of the one before.

FIGURE 3 *Stonehenge: with main circle in original layout as disc for astronomy, also possible symbol of cyclic time.*

As the chaos returns, there is evidence of a huge axial shift of the earth, and global devastation on a barely imaginable scale. The Stone Age returns, and as the Fig 4 diagrams here show, the basic idea of such a cycle emerges in every culture that ever existed, despite being widely dispersed around the globe.

The sceptical reader may wonder if all this talk of a cycle had not just been invented, were it not for literally thousands of points that force us to consider the opposite conclusion. There really are countless physical items that seem to be explainable only by the existence of just such a cycle.

Oddly enough to some of us, such a cycle is already deep in our sub-conscious minds, and now and then it emerges by crossing that subtle and invisible gap between the sub-conscious and the conscious parts of our minds. Many know this from their own lives. Looking back into the thoughts many experienced in their childhood, some people see glimpses of a past cycle of time's events. As noted, there is the strange phenomenon of déjà vu: seeing a scene that appears to have happened before. This can indeed be a genuine experience of an earlier cycle, and subtle evidence that such a cycle exists, just as the ancients claimed. The cycle can also explain why the ancients focused so intently on their devotion rituals, believing that certain actions could influence the future outcome of events. In a cycle of events, they would be right to think this, since the nature of present actions would clearly cause either calm or chaos, just as we realise kindness truly helps.

This gave meaning to those rituals in the past, but it gradually faded from their awareness.

To understand this new thinking, we have to set aside all our earlier thinking that we inherited in our youth; no easy feat. Science and religion disagree about the age of the world... the evidence for a *Cycle* of Time solves all these issues, because we don't then have to invent a world that sprang into being one day, but instead see one that was always here, and just needed a few serious changes to restore order once again. The point where the chaos changes to calm would be the Flash Time zero moment, which would have been so powerful as to move continents; small wonder it is remembered even today, as all the ancient symbols of the disc appear to show [see Fig 4 diagrams].

The finding of young features is therefore very significant to our world view. They appear to disprove linear time.

FIGURE 4: Ancient Cyclic Time Symbols – *Group One*

01 Mayan
    400 AD

02 Celtic Cross,
    Europe 300 BC

03 Egypt Ankh
    1650 BC

04 Africa, Australia,
    Americas 1600 BC

05 Americas
    300 AD

06 Neanderthal,
    Gibraltar c1800 BC

07 Pictish, Scotland
    c600 BC

08 Chauvet, France,
    Neolithic/Stone
    Age

09 Americas, India,
    China, Europe,
    Egypt

10 Global, Ancient

11 Norway, China,
    Global

12 Global, Ancient

13 India, Hopi,
    Roman, Greece,
    Celtic 400 BC

14 Neolithic, Global

15 Celtic c1400 BC

FIGURE 4: <u>Ancient Cyclic Time Symbols – *Group Two*</u>

16 Hopi, Celtic
   CI300 BC

17 Japan, Far East

18 Pictish, Scotland
   c600 BC

19 Gavronis Isle,
   France, Neolithic

20 Callanish,
   Scotland, Neolithic

21 Orkney, Ness of
   Brodgar, Scotland
   1800 BC

22 Egypt 1350 BC

23 India, Europe,
   La Tene, 400 BC

24 Europe, Global
   500 BC

25 Japan, Europe
   450 BC

26 N America,
   S America, Europe,
   India 300 BC

27 Mexico, Olmec
   200 BC–300 AD

28 Pyramids: Egypt,
   Peru, Mayan
   CI650 BC–400 AD

29 Neolithic
   1600 BC

30 Neolithic, India,
   Europe, Hopi

FIGURE 4: <u>Ancient Cyclic Time Symbols – *Group Three*</u>

31 Neolithic, Global
1800 BC

32 Ireland, Neolithic
1600 BC

33 Ukraine, Neolithic
1600 BC

34 Ukraine,
Neolithic 1600 BC

35 Maes Howe,
Orkney c1800 BC

36 Pictish, Scotland
300 BC

37 France, Lascaux
Cave, Global

38 Scandinavia
1500 BC

39 Pitcairn, Pacific,
Greece, Global

40 Saxon, England
500 AD

41 Armenia
c1400 BC

42 Saxon, England
500 AD

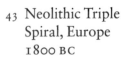

43 Neolithic Triple
Spiral, Europe
1800 BC

Are there young features that may alter our thinking?

Here are a few examples of apparent youth that point to a time cycle. The claim that humans have been living for 3 million years plus, is not credible from the size of our population alone, which in that case would be in the trillions. The current 7.5bn population of the Earth is achievable in 4950 years. Amazingly, it really is possible the experts are incorrect to suggest a 3 million year process for humanity: there just is not the evidence. The rings of the planet Saturn show clear signs of youth, particularly the F Ring; some of these rings are filled with constantly colliding ice crystals ranging in size from a few centimetres to the size of a house, and should therefore have been reduced to powder if their actual physical age were over 4 billion years as claimed. Simple collisions would have this effect, and there are small 'shepherd moons' that keep the particles in the collision zone. Scientists know this, and a long line of time cannot explain it.

Take the distant dwarf planet known as Haumea, located near the planet Neptune at 45 AU (1AU: 1 Astronomical Unit = the Earth to Sun distance), or 45 times the distance between planet Earth and our sun, which is about 2300kms in length, about 10 times more than first

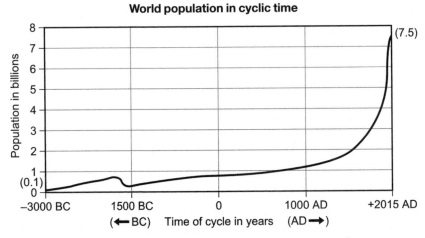

World population in cyclic time

FIGURE 5 *World Population: fitting into 4950 years with minimum of one million people; humanity never destroyed thus enabling continuum to continue in each cycle of time.*

thought[7]. Yet here is the really odd thing: Haumea is claimed to be over 1 billion years old, although it was recently found to have no dark surface dust, but a bright white layer of water ice crystals. This white surface had remained untouched by clouds of black and grey dust that exist in those distant regions, which is clearly impossible if it were truly that old, since it would be covered in dust.

Something must be wrong somewhere, and the most likely error in these age calculations can be traced to how we view Time itself: our very world view. These few examples, and nearly 2000 more found just like them, do clearly suggest the current theoretical version of linear time cannot conceivably function as claimed. They all show a lack of evidence for items being ancient. The proposed dates do not add up, and so the ages assigned to all these structures simply cannot be true. If Time cannot be a linear process, then spacetime may always have existed. This is both logical and reasonable since it instantly solves the problem of what happened before the Big Bang, as Sir Fred Hoyle (*Hoyle et al. 1948*) famously pointed out in the last century with Steady State theory.

This is a very pivotal point: it is quite clear that the galaxies are moving at high speed, but that is no firm guarantee that they formed in an unknown way 13.6 billion years ago as claimed. Even this apparently precise figure of 13.6 can be confusing, because it gives the impression of an exact calculation made with the authority of proof behind it. That is not the case, it seems. Actually even scientists change it constantly, and in 1979 it was given as 10 billion. Where did those 3600 million years come from? In fact it is deeply theoretical in both the concept and the maths, because it simply assumes time to be linear, using the red shift of stars, as we see later.

It is astonishing to find ideas can be so arbitrary, yet they can be.

In spite of all this disagreement among the different branches of science, few guessed that a concept as gigantic and basic as Time itself could ever be false; yet our interpretation of time is of course an artificial one, so it can indeed be misunderstood just like anything else.

When we sit down and analyse the core of all this information, a constantly existing universe keeps reappearing as a likely answer.

7 Nature 12 Oct 2017

This might sound like a bizarre idea, but the possibility of such vast errors is not as wild as it may seem. Even the maths can be entirely incorrect, simply because the equations rely entirely on time being a linear process as a point of fact. Assuming this to be true has created numerous unsolvable 'mysteries', and this may be why both physics and cosmology are in such crisis, and have been since the 1920's.

The solution is readily found when we broaden the horizons of study to include all the key fields, not just a few of them. When we broaden our scope in this way, the research quickly identifies these cyclic patterns which then become both obvious and well supported. We simply overlooked their importance and even existence by specialising in 2 or 3 subjects in great detail, rather than researching the links in 132 fields, as in this study. What produced the most useful results was a tight focus on just the age of items, to see if their 'ages' were justified, and clues of a cycle.

No university could consider funding that, hence the need for fresh research. The possibility of a precisely cyclic pattern within time had never been thought an option, and so was not checked.

Wherever we look in history, the signs of a cycle are there. Our ancestors presumed the cavemen eras were populated only by primitive semi-human beast-like creatures with no sense of culture that could be identified, such as the Neanderthals. This turned out to be completely incorrect, like so many earlier assumptions. The latest evidence shows those prehistoric cultures to have been highly intelligent, with undeniable proof of their art, use of medical plants, and ordered society, tool-making, religious thinking and artistic burial rites, and even brain surgery called *trepanation*[8], with a far better survival rate than modern medicine achieved in the 19th century, millennia later. These are powerful reasons that should change our thinking, but they have not yet done so for one reason: current thinking is still firmly fixed in the old linear timeframe.

The implications are indeed far reaching, but we have to resolve them, because if linear time fails as a concept we have invented, then the dating methods using it also become worthless.

Radioactive methods of dating rocks underpin the whole linear

---

8 The release of cranial blood pressure via a surgical incision in the skull.

concept of time, yet can be based on an error. This, as mentioned, has been clearly pointed out and brilliantly explained by Prof Claude Allègre, who reminds us that it is hardly wise to add analytical uncertainty to geological uncertainty and expect to produce an answer with any meaning. He also poignantly adds, that if key assumptions are uncertain, the results of the maths would be 'scientifically meaningless'.[9] He is right. This has to be one of the most important statements ever made in science, and a point that is repeatedly forgotten in the excitement of modern research: short cycles appear real.

Anyone in geology who has studied the Zanclean period of the Mediterranean Sea region knows it was once a giant dry salt pan which filled up in a matter of weeks when the Atlantic broke through the Straits of Gibraltar. No one has yet had any reason to think this giant and impressive event could have happened recently, as little as 3200 years before present indeed, and not 18 million years ago as claimed. Now we do. This claim that time can be working within short term cyclic periods requires us to do so, because it resolves so many puzzling observations.

Without getting too technical, we can put the idea in a nutshell. Cyclic time is easily explainable if matter acts as a flux of particles, with each one both sitting comfortably by itself, while at the same time being reliant on its neighbour as future motions play out. This works rather like a crowd at a football match which focuses on the movement of one object at the centre of play. When that one football moves in a special way, each person reacts accordingly.

This new finding in quantum physics unlocks a fresh vision of the cosmos as a place of high balance and precision. Even human actions, and thoughts, could be altering that delicate balance in a major way, while staying unseen.

This is very simple, because it means we can see all the matter in the universe as if it were part of a liquid known as a plasma or a Bose-Einstein condensate: a group of atoms has even been observed to behave in this way, like one 'super atom'. This can hold the secret to the motion of all particles, because it means the particles are not

9 Isotope Geology, Claude J Allègre, Cambridge University Press 2008, pp214–215 for further details.

behaving semi-randomly on their own, but are instead part of a coherent and connected whole. This forms the answer to everything, quite literally, because it shows that any powerful event in one place is instantly capable of influencing all particles in all locations. It would even happen without a time delay, making its speed much faster than light [It is possible time switches at this 'super luminal speed' at one moment, but more on this later.]

Could Time reach a peak and then switch in a second?

Thanks to the latest science, we now have this understanding as a viable answer. If the energy has no mass, the cycle becomes possible. Such a rapid shift in the spin of all the elements may only occur at the Flash Time zero moment, as the cycle begins again in a great renewal, but it is a new mechanism we did not see before that can work.

Such speed is presently thought to be impossible because of Einstein's work, but it can be predicted that quantum particles and states will be found to switch in this instantaneous way. There we have it. This may take some thinking about, but it shows how the universe is capable of complete alteration in a fraction of a second when conditions reach the correct, critical state to make this happen.

This can be how time repeats exactly.

In that one moment, when the level of chaos becomes so high it is unsustainable, the whole structure of space-time snaps back into its original state, known here as the 'Flash Time zero' moment. This would occur at the precise time it must take place, when the hands of the celestial clock come around once again to the same point, rather as terrestrial clock hands show midnight. Even people can act as the catalyst for this shift.

All this becomes very easy to understand when we think of all these features as part of a single energy flow, the parts of which act together within space time, and eventually snap back into their original place and role, rather as an elastic band resumes its earlier position, and then the same series of events can follow on from there. Weird as this may seem to some observers, all of it entirely matches what we see both on Earth and in space, and so it can work as a new world view.

As the reader will quickly realise, it seems to be the actual *question* of 'age' that is really at fault, rather than the methods of determining it. After all, if we assume Time is linear when it may not be, the methods could not overcome any error in that assumption. The methods would accept only the answers that 'fit' that notion.

It seems we asked the wrong question of 'how long is our timeline', instead of 'could it be cyclic?' We were never looking for these signs. Now we are looking for them, they are quite easily seen, if we set aside our ancestors' presumptions for a while.

The picture is certainly very different.

We all have to make up our own minds about these issues. Since there are some very major future events which are easily predicted using this data, and have not yet happened, but are bound to do so, it is surely very valuable to know about these trends in advance. If this analysis is correct, then such events of great force would be a necessity we have to live with before the start of the new cycle.

It is intriguing to realise that, even in the 21st century, such major scientific issues are still based on such human impressions as 'Time moving from A to B', and appear to have been incorrect for many centuries, 18 or more. Ancient cultures knew these basic cyclic principles, yet modern thinkers were predictably bound to assume that 'old knowledge' would only be incomplete without the 'brilliant new insights' of each fresh generation. That is an assumption which could prove mistaken. A new answer could change life on earth.

The suggestion here is a radical one: the current linear way we perceive Time itself, especially the pre-history of earth and life itself, appears wholly mistaken. It cannot simply be modified, as we have done over centuries, but needs replacing entirely.

We need a new 'theory of everything', and it appears only a cyclic solution is able to solve these problems and to be that theory. The day of the Line for Time seems to be well and truly over, but most of us are just starting to think about the cycle.

We have to dare to question the 'unquestionable'. Scientists have grown tired of dealing with doubters. Surely the whole point of science is to propose an hypothesis, and then rip it to pieces with experiment. We must never ignore questions and conflicting data.

It seems that linear time supporters have drawn the stumps too soon, since the game of discovering reality is not over. All the mysteries and puzzles outlined in every science journal printed clearly show we remain stumped by many things.

The disagreement about the age of earth and the stars has previously been a straight forward matter of opinion, mainly, and how the maths was done. Now we have some new evidence to check, and a reassessment of key assumptions. [See Fig 18 for Curved Earth photos]

This goes far beyond the quoting of any scientific, personal, cultural or religious references, however strongly felt. The answer is a shock, because there is no way round the central issue, which is this: the majority of what we have written down and decided is 'right' still rests squarely on the assumed passage of Time being a long line from a 'big bang'. This research shows that may be impossible.

Not many of us seem keen even to question the orthodox view of all this, perhaps from a degree of weariness after decades of such questioning.

The latest evidence from space changes all that, forever.

In our pursuit of science, there is a powerful subjective angle. This is why we often find what we are looking for, because we see what we want to see, and so the data we created and tabulated usually fits the framework we made for it. Weird results are treated as just that: weird, abnormal, and thus statistically of low value. This is how we can make a 'problem' go away, leaving the garden looking rosy, and just the way we want it to look. We like the parts that seem to fit, and set aside those that don't, quite naturally. They say maths does not lie, but it can.

As we shall see, some of the computer models can be complete deceptions. They use maths to 'try out' an idea that is a fabrication from the outset, by definition. These models do not use facts, because none are known, so *around 150 variables* are used. This is theoretical, not real. Dozens of such 'models' begin to create a new vision of truth, and can be completely false. Big Bang and String theories are such examples: widely accepted, and yet widely contradicted by observed fact, and unprovable. In no universe can that be called proven, so we need to revise our thinking to avoid bias.

This risk of bias is not a conscious intention of course, but an inevitable effect that is bound to occur via the 'special selection' of data that happens in any research. Any experiment has this element of choice, because it has to test a limited and narrow feature. We cannot test every option, so we choose what we judge 'likely', and that choice dictates the outcome. Even making that test at all, rather than others, is a form of discrimination or bias, because it favours one answer over others. It may be completely false, but if a number of experts in that field agree, it goes into university textbooks.

Wise scientists know very well that each idea is ever only 'the best option they can think of' at the time, because it is almost certain to be overturned one day. This is why so many 'obvious ideas' are indeed overturned, such as the flat earth, and the geocentric earth, despite strong beliefs even to this day.

If no-one else knows any better, having only one life of forty or so adult years in which to study all this, then into the textbooks goes that current version. Only decades of new and contradictory evidence can usually alter this situation, and will often fail to do so for centuries.

Take the red shift of stars, which has long been the yardstick for measuring the age and distance of galaxies and stars. It can show the speed of a body away from us, which shifts the spectrum towards the red end, or towards us, which then conversely 'blue shifts' the light. That is fine, but to go a step further and say for how long this has happened is by no means a certainty at all, as we shall examine later.

As Sherlock Holmes might say, 'from there we move into the realms of conjecture, dear Watson'. We can measure the light...that is beyond question and perfectly fair enough. Yet we are making our measurements in the present, as Hubble showed, and any comment on the time elapsed for this process, we have to admit, requires a step into speculation. It assumes that beam of light has travelled unchanged over time, which is an assumption about time itself. No one usually ever questions this aspect, but the *Horizon Problem* is powerful evidence this assumption appears unfounded. It means that the universe is oddly 'flat', in the sense of being similar in all directions: unexplained as 'by chance', since Big Bang suggests those horizons are not connected to each other.

The early great astronomers, like Hubble and so many others, would never have had any reason to consider a giant cycle for Time. It was off everyone's radar, until Hoyle, Bondi & Gold revived the eternal or Steady State idea.

A short cycle had never been proposed, so why look for one, or question the dating results? Now the evidence suggests one, and we can see useful pieces of supporting information are emerging from the earth and sky faster than we can collate them.

When we boil all this down, what does it all mean? Every day scientists are finding strange impossibilities that show 'things don't fit' their favourite old theories. We have been trying to patch up a theory that does not work at all. Weird as it certainly is, the cyclic time model can answer all these queries, so we surely have to check it.

We assumed that pre-history was primitive. Sure, it looks logical enough, but is it true? Now we find it is not. This evidence shows many examples of unusual finds in archaeology that appear to be out of place in terms of their supposed age and ingenuity.

The *Antikythera* mechanism is a fine one, which shows the ancients around 200 BC were far more brilliant than we ever realised before that find. Called 'the 2000 year old computer', it was found to be a clockwork 'calculator' with exact metal cogs that predicted tiny lunar and planetary movements far beyond mere observation, but using serious maths. One researcher called it as amazing as finding a working petrol engine in an Egyptian tomb. This is covered in detail later.

The point is clear. The ancient cultures were very clever indeed.

How come there were sophisticated drainage and water supply systems in Mohenjo Daro, known as the ancient 'Pure Land' (translates as *Pakistan* in Urdu; *paki*: pure, *-stan*: land), while mainland Europe was barely out of the Stone Age? They were also harvesting vital water supplies in clever split-level cascade lakes, and had underground fresh water and separate waste drainage working perfectly over three millennia before Europe or London existed, which took J. Bazalgette in London until after 1860 to put in place.

Impressive enough, but 3,000 years late all the same, and far too late to save London from the 1849 and 1853 cholera epidemics caused by poor water quality. As noted, Neanderthals were taken for brutish quasi-animals when first found, until later finds of advanced culture proved this wrong, yet the textbooks in schools are rarely corrected. They buried their dead with flowers and grave offerings, made and drilled beads, and performed surgery with great success, even amputations, which finds of healed bone prove was finely performed. Even the flower types were notable, with six of the seven types well-known for medicinal properties to this day in their native Iraq, where these ancient graves were found. So they had herbal medicines, and if they used them, that puts a whole new slant on things.

We like to think, as did the Victorians, that our Stone Age ancestors were 'noble savages', but it is surprising to find those very 'cavemen' were doing brain surgery with more success than they were.

What conclusion can we draw from this? The ancients were smarter than we thought, and Richard Rudgley proved they did do brain surgery.

From these and many similar findings, we appear to have a problem: our thinking is in error. We need to re-think our dating systems, all of them, to include this cyclic time evidence on earth and in space, and then re-write the entire history in our textbooks from 500 BC backwards to what we thought was the 'dawn of time', then wrap it around a 'drum' shaped model of cyclic time, so the end touches the beginning again. This odd suggestion really works, and odder still, the modern Europeans are the only culture in history who did not think so. Older Europeans did, such as the Celts, and everyone else.

If this cyclic model holds true, then writing, maths and agriculture were not 'discovered' by our ancestors, but 're-discovered' by even earlier peoples. These skills were never lost, because we were always here, somewhere on earth. This is an unusual claim, but all the facts do point to the existence of a special era of calm and order that existed before the caveman era of prehistory. Many science books love to say how unlikely such an era was ever real, but that was before this evidence for a cycle emerged.

The rather quaint idea that 'Heaven' existed long ago, and all was well until we became 'physical' rather than 'ideal' and kind, no longer looks like the myth many of us took it to be. The geology shows this era to have been real, with the chalk and limestone as proof of carbon and calcium-rich warm and placid seas required for their deposition; conditions pointedly not in place today. Why do we not find soft drink cans in those strata if people were around then? Perhaps they drank fruit juice without aluminium cans, and their waste may not have been thrown in the sea, as we do now. Is this really feasible, that such a culture existed in prehistory, yet one that was highly advanced? It is.

There is no other way to account for global thinking to agree with this curious scenario, long before the globe's cultures could ever meet and swap stories, so how else could they think the same way and draw the same symbols shown here? So far, there is no other answer, so it is the best fit we have. It even solves, as noted later, the Easter Island heads that have mystified each generation. Their makers came from India, and shared the Brahmin topknot and long ear lobes still associated with ancient Bharat.

Even the time period needed for our current 7.5 billion human population fits this scenario; no other explanation does. DNA traces our current population's original ancestors back to the Far East, and only back to 4,950 years ago. The 'bottleneck' where some assume the global population 'must have been much larger' well before that, would be pure supposition, as would all of the dating of the ancient eras. [Shown in Fig 5]

The primitive species like Australopithecus, Neanderthals and Cro-Magnon etcetera would be small groups of survivors from a still earlier 'mini-Big Bang', when earth's axial tilt sent quakes and tsunamis into serious overdrive. This would explain why we are missing the 600–1000 billion Neanderthal skeletons there 'should be' had they truly existed for 750,000 years or so. Clearly they did not. Even a span of 240,000 years some claim would create around 343 billion full skeletal remains. How many such skeletons have been found? As noted, it is only 137.

Early 'man' is claimed to date back to 3.2 million years in East Africa, although reconstructions from parts found do not look very human, even though the pelvis does.

We will revisit the biology later, but a brief glance here is useful.

Why did Charles Darwin object so forcibly to his own theory?

Here are real, tangible examples of how conventional thinking lacks evidence, and one more key pointer to consider: long time spans were assumed, not actual. In a cycle, Time could not possibly have had so vast a period in which randomness 'might have created order'. If it had, as claimed by Charles Darwin and others, then where are the trillions upon quadrillions of evolving forms? They are missing. Where are the people with three ears, or asymmetric mammals that 'would work later'? We do not see them. Instead, we have superb symmetry, with *mirror image* hands, eyes, outer and inner ears, feet, noses, brains, skulls, limbs, knees, pelvis, spine, ribs, lungs, arterial system and so much more.

If this degree of symmetry had really evolved, where is the billion fold fossil evidence for each and every such step for each such feature? It is all missing.

Darwin agreed that this lack of evidence is another huge problem for his theory, and again put the case clearly in this context when he wisely wrote:

'...why is not every geological formation charged with such links? Why does not every collection of fossil remains afford plain evidence of the gradation and mutation of the forms of life? We meet with no such evidence, and this the most obvious and forcible of the many objections which may be urged against my theory'.[10] He goes on to say:

'That the geological record is imperfect all will admit; but that it is imperfect to the degree which I require, few will be inclined to admit' and also:

'Such is the sum of the several chief objections and difficulties which may justly be raised against my theory...I have felt these difficulties far too heavily during many years to doubt their weight. But it deserves especial notice that the more important objections relate to questions on which we are confessedly ignorant; nor do we know how ignorant we are'.[11]

Where are the human forms alone, of the inner ear 'evolution' steps to what we have now, with those three tiny bones that work so perfectly to detect sound and even music? There should be billions of those alone, along with every other modification, if that truly is what happened. It would take many billions of each form to 'evolve' into what we see today. Yet we see none. They are clearly missing. We can all see that.

Not only is the missing 'ape to man' link still missing, but so are the billions, literally, of forms that 'should exist' to reach every species

10   The Origin of Species, C. Darwin, Penguin Classics 1985, p438
11   Ibid p440

alive now. A cycle may therefore be right. A few hundred examples that look intermediate do not put a dent in the fact that these vast quantities are missing.

To say they did exist but were not preserved as remains also does not hold water. Even shapes or tunnels or delicate life forms are well preserved in rock strata with many such examples, such as at Ediacara in Australia and the Burgess Shale in Canada, let alone actual bone. They included soft body fossils so well preserved that scientists have been astounded ever since the finds appeared. The scientists once promised that could never happen, yet it clearly has. They again promised in 1999 that a find of methane on Mars was a certainty to predict life on the red planet: a 'slam dunk' as one called it. It was not true: it seemed obvious, but it was not so. Methane is no guarantee of life.

They were wrong on both counts, because *evolution may never have had time to occur*. If it had, there would be massive piles of bone evidence, not just enough to fill half a shoe shop (with cave dweller bones). This is a key point: if life did evolve over long linear ages, there must be trillions of tons of dead creatures covering the planet at least a kilometre deep in many places. Do we find this? No, we do not. It is a fatal problem that Darwin himself foresaw, because he realised that a lack of evidence is just that: a lack of proof that life evolved. Biologists quite rightly then ask, if not this, then what? Up until now, the only reply was a religious one, so the two sides remained unresolved either way. Now we have a third option that explains why all these features are 'too young' for life to have had time to evolve…life exists in a cycle that repeats. The geology also moves in a cycle.

Do bones leave traces, and can bones be equally well preserved? Of course they do, and do so superbly, but there is more: they would also always leave marks from their high iron and different mineral content, compared to the nature of the 'country rock', meaning the chemical signature of the sedimentary strata in that location. Unless the rock was also made of bone, which it obviously never is, there is always a mark left where it once was. Bones leave marks, gaps, holes and clear stains as proof they existed. They cannot exist in deposits without these obvious clues being present, so even the recent geological record could not be blamed for losing over 1000 billion of such signs. Since they are not present at all, they must be considered theoretical, rather than real.

Mammoth tusks also preserve well, and can be found on remote islands in N. Russia, just lying around on the permafrost, some having been so plentiful they were used by natives to make huts. Some places in that frozen landscape have relic ice age tusks gathered in huge mounds, pushed into piles by extreme historic tsunamis, rather as in the famous 'bone bed' deposits of Alaska, which includes lion bones...not exactly normal for the cold, polar Arctic Circle region. They show signs of rapid burial by catastrophe, so these were not prides of lions that all fell asleep beneath a tree one day in summer.

Calm conditions by no means, but back to those bones, and the signs they leave.

Whole solid limb bones can indeed be leached away or dissolved by various means, but there are two aspects to bear in mind here.

One, they leave trace deposits of the elements that formed them, which stain the rock in which they lay, and two, there is this: secondary deposition of minerals carried by percolating groundwater such as calcium carbonate, calcite and iron pyrites, which are common globally.

England's famous Jurassic south coast, from Devon to Dorset and beyond, has spots literally full of 'pyritised' ammonites where just this mineral exchange has taken place, where the carbonate original shell (made of $CaCO_3$) has been 'mineralised' into iron pyrites (FeS), also known as Fool's Gold. The atoms are quite readily interchangeable, like small cars swapping places in a parking lot, so water acts as the agent, and they change places so effectively that the whole animal shell can be 'replaced' with whatever mineral is present in the local water table. The original material goes into solution and the iron pyrites crystallises in its place, so the details of the original shell are beautifully preserved forever. Rather like spilling raspberry purée on a white shirt, it is going to leave a mark. Bones in the earth, or strata of sand or mud, leave indelible signs, or an exact replica of the original creature in fine detail.

Since these processes work in every part of the earth, can we really imagine they so widely failed to preserve the remains of literally trillions of tons of bone and shell to deprive Darwin of his vital proof that life evolved? Of course not; the simple answer is that these preservation processes are unavoidable. They happen, and they are permanent.

It is completely impossible for Nature to put a shell, let alone a heavy bone, into neat layers of sand or mud and leave no signs. If those bones had ever existed, we would see the imprint of many more of those processes.

When we see no evidence for them, it means we must consider that they may never have existed. Without that evidence, no one can prove they did. Any theory needs evidence, so without it, the idea becomes mere conjecture. The long time periods required by Evolution simply have no formal proof, and the conventional presumptions do not alter that fact. We can make up theories all day long, but that doesn't mean they are true. Linear time is not remotely feasible, so whatever did happen, it could not be that.

Each special feature of anatomy must have had earlier forms, if they evolved.

Take the perfection of the human eye, or the ear we touched on. Where are those quadrillions of step-wise forms? The auditory ossicles or ear bones called incus, malleus, and stapes that bridge the tympanic cavity so perfectly have no precedent, and neither do the above examples. Where are the earlier forms of the Eustachian tube, which links the ear to the naso-pharynx to equalise pressure?

We have to admit there is a likely answer that many dare not think: that they never existed, and that is why no trace of them exists.

We must always be prepared for great changes in perception, yet it is a quirk of history that we never quite seem to be ready for those changes when they arrive.

As Alvin Toffler wrote in his 1970 book title: 'Future Shock- *the dizzying disorientation of too much change in too short a time'*. We spend half our time confusing ourselves with ideas that lack the possibility of being true.

The old favourites, like evolution and the classic geological time-scale, are filled with presumptions about past conditions that are just not possible; if they were, we would see the evidence. There are many areas of deposits said to have taken vast ages to form, yet are devoid of fossils, such as in 4000 vertical feet of the Siwalik Hills of Burma. Where are the fossils in such areas? Did the animals live there but leave no trace, or go on holiday somewhere else? Neither option is possible or credible. If they had lived there, they must have left signs of burrowing, or bio-perturbation as sedimentologists prefer to call it. They are absent, so we must draw a different conclusion to the usual one, which can no longer convince us.

The linear idea of long, slow and uniform time was accepted as true over 200 years ago, when James Hutton wrote his key book in 1795, but later finds show it cannot be true. It has long been felt 'wrong' to question such famous authors, but we must, and there are signs of circular systems in his thinking too. Even his theory of Plutonism involved cycles of decay and regeneration of rock, so the notion of cycles was there too. He even wrote he found 'no vestige of a beginning, no prospect of an end'…meaning a progression or continuum.

Science detail brief

Most of today's thinkers took their cue from others like Einstein (and George Lemaitre, Gamow, Alpher and Herman, credited with 'inventing the explosion idea' in the 1940's known later as Big Bang theory). They all assumed time to be a line, and thus tried to fit events into that model. Yet they did not show that matter could just appear.

Professor Stephen Hawking, the famous mathematician, used to make the claim of matter arising from a 'singularity', but later changed his mind. Realising it was logically unsupportable, he and others then said that those early lumps of matter must have appeared from a parallel world. Yet this too has a problem that even this famed thinker has never solved, which is this: where did the matter for that other universe come from? They then said that matter came from yet another universe, and so on, ten or more times over, an idea that became known as the multiverse.

Strictly speaking, this is a façade, because it is not answering the question at all. This *'multiverse'* approach is just another theory, and is not a provable answer. This theory is no challenge to cyclic time at all. It just avoids the issue by inventing other universes, for which there is no evidence. It is pure conjecture, and appears to be an error, since it fits neither the facts nor the maths.

We don't need to be Socrates to see this is not logical, but modern thinkers simply could not imagine Time being anything other than the line; apart from Prof. Sir Roger Penrose of course, plus Sir Fred

Hoyle, Prof Turok, Prof Steinhardt, Dr Param Singh and others, whose important ideas we will consider later.

Most interestingly, it was Professor Hawking's colleague at university, the above mentioned Professor Sir Roger Penrose, whose book *Cycles of Time* reveals reasons why, in maths and physics, Time could be cyclic. As we will see, the ideas in his book are hugely influential, and have to be fully appreciated.

A cycle suggests that events move in phases, with Matter always existing, yet simply changing its state of order. Thus it was more ordered, and now it is highly chaotic, as surely every human being appreciates. So far, this makes practical sense, and remains the only viable answer.

The logic is as simple today as it was in 700 BC. Since the latest information from space shows the 'line' of time to be impossible, that cannot impress us as right. It just *appears linear* when seen locally. Time looks like a series of unconnected events because we see it through the eyes of beings that live for a mere 55 years on average. This is far too short a period to witness the long and complex cycles of spacetime that have been detected, but which are not yet fully understood within science, where time is still believed to be linear and largely random.

Even more amazing is the evidence for a hidden network of energy, of which we humans are a part, and hold the balance of power. What this research shows is a state of Nature far more finely balanced than was ever thought possible, and that each person in the solar system is such an intricate part of an energy 'Super Grid', so far undetected by science, that even the very thoughts we have and actions taken can influence outcomes. We people can influence matter profoundly, as some knew long ago (Bell 1964).

This really changes everything, because it shows science was wrong to take the world as a place of 'random' effects. Instead, as the evidence here shows, this hidden 'sub-world' controls the more obvious 'super-world' above it; in the Latin sense of super. Amazingly to some, it is entirely possible that this 'cyclic quantum energy grid' actually controls what happens each day, and is so finely balanced that mere thought energy affects it profoundly. Science just never quite thought of it before, because it has had to focus on what can be measured physically; thoughts being too subtle to measure.

This *'Thought over Matter Effect'* would be working at a sub-atomic level, from the basic fact of our mind minutely controlling our bodies, right up to a quantum resonance effect that affects the whole universe, and does so instantly. Science is only just discovering this quantum level world where even atoms are too big to show the subtlety of how matter really moves, so we will explore just how it can be totally different to what we thought before.

This idea of matter and people being connected gives us a new world which works in a much fairer way. Thoughts really do change our lives, as we all know, but this adds a deeper angle by showing how our collective energy as people may interact with all matter to alter its daily 'state', either towards order or chaos. The Greeks realised that all great change is a negative factor, because chaos will increase. Just look at all the failed attempts to solve road and rail travel issues to see how this is as true today as ever.

Gone is Big Bang as a theory, which never worked anyway because it failed to explain where all the matter came from, broke every law in the book,[12] and was about as useful as answering a question on astrophysics with 'ooh look there's a squirrel', in comedian Bill Bailey's classic phrase showing how we try to divert attention from a difficult problem. We can now see how flawed linear time is, and how only a cycle of matter moving in phases seems able to solve these problems.

Barrelling into its place comes not just some vague circle, but a precise cycle of events. They follow an exact sequence. Solved is the question of dark energy and dark matter, which science was forced to invent as a bolt-on fix, in a desperate attempt to explain these obvious failures of linear time. All will become clear as we fit the few surviving pieces into a new *'non-linear'* framework.

It seems we were asking the wrong questions, such as 'when did the universe begin?' If Time is indeed a cyclic or circular process of cause and effect, then there would never be a start date as we assumed. Instead we would be part of a series of events that are closely connected within infinity, and not random at all. There is actually no evidence of a start or end date, but of a cycle of events. Early pioneers just assumed

---

12 Such as the noted Laws of Conservation of Matter & Energy,
    Cause & Effect etc.

it was all linear because they reckoned it looked that way. The idea of a start date is an artificial one, and we will see just how that is impossible. As so often happens when considering Nature, the answer that best fits what we observe is one we never expected even to be possible, let alone correct.

Modern experts, like the famous astronomer Edwin P. Hubble (1889–1953), found in 1929 that many galaxies were rushing across the sky at huge speeds, and even accelerating, with speed proportional to their distance (Hubble's Law).

That was mind-blowingly unexpected to put it mildly, because it showed something very odd was happening to say the least. How come, they reasoned, could the universe be billions of years 'old', and yet not be slowing down yet? The answer seems obvious now, but it was not so then, and remains unclear to modern astronomers and cosmologists. The answer now appears to be that something did happen very recently that made the galaxies accelerate, meaning they are speeding up. This can only mean the universe would be cyclic, and recently changed speed to be as it is now, or it would definitely be slowing down. Yet it is not, it is doing the exact opposite, and speeding up. The only answer that fits this fact is a short period cycle, *where this motion is recent.*

Modern astronomers are not taught to think in this way at all, and instead are told that 'other forces' must be causing this odd situation of accelerating galaxies. They never imagined, until now, that time could be such a cyclic process, and nearly none do. The experts saw the universe was apparently expanding with this news, and simply 'ran the clock backwards' in their minds to make their next conclusion: it must all have started from a point. Logically, it sounded great, and here we have what Hoyle dubbed Big Bang theory.

It fails to fit the facts, and remains unproved for many reasons; not least that it cannot explain how the matter all came into being, without other universes that share the exact same problem, whether there are ten or more as claimed. They also struggled over the snag that if there was a big bang, how come the galaxies are still accelerating?

This may be why things don't just pop into existence, or happen for no reason. In a cycle there is order, and cause and effect, which is reassuring...if we can see a hidden mechanism that enables it to happen in reality.

CHAPTER 2

The Existence of a Super Grid

It is always the season for the old to learn ... even the wisest of the wise may err.
AESCHYLUS, 520 BC

If a little knowledge is dangerous, where is the man who has so much as to be out of danger?
T.H.HUXLEY, 1877

Essence

One finding set to cause a stir is a hidden 'energy' field or link that fills the space between things. Radio waves are a cruder example of this idea. We cannot see them yet they exist to be picked up by receivers. It means something very new: if the human mind can affect this grid, and both transmit and receive waves of that fine degree of subtle power, then we would be altering spacetime all the time. Are there such waves? We can see their presence via effects at a distance, such as pairs of electrons, so 'yes'. This changes everything we know about life on earth for people, because it means we are making external events either calm or chaotic simply by thinking either way. We already know our actions do this locally, but this would be a cosmos-wide effect.

In science, the discovery that particles are connected by unseen links leads us to a new conclusion. There would be such a Grid of energy that exists in between the atoms, so that all matter is connected all the time, and each part has some effect on all the others. Such sub-atomic 'energy' could exist as a fabric across the entire universe. This subtle aspect is not easy to see, yet is detectable by what we see in Cooper Pairs: their entangled 'link' must be connected by something, and this Grid provides a solution. [See Fig 6 on next page]

Sir Isaac Newton commented in 1730 on the changing nature of things, and our perception of them as 'solid': *The changing nature*

Super Grid concept

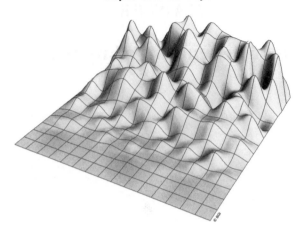

FIGURE 6 *Super Grid: diagram showing a universe-wide hidden sub-atomic energy grid affected by human thoughts and interactions; minds and matter being constantly linked or 'entangled'.*

of bodies into light, and light into bodies, is very conformable to the course of Nature, which seems to delight in transmutations.' The huge space between atoms, and inside them, now shows this to be an illusion, with most atoms being almost entirely empty of mass. The noted example of the entire world's populace fitting into a thimble, if only the nuclei are used, explains this. [Only the nuclei have any mass, so the other parts of the atom have no actual weight as such; take away all that space, and little remains; the thimble would still weigh the same as the 7.5 billion people it 'contains'.]

A huge revolution is already underway...in thinking about Reality. Its implications are so far-reaching they will affect every theory in current use. This revolution, undoubtedly the biggest in all human history, concerns Time. The way we see time is changing forever. The idea of this revolution is the 'circle of sequential events' the ancients were aware of, when the chaos peaks and gives way to calm and order.

Why should we agree? It appears likely because the evidence shows time switches in this perfectly cyclic pattern every few millennia.

Many others missed this conclusion because they never looked for it. After all, we cannot answer a question we have not asked. In a nutshell, new information collected points to an extraordinary conclusion affecting every particle in existence: that Time repeats in cycles.

Yet some leading thinkers do see time rotating, while others have overlooked the presence of a cyclic mechanism. The biggest obstacle in human progress is old thinking. We get attached to it. Some even say 'it worked for 500 years so why change it now?' This is of course a ridiculous claim. Old ideas only appear to 'work' because we don't realise why they are wrong. Some of Aristotle's notions 'worked' 2,300 years ago, but we don't still use all of those today (he lived from 384–322 BC).

One was the ancient concept about earthquakes, which also happened in their era. They had seen moles digging holes, so it was obvious: moles make quakes. They reckoned earthquakes must be caused by bigger moles, so they imagined giant cathedral-sized moles running clumsily along dark subterranean passages.

While hugely amusing now, such ideas were serious solutions in those days. To advance, ideas must change. The deepest problem is the mistake of stubbornly believing our own ideas to be true.

A theory is an opinion someone chose to emphasise. It can look right and yet be completely false logic, even while having apparently powerful 'evidence' to support it.

The key thing to bear in mind is this: theory is not always true. Young students are told to rely on the 'scientific method', and have to pass exams to say why. University students are told the secret in more detail, that theories are often wrong, and may be dramatically so.

Yet students are trained as researchers, not iconoclastic paradigm re-thinkers who could bring 'normal science' to a standstill while everyone re-checks Galileo or Darwin all over again. Researchers are therefore meant to stick to specific research, not go back over first principles on a daily basis....that task is left to philosophers, or the few who stumble on some conflicting evidence, and take the time to explore it themselves. Strictly speaking, we should all do that.

The Ancients saw events as an infinite circle, with Matter always existing. European thinkers brushed that aside, and settled firmly on a long line instead. Yet this created a new problem the ancient version had solved: if time and space were arranged as events along a line, then where did the universe come from? They had no idea. For many years, scientists could not even discuss what happened 'before that imagined beginning', and would not even allow this question to be asked.

The Oxford *Companion to Cosmology*, a respected dictionary, put the situation very honestly, stating that '*...no-one has the slightest idea what might have happened at the Big Bang, nor whether one actually happened at all*'.[13] Wise words indeed, and true.

Everyone is already aware Nature has cycles, yet we never quite realised that every event and part of life can also be precisely orbital, even Time itself. As we walk around the globe, we get the occasional glimpse of a gap in the curtain covering what lies beneath the superficial...the past or the future seen in déjà vu. It can be both.

The revolution is in seeing Time as a cycle, not a long line. Of course Time is old, but far longer than the billions of years suggested. Nature's reality may lead us to conclude that the future and the past are one continuum. All events have therefore occurred before, if that is the case, as an infinite series of events that recur in cycles.

Here is how a cycle really works, and what it can do to help us see ahead.

If Time is cyclic, it will allow us to predict the future exactly, and quite differently to what is thought now. Even the gravity of every particle would change, so it is worth finding out the reasons to check if this is so. It appears there is a mechanism, very like machinery, which connects every person and particle right across the vastness of space...a '*Super Grid*' of energy filling all that apparent emptiness. This Grid can explain the latest quantum effects of Cooper pairs, which amazed Einstein, and led him to call it 'spooky motion at a distance'.

Put simply, this discovery changed literally everything, but no one quite guessed how much. We are only now beginning to see how. It showed that 'all matter' can indeed be deeply connected, so that one tiny movement in one place would have instant and truly cosmic-wide consequences. The big factor left out was the effect of humans on the sub-atomic order of this Grid of matter. This implies our combined human influence may have a deep effect on a daily basis, making it calm or chaotic accordingly. There is no other source of physical energy to have such effects, so it is both possible and logical.

13 Oxford University Press (OUP) 2009, page 28.

Cooper Pair of electrons

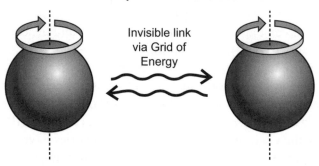

Invisible link
via Grid of
Energy

FIGURE 7   *Cooper Pairs: electrons linked in pairs or groups that spin with same motion; connected via Super Grid suggesting all matter can be similarly linked.*

Sounds like science fiction, yet it has real evidence to support it.

Here is the essence of the whole universe, revealed in this one discovery, and here is how it all works...as one unit or system, not the random chaos it seems.

The key is in this sub-atomic connection between particles of energy that, on the face of it, cannot possibly be linked... and yet evidence suggests they are. Entangled particles show such a link, and won its finders a Nobel Prize (see BCS theory in Glossary).

This link suggests the presence of the above Grid.

Once thought to be merely a local effect, this discovery is evidence of a spacetime 'Super Grid' that takes in the whole cosmos, every particle and planet, from the very tiniest massless dots to whole galaxies, including our own, and all the space between. If it works at a micro level, why not the macro? The key lies in the presence of a cycle, since this changes how we would see Reality, as a constant fact, not one arising randomly. This deeply impressed the most famous thinkers in Greece, so it is worth a check.

This seems the only way to solve the thousands of inconsistencies unsolved by current thinking. It suggests that just a single thought can affect the entire grid, and so a whole world of intense thoughts would have a really extreme effect. We see this effect in miniature every day, as our happy or sad feelings rule our bodily health, or purely emotional upset or worry can cause serious physical illness.

This can be how a force as subtle as thoughts may be so finely tuned into the quantum world of energy that any slight change could be vastly scaled up. This can explain how mind, body, earth and the cosmos too can be part of one energy Grid function.

It is therefore logical that even this human 'energy' may hold that balance of power, if the 'total sum of energy' is as finely balanced on a knife edge as it appears to be. This can explain how a tiny event in one small place can have a vast effect in another, rather like the flap of a butterfly wing creating a hurricane as some theories have said. This does not appear to be literally possible, since hurricanes are created by warming large ocean areas, and butterflies have not yet been seen secretly stoking up fires under the Atlantic, but the point makes a good metaphor.

Some turn to science for a reliable view of reality, but it may need a review.

We are so used to hearing how solid and dependable science can be, that we have been conditioned to think it is nearly always right. Scientists customarily see themselves as the sole arbiters of their own work, while in fact philosophers like Sir Karl Popper and T.S. Kuhn have pointed out such a 'semi-divine power' of perfect judgement is a myth, and should never be claimed at any time. To do so is not science, but closer to religion, and that is a line science should not cross, although it does. As we shall see, even statistics can give a totally false impression, with the usual claim of '95% accuracy' for an idea may have 0% validity. If you hear anyone claim this figure of 95% accuracy, begin smiling, because it is a figure based on methods that can give this exact result entirely falsely.

As Thomas S. Kuhn set out so clearly in his '*The Structure of Scientific Revolutions*'[14], 'normal science' is not set up to deal with revolutions of this scale, hence why they are usually dismissed with ridicule. Science is very good at solving smaller problems, but definitely not equally good at criticising its own worldview. Discontents were labelled as mad or dangerous or both, and personally criticised, while often ignoring the actual issues. Later we will see how this tactic was used to prevent Velikovsky's work being published, but it backfired as people realised

14   Thomas S. Kuhn, 4th Edition, University of Chicago Press, 2012.

he was largely right, even in 1956. Kuhn's work is highly regarded, because he clarified why such revolutions in science are so important, and yet their very existence is ignored in many books, in a move Kuhn calls 'systematically misleading'.[15]

To find major new advances, Science has to be keen to destroy its own old models, yet almost no one is backed to do that. He even said, entirely rightly, that science textbooks *systematically disguise* past revolutions to give the impression of slow but sure 'cumulative' accuracy.[16] This claim is rarely true, and thus often a myth, yet no junior student will ever be let in on that little secret. This was done to maintain the apparent authority of Science, to increase support, and then use it to run the world. It was not meant to be questioned all the time, nor imagined it would ever need to be, so no sure system existed for major revision. Having received that authority, past revolutions were airbrushed out of the history given to most students, to encourage a higher degree of respect. Human nature can even alter science.

Often giant new ideas, like those in 1687 of Newton in *Principia*, were derided when first encountered. They were arguably among the greatest advances in 1000 years. Even Newton claimed he was building on Galileo's work on gravity as a constant force creating a motion 'proportional to the square of the time'. As Kuhn points out '…Galileo said nothing of the sort'. Newton had cleverly linked his work to Galileo's kinesis theorem, making his own work look less controversial and more acceptable, yet he was still misconstructing history.

Time is the rope that binds our perceptions, yet we all perceive it differently. From waking dreams to making sense of our existence, time and our opinion of prehistory are the heart of any such understanding, yet lie just out of sight… below the surface of life on Earth. To have the chance of reaching any deeper understanding at some point, we have to see through that 'crust of the obvious', and to try and reinterpret the world as a means of checking our worldview.

The evidence we now have, if we care to look for it, should have caused the required revolution. It has not done so because the geology

15 Ibid, page 136.
16 Ibid, page 135.

can easily be mistaken for proof of long ages past, appearing to run into millions of years, but we placed too much faith in 'the Present being the key to the Past'.

This famous idea, established around 1795 by Hutton and Lyell as the *Uniformitarian Principle*, has not stood the test of time. While a controversial thing to say to some minds, many current leaders in geology have long since accepted the past history of Earth is not so simple to assess. There have been cataclysms of such immense power and magnitude that even *The Oxford Companion to the Earth* [17], a very valuable volume of superb scholarship, points out that Hutton's principle 'has now been rejected on a number of grounds', and is actually 'no longer tenable'. This appears deeply correct.

This pivotal realisation has never been fully translated into any real change in mainstream thinking. Some firm believers in the old view of geological time may reject this opinion, because it has such colossal implications. Slowly, we are realising the world of Time is not the way we thought it was, and that this old and deeply traditional mind-set has some adapting to do. This research shows there have been some global mega-events in geology and astronomy that happened so fast, and on such a huge scale, that earlier scientists missed their speed and influence, if they noticed the events at all.

If there is any key error, then however huge and impressive a scientific idea may be, it would fail as a result. A path across a stream, like the bricks in a wall, is possible only by finding a firm footing on the previous stepping stone. Take some away, and the footpath is no longer open or probable, just as removing a foundation stone or two will inevitably bring down the whole building. No building can exist on a foundation of fresh air. Each brick or stone relies on the one beneath it. Such errors exist in our thinking, although quite unintentionally.

It seems strange to propose a new world view when so many influential people are quite happy with the current one. Yet there are equally brilliant academics and thinkers who have found serious flaws in the old world view, and realise these are signs of much deeper errors that simply have to be resolved, and never have been.

What is proposed here is a completely different way of seeing reality,

17   OUP, pages 102–103, 2000 Edition.

yet one that fits what we observe. It requires radically new thinking, but we should expect it to. Even more curiously, every ancient culture already knew what we are just discovering.

We must now suggest an entirely new perspective to Time. It seems we humans were wrong about Time.

There is now ample evidence that we have made the greatest error in history, in thinking time is linear; it also implies life is a meaningless line of events that go nowhere. This view is not shared by the Eastern cultures at all. The old debate of *Creation versus Evolution* has never been solved, but it may have a simple solution...a cycle of time that is neat and complete, and needs no magical invention of Matter and Time to start its processes as Science claims.

What is really going on in the universe and on planet earth in particular? We need to know, and fast, with so much order crumbling around our ears, and with the forces of West and East now at permanent war.

Is it possible that all this order turning into chaos is just part of a cyclic process that always turns out positively? The signs both here on earth, and in space too, show it is just this way. Time appears to be what many already thought it was...a Continuum that continues.

This may sound pleasing, but is there any concrete evidence to say so? When we take out the many assumptions used in science today, largely inherited from the 17th century pioneers in geology and earth science in general, we are left with this continuum as the only explanation that fits what we see.

If so, this prompts some new and radical thinking. A cycle makes perfect sense because it is based on order that simply degrades into chaos over time. We see this anyway in every part of Nature and our own lives, so it is logical that Time itself may be part of the same process...the law of entropy, by which order degrades into chaos.

The astonishing finding is that no matter how chaotic and terrible those events may be, it would all calm down in due course, and order would always be restored. This only becomes possible by adding the human factor, which cannot of course be measured.

Today, scientists all agree that chaos will always reach a peak and then subside, yet we think we are so clever that very little the ancients thought, such as time being cyclic, could conceivably hold true now. Yet it does. It takes time to realise our errors are real.

As Seneca said circa 54 AD: '*Let us not be surprised that things so deeply hidden are dug out so slowly*'.[18]

Our deepest ideas have been made to fit the modern mind; then we saw 'proof' to assure us we were right. We even invented the myth that older cultures thought the earth was flat, when they thought no such thing. The Greeks had actually discovered it was a sphere long before the West, as far back as 320 BC, and used maths to compute its diameter to within 60 miles. Now that was clever, *nearly two millennia before the West* calculated the same sums, and saw the earth from space. For those who still doubt all this, we can actually see the International Space Station (ISS) on a clear night as it orbits the earth every 66 minutes or so. [It looks like a star moving very fast, but vanishes when the sun/earth angle stops reflecting the sunlight.]

It is curious to think that Science could be so mistaken, and then rush to pronounce 'we now know' the answer, when it may be just another error on the way.

In error or truth, the key is human thought. No theory was ever devised without a person. Computers don't make themselves. Tables and carburettors do not devise theories, but were formed by them. This is how a superb idea can be spectacularly misconceived, even while living in our most respected textbooks.

In 2012, a Danish geochemist was taking samples in the more gentle coastal area of East Greenland. He was on a research field trip, using a power auger which burrows into the earth like an irate mechanical mole to reveal deeper soil samples, when he had an interesting realisation that touches us all. It suddenly came to him that, while working in science, he was also conscious of searching for answers about himself at the same time.

The earth really does contain clues about our past, and that is true for every one of us. Recent DNA and strontium samples taken across Europe show traces of that past history in the teeth and bones of people who live today, walking about the streets of every village and city in the area. It would surprise many of us to learn that there were around 2 or 4% traces of Neanderthal DNA in those profiles tested, showing that the past really does affect the present. This is very interesting, because it shows how deeply connected we are to the past.

---

18 Seneca, *Quaestiones Naturales* 7, HUP 2004, Loeb, p291

Science has become a monolithic structure that has no real mechanism for listening to 'normal people' who may disagree. Yet there are some wild ideas in non-scientists.

Just look at this example. In one survey, 12% of people thought Joan of Arc was the wife of Noah, as in Noah's Ark. The gap of several thousand years in their historical context is one clue, and the different spelling of 'Ark' is another, but it shows how confused many of us are. Yet odd ideas can work. One is in medicine.

No one would make an experiment that appeared ridiculous or so off-message that its chances of success were zero. Yet often in science it may be just such an off-the-wall attitude that can alone lead to the desired result, such as using the mould of penicillin to cure illness. In that age, it looked plain silly to think this way, yet it would save countless lives. That September 1928 discovery by Fleming would become legend, although Lister and Tyndall had found similar effects from a milder strain of *penicillium* from 1872.

Before this, no one could have guessed that this group of antibiotics could be highly effective in fighting infection, let alone do so by blocking the synthesis of bacterial cell walls. All this shows old thinking can be wrong, even on something as obvious as how Time moves.

Time as a cycle has been big news for all of human history. What seemed normal to the ancient Greeks, a cycle for Time, made no sense to us in Europe, so it faded out of fashion. Oddly enough, it did make sense to the Celts, who are also the ancestors of most Europeans, who hailed not from Europe, but India and Kashmir. Is there any evidence for this radical assertion? As linguists might agree having read Myles Dillon's superb work [19] on Indo-European languages, there is plenty. Now fresh DNA research shows that India is the basic source of humanity, not Africa after all. We will return to this later.

The heart of the problem has always been this: what we presume to be true may not be true at all.

The people of New York would have appreciated more warning than they got for Superstorm Sandy in November 2012, but some was better than none. The same is true for the tragic tsunamis of Thailand,

---

19 *Celts and Aryans*, Myles Dillon, 1975, Indian Institute of Advanced Studies, Simla, India.

Sumatra and Japan. No-one is yet fully prepared for such large geological effects, but we can do much better if we understand what Nature is doing, and why such extreme 'balance correction' is rising in intensity.

The heart of the whole matter is Time itself. The clues to the great enigma of life on earth most definitely lie here, in a better understanding of Time. With a better perception of time we can solve anything.

Science is full of successes that arose from ideas that looked like sure failures. Who would have thought an experiment left to gather mould and rot on a bench could have given us penicillin? Certainly not our hero, the reluctant creator of the mould, and just imagine his embarrassment at explaining he found it by being a poor cleaner.

Many people wince at the idea of probing specialised fields like radioactivity or hieroglyphics, yet there lies a simplicity behind all understanding. A huge advance is in recognizing that no concept is beyond our comprehension. If it doesn't make sense, the explanation is at fault, never the reader. Highly gifted teachers can explain anything and make it simple, for which Professors Feynman, Penrose[20], and Smolin are justly famous, as we will see.

We should also remember the evidence of the Grid being used by the FBI in America to solve very serious crimes, methods that many in Science, and the detectives themselves it must be said, still consider theoretically impossible. Yet they solve baffling murders in just this way, by using clairvoyants who can both 'see and read' those details at the crime scenes, with such precision that the cases lead to convictions. Around 90 episodes of *Psychic Detectives* have been made on a sample of several hundred such documented cases, in which the crimes were solved. It seems the 'matter' at any location quite naturally stores the energy of any event occurring, which can then be 'read' later.

As we see later, this study has checked 96 such cases with names, dates and locations globally, and found them wholly credible, yet only explainable with a sub-atomic grid that stores those events in those locations. Detectives in Australia and New Zealand (See www.*sensingmurder.nz*) have been made aware of such homicide evidence, but so far some found it difficult to understand; perhaps because conventional science has no viable current explanation, at least until now.

20 Fashion Faith & Fantasy, R.Penrose, Princeton University Press, 2016.

It is also reassuring to see from such a study of Time and Nature that events appear to be connected, and are thus not random at all. This would give life the deeper meaning many already think it has. If correct, this changes everything in Science, and makes each person on the planet a vital part of the activity we all observe. In linear time, we become powerless pawns in the game, while if Time is cyclic, we would be influencing its outcome very profoundly, which makes the course of our own lives infinitely more significant. The reader decides.

CHAPTER 3

Cyclic Time and the Oceans

Nothing is wasted, nothing is in vain: The seas roll over
but the rocks remain.
SIR A.P. HERBERT, 1949

Nature is pleased with simplicity, and affects not the pomp
of superfluous causes.
First Rule of Reasoning, SIR ISAAC NEWTON, 1687

Essence

Now for two of the most colossal assumptions ever made in Science, and how they fall short. It has been assumed the planets were once red hot spheres, and then cooled down. The stark differences in the planets suggest this never happened, because they would be the same if the same 'accretion disc' of material was the same 'parent' of all eight. The other great problem this old idea poses for earth is two fold: where did the oceans come from, and life as well? Early writers, like Lyell and Hutton, considered an 'eternal' universe, but could not confirm it.

Centuries later, this created a problem: trying to prove the oceans came from somewhere else than Earth. They chose space. The reasoning goes like this: experts in cosmology claim that earth then cooled down over eons of time, and then a marvel happened. For no known reason, yet at exactly the convenient moment when earth was ready, a huge number of water-carrying asteroids hit earth, and brought the oceans; called the LHB or Late Heavy Bombardment.

This clever invention made everyone happy, and was accepted. It avoided the idea of eternity or cycles, it was quick and easy, and if they didn't look too closely, the case looked solved and could be declared closed. Yet where did the asteroids fill up with water when it is plentiful nowhere else? This is both unknown, and unknowable, being presumed. Like any exciting theory, it was made up.

Any other idea seemed impossible at the time, because they took time to be long and linear, period. The reasoning seemed simple and so 'obviously correct': linear time = billions of years = disc of dust = earth + LHB + oceans = life + evolution = modern society

The problem had not been solved. Linear time relies on supposing it happened; the meteorite 'ages' are not proven either, as we will see; the LHB 'with oceans' is pure conjecture without water oceans elsewhere; the formation of life relies on linear time, with unequivocal proof, ditto evolution; there is no other planet with an ocean of water, and no other space bodies have much of it either. A bit of water does exist in space in the rare comets, but enough for us to get *1340 million cu.kms* of it, with none left elsewhere?

Next to Big Bang theory, Evolution, Accretion Disc theory, and the Geological Timescale, this is probably the most unbelievable idea ever suggested in science; yet it is still accepted to this day, because no one had an alternative they liked. For a start, the Accretion Disc idea appears equally fantastic, because of four things:

1 How could there be a 'clumping' of particles, almost certainly with the same negative charge, when like poles repel? (Spitzer 1941)
2 Why would particles gather in the vastness of space, since like poles repel?
3 The heat needed to form earth would not be generated from friction alone.
4 It assumes the universe is linear, when the facts point to a non-linear existence.

We will examine more reasons why this is beyond unlikely, and a more logical solution that works. The timing of this 'bombardment' is also supposition. The facts point to a pre-existing solar system, which explains the actual variations.

A good clarification to remember often is this one, from the superb *Oxford Companion to the Earth*[21] explaining that the concept of linear time in earth's 'formation of life' theory cannot be confirmed, and is therefore unknown: 'Irrefutable evidence about how life originated does not exist. Hypotheses regarding its origin, however, are

21   OUP 2000, p763

plentiful…the timing of events on the early Earth is open to considerable uncertainty'.

Could the world appear from nothing?

The idea that the human race sits on a planet that once did not exist at all, and now does, is the world view many of us grew up with. So sure are we that this is the true picture, that most of us would readily gamble our home on this view remaining the dominant version over the foreseeable future. That was before we heard of the third option: a cycle of time which no longer has to 'make everything appear' when the celestial clock strikes the cosmic equivalent of 12 o'clock. Instead, if that is the case, all that needs to happen is a simple change to take place. The forces of chaos and order may reach a peak in a second one day. They appear to be oscillating over spans of time that are far shorter than we ever suspected.

It allows the whole universe to be capable of total change in one second, if the right conditions were met.

We all grew up with this teaching that everything formed slowly over time. Our own lives are short by such standards, so it feels naturally correct to take this view, and imprint it upon our consciousness. In this way, it was agreed this linear view should be accepted and 'made fact'.

That was fine, until we began looking for final evidence that all this was actually true. The current idea that the earth has 'formed' from particles that joined together in a disc, and then began whirling around, now has to be challenged. There are numerous reasons that offer compelling evidence that this never happened at all, and could not conceivably have done so; [small particles in space have sometimes been seen to exist in clouds, yet do not show this tendency to form into discs, indeed quite the reverse. Particles tend to acquire a charge, often negatively, for a variety of reasons such as friction, and when these are the same, the tendency is actually to repel, not combine.]

There are other problems with our current view, the water here being one. The oceans are huge, and said to have succeeded after earth's initially red hot state. Yet from this fiery origin proposed for earth, we are asked to believe that frozen comets then arrived at just the right time, like a stream of ice cream vans on a hot day, and just when

the earth had cooled enough to just the right temperature, to begin a
build-up of water on such a vast scale as to form 70.8% of the earth's
surface.

As noted, the oceans are vast at 1340 million cubic kilometres, at
an average depth of 3730 metres. It may only be a fraction of 1%
of the earth by volume, but still a very big figure indeed, and that's
without some sizeable chunks of fresh water, like the poles, the vast
Great Lakes, or Lake Baikal, which is an inland sea really, at 23,000
cubic kms, and 1940 metres deep (6300ft). 3% is fresh, and 80% of
that is in the polar ice, the rest in rivers and lakes mainly.

The cometary water origin sounds nice, neat, but is it true? In the
linear time version, the necessity of long time made this the only option,
but it has not one difficulty, but several. They had to invent this origin,
having 'dismissed' eternity. Of course the universe is vastly old, but the
signs show cyclic phases, not one epoch. Time is therefore not limited
to 13 billion years, but much more...to infinity.

There are at least 12 simple issues about the cometary theory for the
origin of our oceans, and there could well be more. Sadly for tradition-
alists, not one of them supports such ocean transportation, which is
very significant.

Here are those 12 problems with oceans 'arriving' on earth:

1   Why does this not happen today? There should be some evidence
    of water-laden comet impacts on other planets. Mars is cited, but
    it shows very few impacts, and the idea that Mars once had oceans
    also assumes long linear time again.
2   Comets are rare; they burn up rapidly so would not exist for long
    enough to fill a lake with water, let alone the *millions of cubic
    kilometres* we require to tick this box.
3   The little that is known of comets is their make-up of frozen gases
    and dust, so they have been described as 'dirty snowballs'. Water
    ice is not necessarily a big part of their substance, and they remain
    rare sights in the night sky, which does tend to prove rarity, not the
    abundance needed to support the 'oceans from space' theory.
4   Any sediment derived from comets may well have a high iridium
    content or other stellar material, but this is not found here in
    sufficient quantities.

5 Also missing in the oceans are the high levels of deuterium[22] that are seen to be present in comets studied. If the ocean water is cometary in origin, it should also have the same high levels of deuterium in our own ocean water too. It doesn't.

6 Comets would not usually reach Earth, since space is so vast, the chances are slim that they all reached Earth in particular, a small spot in space terms. Their source of water remains unsolved, and would not have all ended up on earth.

7 Jupiter mainly, and Saturn too, the giant planets of our solar system, are much more likely to hoover up any stray comets, due to their mass and thus gravity. This we can see now, such as the Shoemaker-Levy 9 impacts filmed striking Jupiter in 1994.

8 No other planets or their moons have water oceans, so why would earth have such a vast share? Instead they have lakes of volatiles such as ethane or methane.

9 If comets were once more plentiful than now, the other planets should logically have a high water content, proof of a past one, but do not.

10 The neat rings of Saturn, if comets were once common, would be expected to comprise a lot more ice in their rings than they do. The F ring points to a younger formation date, not 3–4 billion years as claimed, with its pieces still unpulverised.

11 There is no evidence that there was never an ocean. Quite the reverse. The oldest fossils and the oldest amphibians would all require one, as do all marine sediments in order to be formed in layers on the ocean floor. An earth with no ocean is speculation.

12 A huge coincidence was needed. The old view of Time as a very, very long line required earth to have been formed slowly, building up its shape from particles of just the right size that 'came together' in space at just the right distance from the sun, so it didn't boil or freeze, called the *Goldilocks Zone* [after the 3 bears' porridge children's story: not too hot or cold, but just right for water]: very unlikely to happen if Time was random.

We may therefore conclude that ocean water may not be derived from millions of cometary snowballs hitting earth as first thought. In our

22 A form of hydrogen known as 'heavy water'.

galaxy, as perhaps in others by definition, comets are not expected to last for very long, due to their loss of matter on each pass of the sun, so their very existence suggests a cyclic solar system, by decaying rapidly in both orbit and mass.

The astronomer J. H. Oort invented the Oort Cloud in 1950 for this reason, as a *theoretical place* beyond telescope range which was the source of such comets. A cycle of short period would explain this without creating this cloud as a source. The mere idea of long linear time 'forced' him to invent it, and others to accept it, showing how cosmology often works: if you need anything…just invent it.

The Sun's ionic or 'solar wind' is the cause of their long tails that so entranced the ancient Greeks and Romans, who viewed them as strange portents of great change. This is not a small loss of a few surface molecules, but the wholesale disintegration of the comet itself, so they often break up and fall apart never to be seen again. The short period comets cannot be very old for this reason, and even the long period comets with distant orbits cannot last for too many years, since every pass of the sun removes still more tons of material. Very ancient they could not be.

To say the oceans must have formed from these rare items, is just not likely. Yet this is a central tenet of linear time, claiming the oceans '*must have*' appeared in this way.

If they did not form like this, then linear time as a concept is over, and with it our view of how the solar system formed. In a cycle, it does not need to form.

This extraordinary suggestion may seem absurd at first, but our pledge to the scientific method that forces us to follow where the evidence leads us, must take precedence over our own preferences.

Another shock from space was the find reported in Nature in April 2012, that the Neodymium ratio of isotopes 142Nd and 144Nd is not the same as for the stony [chondritic] meteorites earth was supposed to have formed alongside, 4.5 billion years ago. This appears to support cyclic time.

Why is this such big news? Those speedy meteors we see flashing across the sky now and then, and which land from time to time on earth, often at the poles where it is easier to see and collect them, were 'meant' to have formed when earth did, from a big cloud of gas and dust particles...they were expected to be the same, but aren't. This allows for the conclusion that earth was always here, and the meteors are not relics of the solar system's birth, as nearly everyone assumed they 'must be'.

As a race, we humans tend to be decisive about things we believe in. In regard to theories, we must be ready to change them, but this is not easily done. Who is to say that certain items of theoretical physics are right or wrong? Mistakes can persist for centuries. Each era thinks it is the best ever, which is true in its way, with more data.

The British industrial revolution was fuelled by the arrival of steam power, and the burning of coal to create heat and iron for rails and machinery in general. This spirit of change was embodied by several people, such as I.K. Brunel, his father Marc and others, who were so passionate about the new metals that one person was even known as John 'Iron-Mad' Wilkinson. It may be a long shot, but he might have been quite a fan of cast iron. He was certainly a great material success, and became so wealthy he once offered to pay off England's national debt.

We tend to think of modern times as *the* great age in which all old notions are discarded in favour of perfectly formed, new, better and entirely proven facts of modern science. The myth of the flat Earth is an example. Anyone who has steered a small ship at night has seen how an approaching vessel's lights appear some time before its wheelhouse is visible, even when surprisingly close to their own. Only a spherical Earth explains that...and the lack of pictures ever taken of the mythical 'underneath', were it to be flat. It is often said that a wish for clarity can be answered with one answer, while a person's doubt is not resolved with ten correct replies.

Most people were taught the view, perpetuated over many years, that the older thinkers in our history all thought the earth was flat, and that only modern science was able to prove it was spherical. This is entirely untrue.

Roger Bacon, the English philosopher and mathematician, mentioned the earth's curvature in the 13th century, but that was very late in the day compared to our first records of earth as a sphere. The ancient Greeks and Romans as far back as the 250 BC used the stars to calculate the curvature of the earth, and its size to within 60 miles.

They were certainly not the first, since their maths and many other skills were in large part derived from India, where the invention of the zero in maths altered the speed and dexterity of calculations forever, and that was 1800 years ago.

Roger Bacon, born in 1214 and later known as the Wonderful Doctor, was very perceptive about the means of research. He reckoned there were two ways to gain 'knowledge', which were Reasoning and Experience, but his great concern was especially focused on the human limitations when he pointed out that: Reasoning 'does not make the conclusion certain, nor does it remove doubt.'[23] Reasoning by itself can be too subjective, so we need much more to be sure of that elusive certainty. Very clever, and that was 750 years ago.

A long line of time would be fine, if it wasn't for modern discoveries. We even found larger mountain ranges below the ocean than exist on land, which the 19th century geologists of the Victorian era knew nothing about. In those days, even glaciers were a mysterious novelty of strange power long vanished from sight in most places, while balloons were a newfangled form of air travel, so most major advances were yet to come.

How good were those early pioneers at working out the structure of Time and the cosmos under its apparent control? Not good, it has to be said, with none of our modern data. Steam power was almost magically clever, metal ships were held in deep suspicion of imminent sinking (they were iron after all, not known for its natural buoyancy) while the train was considered the work of the devil by many, who felt certain the brain would boil if moving at the huge speed of 40mph. It was all too hasty. They were keen on building all right, but nothing too fast that bordered on the unseemly.

A basic form of atomic structure had been deduced for two millennia, by the Greeks, Indians and Eastern philosophers originally, but the big quantum stuff was to come much later after 1915. Not by chance were these giant leaps in thinking made by Einstein and Nils Bohr after the First World War, while the older generation of scientists had largely died in the war, as Prof. Lee Smolin shrewdly points out:

---

23 Opus Majus, 1267, from Chambers Dictionary of Quotations, 1996, p60.

'There simply weren't many senior scientists around to tell them they were crazy'.[24]

It only takes one person to speak up, and science advances.

Our impression of Time is perhaps the biggest, broadest and most far reaching of all physical ideas.

The consequences of getting this wrong are serious indeed, with some of the most major failings in future prediction. If we had predicted a major Indian Ocean sub-sea tectonic movement before the 2004 Banda Aceh quake of 9 on the Richter scale, we could have had more warning time, or created better tsunami wave detection systems. There are other areas at risk from large events we consider much rarer than they are. In linear terms, they would be rare. If time is cyclic, then that changes everything. They are no longer 1 in 1000 year events, but more like 1 in 4.

Even the cycles of life and daylight are not fixed. It may sound counter-intuitive, but not when we examine the nature of space, and the systems which rule nature's biological connections. Unless we live at the latitude of Iceland or Spitzbergen, which has months of night without day, and day without night, we live with the cycle of day and night in 24 hour chunks.

The evidence now points towards a quantum flow of energy that ebbs and flows in spans of time that are also connected, very like the solar maximum that twists the sun's magnetosphere in a knot, and then unwinds much more rapidly, with powerful releases of energy as coronal mass ejections, known as CME's for short.

The process seems to work a little bit like the ocean's tides that build into a bulge or mound, and then ebb. This cyclic process is so exact that it can be predicted exactly, even accounting for the spring or neap tides when the sun and moon combine or separate in their effects during a tidal day of 24 hours and 50 minutes. There are so many cycles of all the components of earth's surface, and interior, that we may well not yet have found them all.

We are literally surrounded by cyclic patterns of change, even within our own bodies. Our own blood never flows in a line, but always in a circle. Our neural and so many other biological systems are also circular.

24 The Trouble with Physics, L. Smolin 2006, p348

These may seem like small scale examples, but from the very small, to the seriously massive like water, carbon and nitrogen, cycles seem to be nature's way of running almost everything. The process of rotation appears to be the central pivotal method of motion, almost a default mechanism for life and space. Could Time also be repeating events? It seems it can.

Change is never easy, but improvement in our thinking must prepare us for the future. From geology we can see the ancient sea level was 300 feet higher than it is today, thanks largely to the trapping of water in the polar ice caps today, which makes it 100m or 300 feet lower, with extra land made available.

Many huge events, such as the formation of entirely new seas, were always thought to have happened very slowly over long spans of time, until now that is. The latest evidence all supports the cyclic view in which events happened much faster than thought earlier. Two spectacular examples are those of the Mediterranean and Black Seas.

The Zanclean sediments recently located in those areas of Gibraltar and the Bosphorus respectively show clear proof of very rapid water movements as reported in Nature in 2016. There also seems to be a link between these huge events, when cubic miles of water began to spill over the earth's surface to flood previously dry areas, perhaps when the axial oscillations altered the earth's tilt angle.

We cover all this later, but the oceans are a major item to come from space. It seems they may not have done so.

CHAPTER 4

A Quick Q&A

Are there errors in our notion
of Time itself?

But where is everybody?
DR E. FERMI, 1950; Fermi Paradox on the lack of aliens

I make myself laugh at everything for fear of having to weep at it.
C DE BEAUMARCHAIS, C1760

Here are some facts that alter what we think…
Q. *The origins of the earth & space: All neatly sorted out and accepted, right?*
A. Actually, not even close. Some of those 'accepted facts' were made up a century ago, but never worked. We are taught that science knows most of what there is to know. Top scientists say this. In a triumph of modern science, the great pioneers have worked out nearly every detail, from the deep ocean to the farthest stars, and even way back in time to a dizzying distance only measurable in light years. This is how we see the world of earth, and the universe: from a claimed perspective of great understanding.

In the small scale, science has changed the world with many benefits, but on the space scale, the story is full of errors. Slowly, the presumptions of our ancestors were transformed into facts, written in textbooks, and taught to our youth of each successive generation.
Q. *Did no one say anything?*
A. They did. Thousands of lone voices were raised about some of the glaring errors in this plainly mistaken conventional worldview, with the world's people barely looking up from their desks. Religious views posed a risk to that viewpoint, it is true, but they were carefully ignored where possible, challenged in court whenever possible, and dismissed as gullible and essentially deluded.

Then something odd happened. Many mainstream scientists of very high calibre began to realise things were not all rosy in the garden of science. Some trees of theory were rotten, some flowers were not at all as they were described, and many items with clever names did not actually exist. We had made up whole parallel universes in attempts to plug some of the huge gaps in that old and very artificial world view. That 'multiverse' is not an answer, but a desperate invention with no evidence. The old view had failed.

Then in the late 20th century, a new group of people emerged, almost entirely unconnected with each other, comprising thinkers in maths and science who had independently worked out reasons why the old views simply did not add up. Many such thinkers had studied both science and religion, and found no key contradictions between the two, yet seeing connections that showed subtle ties were interesting.

These new thinkers pointed out that nearly all we 'know' depends on several key assumptions. Take them away, and we've got nothing left. These old notions, taken to be rules, were all sharing one common theme: they were linear.

Q. *Why is that such a big deal?*

A. It is ok if it works, but if not, it would stop scientific progress, and even destroy the understanding of knowledge. Time underlies all we do. If this concept is wrong, then we would be in trouble, because it would invalidate every big theory we have. The problem is huge: we think we know so much, yet nothing in 'giant scale' physics works, so we cannot be right. It was vital to check deeper. As others have pointed out, we actually know more about the surface of Mars than parts of the deep ocean. Even the moon is more familiar, the side we can see anyway, and English astronomer Sir Patrick Moore had mapped it with such accuracy that he was consulted by NASA about good landing spots before the 1969 touchdown.

Q. *Why do some say a cycle of time is the most profound change in modern times?*

A. A cycle would change the reasoning we use in all we do. If we are approaching the end of a cycle, we may need to alter how we live each day. It would turn upside down our vision of our own origins as people, and of the planets, and even suggest new purposes in life by showing the universe is not the place of chance some have claimed. A cycle would give a value and importance to everything we do that was never realised.

Q. *Why the need for a new worldview at all? Is science not largely right?*

A. Alas not. No one realised our impression of Time was even an issue, and no one imagined *our vision of Time itself* could conceivably have been the flaw. All this new evidence and thinking shows the old mechanistic vision of reality has deeply misled us in every aspect of human awareness. For our plans to have meaning, that needs to change.

Q. *How would anyone know things were not right at such a deep level?*

A. For so many old ideas to be failing, something must be wrong. That is the sign the old thinking must be invalid. No one realised our whole vision of time itself could be to blame. Even Big Bang theory was in trouble, being broadly accepted by some, yet seen as 'impossible' by other top experts. Yet the obstacle still existed. We had accepted a view that no longer explained the latest discoveries of science, *which really were facts.*

Q. *Which discoveries?*

A. At over 1,200 examples, the list is surprisingly long, in space and on Earth. The Lydia family of asteroids have an 'origin problem', having a great variation in their composition. This would be impossible if they formed from the same gas cloud in a neat 'line of time' as thought. The largest is 185kms across, so they are big. Then take the distance of Jupiter from the Sun; it should not be there as a gas giant, if time were linear. So experts invented a 'migration' from somewhere else, and carried on. The different planetary compositions are a big issue as well, some with magnetic fields and rocks, others of gas or ice, but lacking the uniformity required if they truly arose from the same cloud. The F Ring of Saturn we touched on, which would have only small ice pieces in it, had it truly formed 4 billion years ago as claimed. These pieces are constantly abrading, so they would be largely dust by now, yet they aren't; a sign of clear youth.

Q. *Is there a more down to earth example?*

A. There are hundreds. Recently[25] an intriguing new example joined this list: a nematode or tiny worm less than ½ mm long, called

25 Nature, vol 474, no:7349, 2 June 2011 pages 79–82

H.mephisto was found inside deep rock water at a blistering 48°C in the South African Beatrix gold mine, up to 3.6kms below the surface, and in level 26, and *yet not in the mining water*. This shows they were there when the layers formed, and that creates a big problem for the old 'long line' of time idea still used. The original sediment, with the worms inside, must have been part of a huge 'overturn', in which calm conditions suddenly became very turbulent, as in an axial tilt, and did so recently, allowing the worms to survive and be found today. Millions of years are not needed.

Q. *Why so hot, and so what if there are worms so deep in mine shafts?*

A. Deep mines are extra hot being nearer the red hot magma below the earth's crust. It can be 5–10°C hotter for every kilometre of descent, as in a mine shaft.

This find is astonishing because it shows science was wrong to presume no life existed at such depth. It contradicts current thinking. It shows the worms were present before any recent groundwater entered the mine workings around Shaft 3, where many samples were taken. Carbon-14 dates of the water material gave extreme variations of 3–12k years, a huge range of inaccuracy which casts doubt on this method of age determination itself. The deep water is also assumed to be very old, since it 'couldn't be young' in rock that deep and thus that old. Linear theory cannot begin to explain the worms' existence rummaging around inside rock claimed to be 2,700 million years old by some estimates. This is just not credible, but there is another snag. Evolution theory claims only bacteria lived that long ago, so where did these worms come from, without any ancestors? No such creatures were meant to exist then...a serious problem for the troubled linear time theory. Also, if they really had lived inside those rocks for so long, there would be many tons of their dead ancestors. No such finding was made. This is where science has invented solutions which are not possible, and point to errors in the very thinking about timescales.

Q. *So does any of this help with solving the 'origin of Earth' puzzle?*

A. It appears it can, but the answer suggested is so bizarre that it takes some extra consideration, existing as it does on the edge of what most of us are willing to accept.

Q. *I'll be the judge of that, so try me: I want details...so what is this strange solution?*

A. We seem to have two schools of thought on the origin of the Earth, but neither is able to win over the opinion of the other group. One may be right, but which? Instead of slow, gradual events over billions of years as claimed, the signs show rapid and truly extreme, dynamic changes in earth's geology. Clues to this lie in the spectacular Monument Valley, made famous by films about the Wild West, just north east of the Grand Canyon. Both are claimed to be millions of years old, but the valleys' isolated pinnacles all have the same exact height, showing the level of an earlier plane of sediment. The fact that these pinnacles remain, all neatly similar with the red colour of an iron-rich reducing environment, suggests a very different scenario. Now 5–6000 feet (1830m) above sea level, the valleys could have been formed by a very rapid land uplift, so the earlier ocean water that is known to have existed 'above' what is now western America, would have rushed west with great power, removing the sedimentary layers between and around those towers of vertical rock, leaving them as we can see today.

Evidence of this colossal power, and massive scale of such turbulent water movement, can also be found in Zion National Park to the west, which has a large hole around 1000 feet (320m) above the valley floor. To form such a hole at that height confirms +300m flood depth at the time. That hole, and others like it in that area, were not chewed out by mice, but by huge scale flooding moving a great speed. Those holes and canyons could not have formed slowly or gently over long periods, but only with highly active sediment-laden water vortices of great depth and force. The Grand Canyon and Monument Valley could have been cut by such forces. Such conditions would arise from an axial tilt of the earth, and the continental uplift as well, as the continents were rapidly forced to find equilibrium in new positions...the break-up of Pangea, the old supercontinent, of which America was of course a part.

This would also allow for the cutting of the Grand Canyon, about a mile or 1800m deep, which need not require millions of years for its formation. Such speed brings to mind the huge ripple banks in Washington State's Columbia River area, just east from Seattle in the spectacular Pacific north-west of America, where a rapid outpouring of the water in glacial Lake Missoula (see Glossary) cut a path westwards, and laid down those huge glacial deposits. The quantity is estimated at about 2300km³, or about 550 cubic miles of water, which is a lot. This re-shaped 60,000 sq.kms of land in a few weeks.

Bearing this in mind, the idea of a short cycle begins to gain ground.

Q. *Have you a point or two that shows time is now wrongly dated?*

A. There are so many, and here are a few to get you started. The population of Earth's humanity is put at millions of years in the making, yet it oddly fits into 4,950 years, even with huge disasters over history, and then there's this. How come there aren't more than 137 skeletons ever found of the Neanderthal, and a few early types of hominid, when they were 'meant' to have lived for around 5–750,000 years? As noted, *there should be 600 billion* of them. This problem is just ignored, because it shows all is in disarray.

There should be islands of such bones, as there are with mammoth remains in northern Russia's huge Novaya Zemlya island. This is explained by Neanderthals not being as successful as modern humans, but that won't wash at all. They were heavier, stronger, better built than *H. sapiens*, and often with a 13% larger brain than we have.

First wrongly thought to have been brutish ape-like creatures with no human qualities or culture to speak of, it turned out this was a big mistake, when beads and flower-filled burials began to turn up in excavated Neanderthal sites, such as in Shanidar, northern Iraq. We will return to how these apparent misconceptions arose.

Q. *That is shocking, but what of time itself. Surely the long line of Time is a well proven truth we all know and accept, so why bother with a new version?*

A. This concept of a universe that rotates over the course of time works as a way of explaining what we see. If not a cycle, then what else? Put bluntly, since present models of the long line of Time do not appear viable, then what are we left with? Only a cycle works. A spiral is still just a line with a few twists, as is a single or double helix, so that leaves us with a ring or a Mobius strip [26], which is at least fully cyclic; and a continuum.

---

26 ∞ is the symbol for infinity and this cyclic time motion, with two 'switches' of matter state: order to chaos, and back.

Q. *But surely the long line of time is still an accepted fact these days, isn't it?*

A. It is accepted by many, yes; but well proven...not at all. Is it beyond dispute? Definitely not. The extraordinary reality is that current thinking about Time is still theoretical conjecture: experts don't know what happened in the far past, so ideas are suggested. We can make informed guesses, but they stop well short of working out exactly how the cosmos clicks. Even the long acceptance of linear time does not amount to evidence, so Time remains a mystery to solve.

Q. *Has anything changed in the last decade or two?*

A. Yes, a lot. Thanks to science, we have a great deal of new information about both earth and space. The Horizon Problem radically changes our centuries old situation of the classic stalemate, usually between religion and science. Actually both are similar in their views of time, even the way it could be cyclic.

Q. *Why have I not met more people who know about this?*

A. You will meet many more. Like all new ideas, this too takes time to be seen and assessed. This book gathers a large body of fresh evidence never seen in one place, and finds new conclusions which take a while to be considered. There are now a lot more people who like the natural fit of a cyclic cosmos.

Q. *Why do few experts seem to agree with this cyclic analysis of time?*

A. Two answers to this: first, it is new to science, so they may not have seen a comprehensive account of these new data, which is likely, because this author had never seen one either. Other versions of Time are current, but are very different; this makes an entirely new world view, like this one, a challenge even to consider. Secondly, many people simply don't have 20–30 years to carry out a root and branch reappraisal of so many such involved issues. Many lack a reason to find new answers; each side is firmly convinced that it already supports the winning team, job done. While we remain fixed in an old deep-seated mind-set, we may never see a need for change.

Q. *So why all the media excitement?*

A. A new world view that works is exciting news, and explains why several top scientists have focused on cyclic alternatives. The other key issue at the centre of this debate of Earth's origin and nature is its exact age. Even this question is incorrect, and not as obvious as it may seem, nor is the answer.

The right question to ask is: 'Does Time last forever, and always exist?' If so, we have new answers to all our questions, and the old question of 'when did it start?' no longer applies. That was the old question to ask, and because it had no true answer, it never worked as a solution.

Q. *Could it counter 2000 years of our comfortable, traditional linear thinking that most people seem to think works; and is religion involved?*

A. Each of us has to decide this, but many think it can. The heart of the matter is not a Science versus Religion issue, nor the old 'did it evolve or did God create it?' frontier. A cycle is about a third option that finds reason in both ends of the spectrum.

Q. *Could this version of reality ever change our global thinking?*

A. If this cyclic model is correct, it would enable us to predict the natural future with accuracy. That would be very useful indeed.

Q. *How could just a different concept of Time change so much?*

A. If this model of Time does fit the facts better than the old one, it forces us to rethink our entire worldview. Huge holes are appearing in that world view, as whole galaxies are in the 'wrong place', moving at the 'wrong speed', and are far bigger or heavier than they 'should be'. Even the amount of matter we see cannot explain its own existence or gravitational effects. Current answers cannot explain all this, so Dark Matter and Energy may seem to plug the gaps, but cannot be found, and so may not exist at all.

Q. *Why is any of this a problem?*

A. It shows the 'standard model' of the cosmos needs radical revision.

Q. *Doesn't everyone in science know this and are responding?*

A. Many do, yet many others are still trying to bolt on new fixes to revive the old model. These fixes may solve nothing, and imply the need for a profoundly different approach, as suggested by Sir Roger Penrose and others.

Q. *How does a cycle help all this?*

A. Surprisingly, it solves all these problems. Gone is the need to create the world 'out of nothing', which both science and religion continue to have serious trouble explaining: where would all the matter come from? Science then invented other universes from which the matter would magically spring. This is not really a solution, but another invention which remains un-provable. In this cyclic time fashion, the cosmos is always in existence, and never ceases to be present. This may sound peculiar at first, but Nature was never easy to predict, and our artificial linear version of time may prove to be the peculiar one after all. In its place is the apparent existence of a natural rotation.

Q. *Surely our account of deep history still works.*

A. Very oddly, there is clear evidence to show our classic view of prehistory could all be mistaken too. The further back we look, this cyclic view of Time was common knowledge in the ancient world, and appears well understood. Naturally we feel sure our modern thinking must be better than the best the ancients could produce. Yet the truth of the matter may be very different to this presumption.

Q. *What about the dating of rocks and artefacts that tell a different story?*

A. This is the great challenge for science: all these methods rest on the assumption of long, linear time. Take away that, and these dating systems no longer prove the dates the rocks formed, or when the artefacts were in use.

Q. *How can solid rocks be wrongly dated as this suggests?*

A. With alarming ease, and here is how: tests show that elements once thought to have formed over time are actually present when volcanic rocks formed at their eruption from below the Earth's crust. This invalidates the primary basis of linear time.

Q. *Is that it?*

A. The chapters explain the process in detail, but this problem by itself is sufficient to change the way we have dated earth's entire history. Evidence also shows that the state of gravity, thanks to particle spin changes, may be the switching mechanism for chaos to flip back into order, and vice versa.

Q. *Isn't all this rather improbable?*

A. Indeed it can look unlikely at first glance, but it coincides with the natural processes of Nature, which show continuity. The cyclic model does appear to work better than linear versions of time. On this basis, it can be true.

Q. *What is the reaction to all of this?*

A. The response is very encouraging. The majority support it, while being understandably puzzled by its implications. Some observers react by being excited at the potential for progress in several sciences. Some refuse to accept anything is wrong or out of place, since the heart of these old inconsistencies in science have been emerging here and there for centuries. The fact the big problems have yet to be properly solved is strong and compelling evidence that all is not well with the conventional theories. At least we have to discuss these matters and problems, and be ready for profound revisions if they are felt necessary.

Q. *Does all this matter much to the average person?*

A. Indeed it does, and more than we may appreciate. It is possible the extreme natural events we are witnessing may be happening together for other reasons than pure chance. In that case, we may be approaching the cyclic time equivalent of an extreme meltdown of order, before calm is rapidly restored. If this is correct, then all our future plans would need to change to accommodate this natural process.

Q. *How does a new world view help in any of this?*

A. So far, the cyclic version is the only explanation of how Nature is in this state of increasing upheaval, and what may happen next.

Q. *Any evidence for that?*

A. Here's one piece among many. The 2011 Sendai quake that occurred on 11th March off the coast of North East Japan was not expected in that location by many experts, yet was predicted by one team in 2001, led by Koji Minoura, who found evidence of a marine inundation from a great tsunami in AD 869, 4 kms inland [27]. That had a farther water penetration inland than even the more recent event, which was graded nine on the Richter scale. Using the linear prediction techniques, they judged it to be a once in 1000 year event. Sure enough, an 8.4 quake did hit the area in 1933, but only 78 years later came the magnitude 9 quake of 2011. This would have been 922 years sooner than expected, if the linear statistical techniques were right. Sadly they were not. It was thought that old rupture zones that moved slowly could not react this fast, so long after the tectonic plate margins actually formed. It is therefore probable that these rupture zones are not as old as science has claimed. Calls are now being made to tear up

27 New Scientist, 23.4.11, p3

the old statistical rulebook, so profound was the error of assumption made in this case.

Q. *Curious, but how does that affect the future?*

A. This is the key value of the cyclic time model. If we agree there is a faster pattern of these giant events, thus more frequent quakes to come, then if we can react in time to prepare for that, the outcome could be very different in terms of potential loss of life. Usually we are all surprised by these events. If we use this cyclic process to predict them, we may be able to change that reaction into preparation.

Q. *I don't see any evidence in the modern 21st century world that a cycle exists, or is about to begin another roll of time. Is there any?*

A. It is all around us, and the clues are in the chaos we see in both society and Nature. Chaos increases. It reaches a point of maximum and then stops. We are seeing abnormal extremes in every area of nature, from melting ice to quakes and tornadoes, to wars and social violence. Local government takes extreme steps to raise money, ignoring the stress caused. With over 7.5 billion people now, we have never seen this scale of such unrest, and nature is also subject to these forces of rising disorder. This is also why the acceleration of the galaxies is such powerful evidence of a very recent switch between cycles, rather than a far distant 'bang' as usually suggested, which would be slowing down as everyone predicted it must be. The fact it is the opposite, shows the reverse must be true, meaning that the universe can indeed be alternating back and forth between Order and Chaos on a regular, and rapid basis.

Q. *Can we sum up why a cyclic cosmos could explain how nature works?*

A. We can try. The linear model has the fatal flaws so well explained by Sir Roger Penrose, as mentioned, in his fine 2010 book *Cycles of Time*, and by Prof Lee Smolin in his equally impressive 2006 book *The Trouble with Physics*; as Penrose so rightly pointed out, if that doesn't work, what does? As his book explained, only a complete circle for Time appears to fit the facts we see. The vital need now is to re-assess how long each cycle takes to turn. Now that the evidence seems to point so overwhelmingly towards an ultra-short sequence of identical repetition, this could be the 'very different' type of answer predicted by Penrose[28].

Q. *Can we improve our realisation that 'what we think' may not be real?*

A. We always struggle with our subjective viewpoint, and inherited errors.

Using a global perspective, which we may call 100% reality, if we take a quick tour of the planet, we can observe a very different perspective beyond the purely local one we may normally use. A very local view may be completely different, with no apparent signs of much that is wrong, unless we are living in Baghdad. Some areas of the world are calm, while others are caught in the grip of war, where even the sharing of beliefs has been weaponised. This welding of weapons to scriptures is a mistake according to reason, while the real need is for great tolerance and understanding.

The modern era has fallen into a deep canyon of uncertainty, which is not quite the look we were going for. We see the effect of our differing levels of discrimination in every sphere of life, and how we plan to react to every change. At the heart of all these problems is a loss of mental energy, and our interpretation of how reality works. It is as if the human mind is losing degrees of energy.

Many think it is very plain and obvious to judge what is real and what is not, but in fact we make serious mistakes in such judgements. Now that science has moved further ahead since Einstein's singular era in 1915, we have not yet adjusted to account for the findings science has so skilfully discovered. Some serious problems within science have yet to be solved, and mainly because of one aspect: our interpretation of what it all means.

Q. *Can we be sure of what we 'know'?*

A. Often, when we think we have acquired new knowledge, what we actually have is new theory, and the result has placed science in turmoil. This is no exaggeration, as many now realise. Not all of science is wrong, but a great deal of it is, and so not all of it is right either. This is the challenge we face.

The curious fact is this: recent discoveries in the last 10 years have produced results so strange that scientists are both unsure what they mean, and unable to explain them. What does all this mean? We now

28 The Road to Reality, R.Penrose, Vintage 2005,p1033

have enough new data to form an entirely new worldview based on all this information, yet no one has created one that actually works.

Q. *Why not?*

A. One reason is that the implications are so unusual, peer pressure makes us unwilling to draw the conclusions the data are indicating. Science is also struggling with the enormity of this new set of data, because it shows that the central structure of our worldview has to be mistaken. The simple fact we now have to accept is a new one is needed. We have precious little time in which to switch the direction of humanity's aims to include all this new information about what the future appears to hold, before the new passage of time becomes all too obvious to everyone, at which point it is then too late to change.

As recent tragic events in the tectonic plates off the coast of Japan, to the west of Sumatra and off the coast of Thailand have shown, the structure of the earth is undergoing some major changes. Some claim that this is nothing out of the ordinary, but the same data they use can be interpreted in an entirely different and rather unsettling way. It is possible they are profoundly mistaken in thinking this tectonic activity is nothing unusual. If true, we have some major rethinking to do.

Q. *Does it matter what science thinks?*

A. Indeed it does, and very much so, because many people have come to rely on science, and do so because science appears to address the changes that are happening in the world, so that many people regard it as the method to avoid disasters nearly all of us can see in the future, as events move to a chaos peak. Even science fiction has a say in this. Indeed many of the wildest ideas within science fiction have either become science fact, such as mobile phones and space travel, or have become accepted ideas within science as an institution, such as aliens from outer space, for which there is not the smallest trace of proof of any kind. Yet many in science regard their existence as true, while other scientists accept the real position of having no evidence to support this conjecture. The makers of the Roswell film admitted it was a fabrication.

While science has made some brilliant discoveries, this does not mean that all scientific theories are similarly correct. If we look at a deeper level of both our humanity and science itself, we find that science would be entirely unable to save the Earth from the disaster.

Yet this evidence shows the outcome is always good in the end, because the cyclic processes that ensure this are bigger than any of us; and Time is not random, but pre-existing, so it always runs to order.

Q. *Has science seen new chaos patterns in Nature?*

A. The speculation of disaster frequency currently discounts the potential that Nature may have her own way of changing the way life on Earth works.

The good news is that we are still here, and if Time is indeed a cyclic process as this book suggests, then our continued presence on the planet is strong evidence that no matter what disasters may occur, humanity wins through and continues to thrive. Science does have quite a record of being seriously reluctant to accept its own new findings, along with their implications, even within its own ranks of experts, and is famously slow to adapt to new reality as it appears to be.

Cyclic time predicts we always survive, and here we are to prove it.

Luckily for all of us, there is sufficient time to put all this right with a series of new discussions on Time itself. Some believe such radical changes are not yet needed, and that greater tectonic activity on the horizon sounds rather unlikely.

Q. *Surely someone in a university would have told us if it were so.*

A. They don't tell us because they don't know.

Since the giant category nine earthquake off Japan in March 2011, along with the destruction of all the Fukushima reactors behind the almost useless 5m concrete seawall, not to forget the tragic loss of 23,000 people, this academic group is smaller than it was.

For all its successes on smaller scales, science has never been able to predict the deep future. Yet if time is a cyclic process, then we should now be able to do so, and this book is a small attempt to combine the few solid facts and clues we have to see if they amount to a new understanding. If science were a perfect process, which few dare to claim, then its practitioners would have perfect thought processes and ideally balanced minds, and we would indeed have received due warning and notification about all these disasters, including the Chelyabinsk meteor that exploded over Russia on 15 Feb 2013, but sadly that was not the case (see Glossary for details).

Many such examples show that our understanding of the real world is grossly incomplete. The solution is brutally simple: both we and science itself have to be ready to take it all apart and start again, if need be. That moment has arrived. Just as before, Science can also take a leading role in resolving many of these profound issues, and is bound to do so.

Q. *Does every generation think it is the smartest ever?*

A. It seems so, but the news is full of people finding their rose-tinted view being snapped into 100% real in moments, and how shocking the experience was.

We even lead our lives as if we would never die, and act as if no one else will either. Sometimes we remember briefly, and appreciate our family and friends within a more realistic timeframe, but not often. Some people live each day by being just as kind, helpful and gentle as they can be, aware it will be better for all by living like that. Being aware of such feelings, thoughts and ideals becomes our philosophy, so we study the ancient texts of India, China, Egypt, Arabia, Greece and Rome, to see if they perceived the world differently.

The Greek world was also full of chaos in ancient times, but the Stoics had a wise take on it all. They reckoned that by changing local situations as little as possible, the resulting lack of change would carry the least disruption in the process of time's passage. Today, we don't even run our big cities with such wisdom, as the parking laws clearly show. Cities like London have many good shops and tourist spots to see, but the tough parking restrictions make it harder to reach them. The Greeks would never have done that, had they had cars, and nor did they prefer to enrich local councils with heavy fines, rather than helping people and trade to prosper fairly.

Q. *So how much do we really know about the reality of life, even if we could read all the books in the world, how could we ever work out which of their many messages were true?*

A. The key task is to separate pure speculation from absolute certainties. We have to be careful what we accept. Even the US president would be in the same position, receiving only a well-sieved version of news. As many have noted, even the most well-informed leaders are not given a broad view of situations on which to decide their actions; so how should we proceed?

Perhaps the first step is to winnow out some of the wilder offerings. Accept very little via the net. This is the specific and necessarily single-minded quest for true reality, where even the desire for a specific outcome has to be set aside if observations do not support it.

Q. *Does the future look good in a cyclic world?*

A. It always turns out perfectly in a cycle, but not in any other versions. This is great news, because it shows how science has proved this to be the outcome we can look forward to. Some in science may disagree, but none of the other models explain reality. All the evidence points to this eternal outcome, which could not be better, indeed the best it possibly can be.

Brief Point Guide to 'Flash Time'

Just because Einstein and Prof Hawking chose an opposite view to this one, does not mean they were right, or that anyone may not form a viable opinion of an alternative. It shows even the greatest experts can make mistakes. Here are some key points:

- The theme is simplicity itself: every few years a vast change happens in a 'Flash'
- Proof of this appears to be the 'flatness' of the universe, meaning the energy and density are equal or 'flat'; either unlikely or impossible.
- The human influence is a key factor science is only now considering as a cause
- This book shows evidence Nature does this in a short period cyclic pattern
- These details point to this event cycle repeating as a precise play of steps
- If so, this is the best news in history: it means life would always return to order
- 300 year old ideas can only now be shown as mistaken eg time as a long line
- Our population of 7.5 billion needs only 4950 years to form in each cycle
- The *Flash Time Zero* moment is when the old cycle switches to a new one

- The claim of millions of years passing fails modern science tests of 'proof'
- Famous ideas like Big Bang & Evolution theories were never compared to cyclic time evidence, and now seem to fail such tests; science no longer supports them
- Did matter arise from nothing or was it always here as a continuum?
- Only now have we the latest science to compare with ancient awareness
- Some prefer old ideas to new ones, but only we can tell if we are dreaming
- Many people have a subtle awareness of the world being far better than now
- How can there be a deep memory of a past cycle...unless it existed?
- The chaos wave becomes unsustainable, falls apart, and then returns to calm
- Nature is circular, decaying into a chaos peak & then collapsing into calm again
- Extreme storms always equalise extreme imbalance
- We may agree or disagree, yet science cannot prove this cycle does not happen forever as part of a natural process we are only now detecting as realistic
- Time as a line fails because it uses assumptions; cyclic time works without them
- Our future is bright because nothing can prevent the return of the old Calm Era
- Even Stone Age people knew this, as their disc symbols seem to suggest
- Conscious people can play a central role in guiding this cosmic event sequence
- The link is that human minds can alter the spin of matter...across the universe

Scholars in both science and religion agree this can be how Nature moves along.

CHAPTER 5

How Correct is Science?

Science has 'explained' nothing: the more we know the more fantastic the world becomes and the profounder the surrounding darkness.
ALDOUS HUXLEY, 1925

If you are absolutely...and persistently wrong you must, one day, have the extreme good fortune of knocking your head against a fact, and that sets you all straight again.
T. H. HUXLEY, 1890; attributed

Essence

In all our searching for knowledge, we encounter one major limitation: the mind. New results need new methods of thinking. This might sound rather obscure in a hunt for facts, but it lies at the heart of the whole of human understanding: how we choose what is likely to be true. That is never going to be an objective judgement, because we have to leave out nearly everything. Choose one, leave out 10,000 items. Now that is selective.

As Mark Twain remarked in 1883: 'There is something fascinating about science. One gets such wholesale returns of conjecture out of such a trifling investment of fact.'

Even the use of evidence will be cherry-picked to suit our aim, and is thus predisposed towards our intended outcome; not intentionally to mislead of course, yet it creeps in via the selection process, despite attempts to exclude it. Take ten or 100 such linked outcomes, and it can look like proof. Such apparent proof may look convincing, and yet can also be very wrong. It was Robert Oppenheimer, who led the atom bomb team in World War II, who warned later in 1967 that 'No man should escape our universities without knowing how little he knows'.

Science explores ideas or 'hypotheses', which are informed guesses of what 'may be so'. Whether they may be right or not, no one knows, as Dame Jocelyn Bell Burnell, the respected discoverer of pulsars, explains so clearly. As she said, research is always a work in progress, so we can never trust ideas completely. A 'solution' is like a 'tame' tiger in the kitchen: it has to be checked on constantly, in case it goes horribly wrong.

As Sir Karl Popper said in 1934 that 'Every scientific statement must remain tentative forever'; and that should be the case, yet few live by it.

The more we check up on big scale science, the more we have to admit it is not the collection of solid indisputable facts claimed. In the older days, scientists knew this, and kept using phrases like 'could be' and might be'.

Today scientists use much bolder language, hoping to be more persuasive, yet not always wisely so; they often set aside the tentative nature inherent in research about unknown things, and jump in feet first with certainties like 'is' and 'we now know' this. This implies clearly that the earlier version was all wrong, but that admission is left out. We are therefore looking at a mixture of wonderful precision and outright guesswork, with no admission of the latter. Experts know this too, and many realise they do not have a monopoly on truth just because fridges and steam engines have worked quite well (though rarely for long enough with a hint of built-in obsolescence).

As J.Krishnamurti pointed out in 1970, nearly all experts rely on others for their influence, not only because there is a lack of time in one life to check everything, but also the unwillingness to take risks: 'One relies on authority because one is afraid to stand alone'. Some think that life is complex, and that escape is the answer. Reality tells a different story, because the clues point to a cycle of short duration, and that would mean we have to face the music here on Earth, and will succeed in doing so.

Arthur Koestler wrote in 1953 that 'Space-ships and time machines are no escape from the human condition'. The temptation is always to desire an external solution, rather than use the laboratory of the mind and find a simple one there: 'Free from desire, you realise the mystery. Caught in desire, you see only the external', which could not be the essence, as Lao-Tzu observed as far back as 250 BC.

Sometimes we hit serious pay dirt when one of our theories works spectacularly well, such as Priestley's discovery of oxygen's properties, in which he found this novel gas also stimulated fire very effectively. Sadly for him, he went to Paris before declaring his find, and told the brilliant chemist Lavoisier his secrets, only to find his 'new gas' discovery had all too soon been renamed 'oxygen' by Lavoisier, and presented to an impressed world as a new element. Priestley never quite recovered from this loss, and now we have other means of showing copyright.

It does come as a shock to the budding scientist, to find out that some of science is literally invented. There is much philosophy in science, and armies of learned thinkers devoted to its nature, and the study of its effects. The very word philosopher has inspired terror in many a casual thinker, because the subject goes into minute detail about subtle assumptions that often creep into mainstream science, and invalidate it. The notorious Nietzsche once described a 'philosopher' as '...*a terrible explosive in the presence of which everything is in danger*'. As we will see, much of modern science will fail such tests of accuracy.

Even maths is not a solid reason to believe one version over another, since the equations are full of human invention, and others known as 'constants'. This is a neat way of making the maths turn out as you thought it would, and then declaring 'Look, it works!' Not quite...it turned out *as expected*, but with so many human insertions, it may not be true at all. This is a deep problem, and one way even Einstein can be mistaken.

One would expect maths and physics to be as solid and factual as anything can get, which can be true in some examples. When we get the least bit theoretical, the whole situation changes: Theories dominate. Now we have the challenge of picking out the faulty 'guesstimates' of the last 3000 years from the real evidence.

The modern thinking that emerged since the Renaissance in Europe still rules lives to a large extent. This shows the trust most of us place in what we are told. We take it as read that it is the purest form of knowledge we have. After all, people wonder, how can the makers of such complex inventions as spacecraft, computers or nuclear power plants be wrong about anything? Yet they are, and deeply so.

These clever inventions are not one thing, but a combination of a large number of innovations to achieve a particular purpose. Yet while we can put people on the moon and send probes to Jupiter 400 million miles away, we seem unable to resolve the human problems here on earth.

Our trust also stems from the real wonders of central heating and food preservation, which sustain us all in some way. These are major advances that, along with refrigeration, extend the time we have to work and live by freeing us from the daily chopping of wood and subsistence food harvesting.

Being kind people, we naturally like to extend this guarantee of excellence from our peers to cover any area requiring expertise the rest of us have neither the time nor wish to understand. So much of our current thinking has been thought out to such a degree, it seems only right and respectful to accept the bulk of it at face value.

Surprisingly to many of us, this trust has been misplaced to such an extent that much of what we thought we knew is not 'known' at all, but based on a best guess with little to support it. It is time we worked out more for ourselves.

For example, our perception of advanced engineering is often one of complete thoroughness and precision. The reality is rather different. The Titanic was called 'the ship that couldn't sink', which was tempting fate a bit too far with no-one monitoring icebergs in the North Atlantic, as they do now. Even computers can fail, as we all know, and it happened to the warship USS Yorktown in 1997, when the ship's systems crashed after the computer tried to divide a number by zero.

The list of our errors is almost endless, even in reference books.

Even written dates can be questionable. Many of us tend to take things like dates in learned text books to be almost godlike in their accuracy as solid stepping stones to mapping out the path of recent reality. Sadly, this is all too frequently a myth.

In ancient Greece a meteoric fireball was seen flashing across the night sky. We have a date of 466–467 BC, because the calendar has changed that much, no-one is quite sure which year it was. Many dates in books have a question mark after them: even for past kings, whose reigns were really important, yet we do not know for sure when they ruled.

Even the order or sequence of events is uncertain, because the records are incomplete. We then have the tough task of the archaeologist to consider, whose life is spent in the fascinating endeavour of piecing together pottery and other finds to fill in the gaps. Since many items have a query beside them, we have to ask ourselves this rather uncomfortable question: how much of what we think is provable fact may actually be mere invention? The answer is a shock, or should be.

Some may feel the finding of giant errors in our thinking may be seen as a bad thing in some way. Actually it is quite the reverse. Seeing what is incorrect is every bit as valuable as learning what is right, since by simple elimination we can then move forward to the only possible remaining answer. As the famous Sherlock Holmes used to say in Conan Doyle's stories, once the impossible has been ruled out, then whatever is left, however unlikely it may look, must be the solution.

The past is far from clear. It is time we re-checked *all of it*. Beyond around 900 BC, history was not recorded, and can only be deduced, and thus open to huge errors. For instance we have found traces of Neanderthal and Cro-Magnon man, yet we do not know if they used a spoken language.

Before and since this line of 900 BC, our version of all history has been formed by dating methods we will see cannot be relied on at all. The whole of pre-history from this period, right back through the entire geological sequence, has been tied to methods that cannot earn our trust.

Are there clues in history?

A quick sidestep into the past shows this clearly. We think we know what took place, but there are errors in the old deductions. The victors wrote the history books, which matched their linear thinking of who held supremacy. This is hardly surprising, since the foundations of linear thought gained force in the world with the rise of the Eurocentric culture, formalised during the ancient Roman era. Before that, the Celtic and related cultures had an equally advanced society in many ways, and so much gold that it drove the Romans to annihilate the culture. Celtic gold was a reason in itself, as well as the Druids, who disliked this plan. As we realise now, they were called 'barbarians' as an excuse for this conquest, when all that name meant was 'non-Roman' or foreign.

In linear thinking, we still have that old problem of 'what happened before the beginning'. Until recently, scientists would often not even discuss a 'pre-big bang' era.

This 'before the beginning' period is the pivotal time which explains all of Time itself. The evidence shows this quantum re-set or 'flip' restores the 'cycle' of Time, the details of which can work.

To paraphrase the eminent Monash University palaeontologist, Dr Michael Waldman: '*If a different version of events fits the facts as well or better than this one, then it may well be correct*'.

This is one of the best answers ever given to science students.

It is amazing that such a major error in our very idea of Time can exist for three centuries, but it has done so. The entire linear foundation of our worldview rests on the methods of dating rocks and other items. It looked reasonable, and was accepted.

Then came apparent agreement with carbon dating for organic remains, after a few 'adjustments', and the major 'break-through': the Uranium-Thorium standard, on which it is now all based, seemed to solve the question once and for all, and set the stamp on linear time as the true version of all past events.

All very good, but for one serious difficulty. It has an error in its conceptual thinking. The snag is this: the dates relied on the same basic concept of long periods of unchanging time. By assuming there was a line of time that never changed, the confusion grew. Put simply, no one guessed time could be a circle of events…until the new evidence we see today forces us to do so.

Some very telling errors appeared, which were quickly written off as anomalous flaws in the sample which didn't really mean anything, but they persist to this day.

One reported test used clam shells from the Murray River in Australia. Using carbon dating, the shells were 'dated' at 4,000 years old. Excellent, except for one small difficulty: they were actually *fresh* clams fished out of the river just days before, and so were not old in any way at all, let alone *that* old. How could this possibly happen? We cover this later, but in two words it was '*natural contamination*'. This can come from other sources of active carbon which misleadingly increased the true background level, giving a deeply false 'age' result. This is a common effect in shellfish like clams, being filter feeders, and thus tough to assign dates for, because they filter so much water [220 gallons a day or more] that they absorb more carbon, ruining the method's validity.

There are 1000's of examples of apparent error in such calculations, because they are all based on the assumption of unchanged conditions in the past. If the world changed in the past in any significant way, then those results would be mistaken. The signs show this did happen, and in several spectacular ways. Remove these errors, and we have a new version of Time which becomes so short, that it appears unlikely. Yet it works.

Sometimes science creates its own facts we may not like. They need to be checked.

The great questions of how we arrived on earth have puzzled humanity for all of time, and still do. Yet the most basic starting point of all, *defining a fact*, has never been fully resolved. Subjectivity does play a part, because we decide what passes for one. We often think we have found an undisputed fact that no one could dispute, or even doubt. Try thinking of a few, and you will find there are not many. We breathe air, the sun shines when the clouds clear; this kind of thing is tough to argue with as factual. These are truly indisputable things we can see, and one more useful thing: they are solid, large scale lumpy things we can understand and get to grips with.

Quite separate would be the use of reasoning to assume larger things, such as all the geese we may have seen are white, therefore 'we judge that all geese are also white'. That would be rather like saying if you have seen one bird, you've seen them all. This does not of course follow at all; it only means 'the geese we saw were white, which tells us nothing about other geese we have not seen'. Swans were once all thought to be white, until black swans were found. [Today a 'black swan' has been taken to mean an unexpected event no-one predicted.]

Next we have to consider the degree to which our minds can be influenced by our family or education. Logic can seem flawless, yet peer pressure can turn it upside down. There have always been these fine lines of judgement that puzzled even people like Socrates and Plato and other famous thinkers; indeed especially them. Other people felt more focused on the physical, and just worried about what to eat next. They were not bothered by such deeper meanings. Societies judged themselves by how 'physical' they were, agreeing the spiritual concepts were somehow cerebral and 'more elevated'. We feel divided by such degrees of concern to this day.

In history as now, hermits are praised for their detachment from worldly life, and who can forget the European priestly anchoresses, such as Julian[a] of Norwich, who had themselves walled into a dark room to connect better with God. Aristotle was a famously great thinker, and these intellectual giants would spend years assessing how to remove subjectivity from the use of reason to determine reality. This is no easy task on occasion. Many other less impressive observers were dismissive of his caution, and perhaps lacked his focus on accuracy and quality in thought above all other considerations, such as lunch.

Some questions are easy. Is the cat inside the house or not? Just check which side of the door it is on to solve that. Some tempt us to assume giant things on a space-wide scale. Does the universe have an edge, or run in a loop? Has the sun always shone every day the same way, or have there been changes even to that daily pattern? Coral growth lines show it has not. Is the mind spread through the brain as electricity as some think, or a point of energy? A more complex issue to solve. Are any such ideas factual? We do need to know, because we have to live our lives relying on the answers being correct. What is now clear is that many of our 'facts' are not actually reliable as truth.

Philosophers have fussed over this difference of fact and fiction forever, and with good reason. The answers are ruled by the way we think, so we cannot trust the strong wills of those who say 'it is self-evident', because that too may be another invention.

The ancient Greeks, Indians, Chinese, Celtic, Mayan, Aztec, Toltec, Hopi and every other serious culture that ever lived were deeply focused on such matters, and made them the centre of their lives, knowing their answers would rule every second that followed.

Even this is not accepted globally: what is the scientific method?

Sir Karl Popper was a famous thinker in the 1950's, who had some interesting points to make on this subject of how to check if we are right. It is a shock to realise that even today, with so many brilliant advances in super-conduction and quantum mechanics, we still do not have a clear definition of how to do this.

Too many of us take for granted the earlier work of admittedly giant pioneers in one field or another, without checking if they were quite as right as we were told they 'must be'. Indeed many of us avoid thinking too deeply about such imponderables, preferring to concentrate on a smaller more manageable aspect of our chosen field. This is partly why we have become over-specialised in ever smaller parts of one type of study.

In archaeology it may be a global choice of focus, on pottery for example, whether a find is pre Roman, post Roman, or near East cultures, or Sumeria, or the Gupta Period, Saxon, Xingu in South America, Clovis in America. Or there are complex sciences like geophysics; just one such major field would take a lifetime of effort to master, which could not include all of them. It simply cannot be done. This means that none of us has a full picture of what is happening in the present, let alone over all of history, or the future.

We arrive in the world within this cloud of confusion, realising over time that no one may know how we got here, and what the point of it all is. With perhaps 1,000 recognised ideas offering answers with varying degrees of unlikelihood, it is tough to find truth at all.

Let's take a glimpse at human knowledge itself. How can we know? We cannot be fully informed by relying on what others say is 'known'. Science teaches us to ignore second hand evidence, yet relies on it all the time.

Astronomy is also spectacularly and famously diverse, with solar plasma specialists, stellar spectroscopists, moon dust or water experts, nebula experts, cosmologists, conceptual theoreticians and planetary geologists who peer in wonder at Io hovering near Jupiter, and the giant volcano Olympus Mons on Mars, and at least 100 other subjects, and offer ideas that often change later.

Geology is a case in point: it is so specialised that a gap remains inevitable between the palaeontologist who studies fossils, and the sedimentologist who studies what you would expect, and the radiogenic expert on age determination, and so many other divisions. Not one single person is always aware what the other branches of science or philosophy are thinking, and which parts of what they have heard or read are accurate, or just more inspired theory.

Then there are the computer simulations, a firm favourite in cosmology, where so little is known that hundreds of 'parameters' are fed into a powerful mainframe computer, and this produces a pretty cartoon of a few seconds showing a guess at 'what might have happened'. This is speculation run riot, because while they look intriguing, these simulations are based on past thinking of what was 'assumed', which is often unconnected to reality.

We are therefore left to figure this out ourselves, so figure it out we will try to do. First of all we need to treat all earlier work as interesting, but potentially incorrect, just in case it is. To arrive at a better understanding of anything in science, it is essential to appreciate that earlier work may be so wrong 'in fact', that to use it would not just endanger the validity of future work based upon it, but destroy the value of all future predictions. Linear time may be such an error, so we have to check everything.

The finding of such a marked lack of facts showed that Socrates was profoundly correct in his famous assertion that we actually know nothing. Knowing is very different from thinking the obvious must be correct. Science has a very serious problem with this single factor, and has become so desperate that some scientists now refuse to discuss the main issues. Any result may look good, with the 'elegant maths' everyone wanted, but this is no guarantee of accuracy. Even maths can be designed to create an answer, and statistics will have a separate chapter later on to show how even a '95% accuracy' can be 100% untrue. The answer is 'very easily'.

This problem of making a false concept 'look correct' is a real and giant scale risk. If so, such an error would still be 'scientifically meaningless', as the celebrated French geochemical scientist Prof Claude J. Allègre explained in a similar context in his 2008 book *Isotope Geology;* specifically about how the scientific 'method' can be misleading if we draw the wrong conclusions, which we will study later.

The hub of the matter is a problem existing in science...seeing time as a line.

We have made a really fundamental one which upsets how we see reality: that time is a line, with a start date, a middle, and an end. It looked right, and it felt right, not least because every single human being's life seems to run this way. No one escapes being born, or the fact of the body having to die one day, so the whole concept was duly superimposed on Time itself, and Earth's own history too, along with literally all of physical reality...even though not a single one of us ever saw Time do this.

We took it on trust that this was one 'obvious fact of life' which pretty nearly every person on Earth was firmly agreed on: events follow a sequence we can all see, so it must have had a beginning far in the past, and an end sometime in the future, which must also presumably be unknown. Or is it?

This is the picture we all inherited, and almost no one stopped to question it, but simply got on with proving *how* it must be right, not if it could be correct in the first place. It was just too obvious and apparent to doubt, let alone waste any time at all on mulling over such a 'given'. Time became a line in everyone's mind. It was taught in schools, by learned scholars in universities, and almost never questioned. Alas it is now in direct conflict to observed reality, because everything in nature is circular.

Now it is being questioned, and not a moment before time. A few maverick thinkers did begin to question it, such as Hoyle's group with their Steady State Theory; but they were not accepted as right, and were crucially unable to explain many of the stranger findings that emerged in space research. Linear time was barely dented in its status as a world view, and everyone continued to believe it, and got on with their lives.

Then a change happened. After World War II, the amount of money put into space research began to increase rapidly, now that peace had been established. Powerful telescopes were made, and as the cosmos began to shrink, it revealed a long list of secrets. Scientists had their linear model of Time reassuringly fixed as a long line that stretched back into antiquity, and an equally fixed set of results firmly in mind as to what they expected to discover. The experts set out their 'perfect account' of spacetime history. It was, however, mostly imaginary, but we only know this now.

Alas the findings did not support them, but they pressed ahead anyway.

How did their line of time thinking develop?

They made up a scenario, and the big idea ran like this. The universe *must have* cooled from a fiery start billions of years in the past, and, with equal certainty, the planets of our own solar system *must have* formed into the spinning the spheres we see today…from the clumping of dust particles. This was a guess, but nearly everyone agreed, because almost no-one imagined any other answer.

The reasoning looked ok at first, so the same logic was applied to the entire picture. Earth *must have* cooled from its own fiery beginning, since everything *must have begun* at some time, or so the thinking went. The perceived neatness of this way out was hailed by all as a triumph, and an increasing number of researchers, well into the thousands, began to work on different solutions as to how this may have happened, and suggest when. We need to remember they were choosing between two ideas at that time: creation as per the Bible, and any other version they could think of. So they chose the line of time with great length, giving everyone plenty of time to work with. Indeed this was almost identical to the creation by God version, but with a tweak or two.

One snag arose, but was quickly ignored; this was that matter could not have appeared from nowhere. For many years top experts would say 'you cannot ask what happened before the beginning'. This too is not an answer. Only later were other universes dreamt up to 'solve' this problem, even though they don't provide an answer at all. All the 'multiverse' idea does is move the problem to another room, and then another, until we lose the will to count more rooms. That answer is without evidence or meaning, like the world being on a turtle's back, with 'turtles all the way down'…nonsense.

As noted, the source of the world's oceans was a bit of a problem; at 13,000 million cubic kilometres in volume, their origin took some explaining away. Their origin became a matter of great controversy, until a bright researcher pointed out that since everything else *must have* come from space, as there was nowhere else it could have come from, then the water *must* have also originated in space.

Everyone breathed a sigh of relief, and got on with other aspects, even though the oceans from space idea was not supported by the vital required finding of large amounts of water anywhere else. They ignored that problem, and hailed it a brilliant success: the cosmos had made itself, and the oceans fell out of the sky.

A wild idea indeed, but they ran with it. There was no clear evidence for it, but the idea could sound quite convincing with nothing else on the table at all, so this became the only game in town. No one guessed nature would ever reveal signs of a cycle.

Papers were written, wonders were proclaimed, tenures granted, funding arranged, conferences rang with applause, and progress was declared real, just as it is today. Few wondered if it could be real after all, and apparently not one person held it all up beside the Munchausen trilemma.

Experts realised they were writing history as sole judges

Without a source for those oceans, we may fairly think this a non-starter, but they did not. It was all they had, and like Darwin with his missing trillions of fossils, they neatly reckoned the evidence was just hiding, and would all magically appear one day. It never has, but their answer still made sense to them...space is huge, the water could still be hiding out there. Any naysayers were easily brushed aside as dinosaur thinkers of the past, or mad, or both. These new ideas were the future, and full acceptance should be the only response, or so they felt. We believe what we want to believe.

This new idea method was exciting. Whenever a problem arose, they just invented an answer to solve it. It all seemed perfectly reasonable: the water on Earth could not have been present before the fiery beginning of Earth as a planet, since it would all have boiled away in the heat, and so it *must have* arrived after that, as if by courier from somewhere in space. From where? Another idea arose: perhaps in the form of frozen comets. That would be very unusual, they reasoned, so they needed a mega-event...a 'heavy bombardment' period of intense asteroid activity was invented: job done.

They were inventing the cosmos and its entire story all over again, and it was fun.

This assumed a great deal, and it all had many problems. For instance, if so many watery snowballs were rushing about the solar system, then where did they come from, and how come no other planets were equally splashed by the same cosmic deluge? [Some claim they were, but the lack of great age to the F-Ring of Saturn etcetera suggests not.] Also, how come this mass of water sat in a dark corner and then waited a measured 2.5 billion years for earth to cool down before arriving as if by perfect taxi, right on cue?

Who is to say the date is right? There is no way to be sure if the figure was not 3,200 years ago, and there was no water to deliver at all. That is unknown in science, but the evidence points to this unconventional answer being correct.

As we will see, this space ocean origin idea is just not believable.

How come, some asked, we don't still see such furious large-scale activity in space these days? Simple, came the answer, there *must have* been a period of extra intense planetary activity, with watery comets flashing across the sky and hitting Earth and other planets. The craters on the moon, Mars, Venus and other celestial objects *must have* happened around the same time, and so this solution must be the right one, or at least good enough for the time being. And it was so. This period of intense activity received an impressive name, the *Late Heavy Bombardment* or LHB for short, and was soon written in textbooks as the great solution.

No one expected that to change any time soon, and so it didn't. To this day, this is the accepted account of where we all came from, where earth's water is from, and how planet Earth came to be as it is. This explanation has been in such common currency for so many years, that in the minds of many who hear it, this is a piece of indisputable truth. It is widely disputed, and clearly unworkable, so we'll deal with this vexing blemish in linear time later, as it is a serious shortfall in the standard model of reality.

There was only one problem...new findings did not match what was expected. Only early in 2016 did scientists begin to admit the LHB may be wrong. This came as no surprise to some, because the LHB was always an invention. Sure, there was some evidence of impacts on planet earth, but to claim they nearly all struck in one era, and just when water was needed in great quantities, stretches belief too far.

Theories have to be invented of course, or science would have no ideas, but there comes a point when no-one can tell which ideas are close, and which are pure fantasy of such wild inaccuracy they have misled everyone for centuries.

Other errors became clear as science found out more. Take the planets as examples. Our entire solar system was fully expected to be cold and dead, and 'must have been' so for billions of years. The world's top experts in 1946 predicted that when a probe could land on

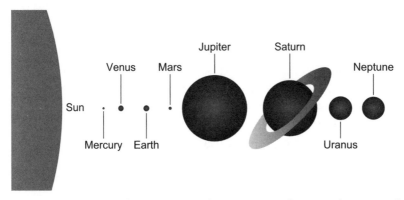

FIGURE 8 *Sun & Planets: our solar system's planets relative to the sun's size at 1.39 million kms wide, placed in order [but not relative distance apart].*

Venus, it would certainly find a surface temperature very like that of Earth. They were almost the same size, and the same age, as everyone had already decided, so why should it be any different? They decided it should not be. It would therefore be very much like Earth, about 17°C they guessed, like a nice Spring day, with a similar amount of latent heat, and similar greenhouse effects to keep it stable.

No surprises expected there, yet that was not what happened at all.

They were not just wrong, but spectacularly so. Venus was hotter than anyone expected, except Einstein's friend Velikovsky. As noted, it turned out that the Venusian surface was 480°C when first measured, and much hotter than even the melting point of the metal *lead*, which melts at a rather milder 327.4°C. Compared to the boiling point of water at 100°C, that is blisteringly hot. Venus 1, Spring day 0.

Even the very latest discovery just heaps more mystery on to the growing pile of puzzles which all share one theme. They show that our current worldview is not actually possible. Yet perhaps all this was a continuum, as we shall see.

Extra science detail

The vast reaches of interstellar space were firmly expected to be entirely cold and dead: it simply had to be so if the cosmos was 13 odd billion years old as claimed. Yet it was no such thing.

As noted, a big issue became known as *The Flatness Problem*, because the universe could not remain 'flat' for 13 odd billion years as so wildly claimed which became known as *The Flatness Problem*.

As top astronomers have pointed out, this finding was utterly unexpected, because it is the cosmic equivalent of trying to balance a pencil on its point for an imagined 10 *billion years*. This is clearly impossible. What fits better is an idea we will come back to later, which is a cosmos of energy that follows a cyclic pattern. [In a nutshell, it points to a 'power' density which becomes unstable, as now, and will then 'flip over' to order. We may therefore replace the line with a cycle, since no other answer fits as well.]

This single discovery, all by itself, heralds not only the end of linear time as a theory, but also everything based on it, which includes much of modern scientific theory. Many cosmologists are puzzled by this, but a few began to wonder if the motion of time's events could be circular, and may never have been linear at all, ever.

Here is a summary of key clues that suggest a short cycle of time, by subject:

Spacetime

1 Large Magellanic Cloud has far too many heavy stars: classic ideas fail
2 Both key methods to confirm Hubble constant contradict their own results
3 Energy and density are too 'flat': impossible or unlikely in the linear Big Bang story
4 Huge planetary variation shows solar system did not form from one cloud
5 Matter cannot be created nor destroyed, a law that confirms cyclic time
6 Ocean water could not have come from space for eleven reasons
7 Sun has not burned out yet, nor galaxies slowed down: a cycle
8 Saturn's F ring shows clear signs of young age: a recent cycle/continuum
9 Big Bang theory counters basic laws of physics as above ie not possible

10 Multiverse idea of many worlds has no evidence to be true
11 Galaxies are speeding up, not slowing, so not billions of years old
12 Haumea dwarf planet is 'too young', being covered in ice not dust
13 Jupiter location far too near sun for usual theories to be correct
14 Huge voids in space support cyclic time continuum, not Big Bang
15 90% of 'normal' baryonic matter is missing from linear time version
16 Spiral galaxy stars 'should have' spun out long ago in linear version
17 Finding of 'hot Jupiters' near stars confirms cycle, not Big Bang
18 Missing matter in universe fits continuum, no need for Dark Matter
19 14 dwarf galaxies found in same plane; not chance. [New Scientist 10Feb 2018]

Energy

1 Balance of power easily altered being so finely balanced
2 Existence today suggests a cycle since linear time creates a collapse
3 Super Grid explains cyclic energy flow where conventional ideas cannot
4 Future linked to past as double slit test shows (see text)
5 Energy Grid as affected by ourselves provides means for a cycle
6 Entangled Cooper pairs of electrons shows matter is vitally 'connected'
7 Grid can alter energy state at super high speed enabling cycle

Age dating errors in methods

1 Ice core dates unreliable by assumptions; can be rapid by axial tilt
2 Tree ring dates do not match Carbon dating method
3 Carbon dating sample corruption common via water and air
4 Geological Timescale miscalculated via world view assumptions
5 Fossil record does not prove ages: a billion year myth
6 Prehistory assumed theory, without solid facts to prove the story
7 Chalk taken as ancient and slow-forming: yet flint bands can be annual

8 Atlantic ocean floor can be very young: lack of sediment at mid-points

9 Blake Outer Ridge wholly unsorted grains shows recent axial turmoil

10 Radiogenic decay method fails due to unsupported assumptions

11 Anomalocaris fossil far too complex for early linear time theories

12 Trilobites appear in separate ages globally, not in linear sequence

Earth

1 Evolution lacks the fossil evidence to prove linear time as correct

2 Fossil record also lacks the variety of forms required by Darwin as proof

3 Geologists have not found the vast quantity of fossils, as Darwin predicted

4 Grand Canyon and Monument Valley could have formed in 1200 years

5 Coal seams all show rapid coverage by mud and sand, possible in 200 years

6 Mass extinctions can be shown occurring in every time era, not 5 times

7 Maths showed waves could only move 200 ton rocks, yet 620 ton rock noted

8 Current axial tilt would have been very rapid: the signs are everywhere

9 Dinosaurs did not exist for millions of years, hence trillions are missing

10 T-Rex recently found with unfossilised collagen, as expected in a cycle

11 Entire fossil record can be accounted for in 4,950 years of short cycle

12 Chalk not entirely composed of shells, but also of rapid precipitate

13 Lazarus fossils show Darwin's claims were incorrect, as he noted

14 Cambrian Explosion of Life shows the Flash Time cyclic switch was fast

15 Burgess Shale in Canada has fossils showing life then had no ancestors
16 Chalk fossil urchin shells fail to show vertical evolution: they counter it
17 K-T event crater shows it could have been very recent, not ancient
18 Pangea split of giant land mass could have been very recent: axial tilt
19 Coral growth a known rate, yet only enough to last for under 5,000 years

Human history

1 Cavemen species are recent, as shown by 620 billion missing skeletons
2 Neanderthal skeletons are an example of cycle: only 137 found
3 Our human population needs only 4,950 years to reach current 7.5 billion
4 Ancient cultures all had same cyclic time symbols, yet never met to share them
5 Ancient cultural traditions/writings show the cyclic switch; very near their era
6 Pyramids common globally, yet the builders were separated and could not meet
7 Easter Island moai statues show Indian Brahman signs: since split of Pangea

Human mind

1 Common experience of déjà vu in 99% of people shows cycle is real
2 We choose a world view rather than work it out, as Trilemma shows
3 Human mind energy can be the anthropic factor that moves the cycle around
4 Our theories in science rely on idea creation rather than objective proof

PART 2

Checking Earth's Ages

CHAPTER 6

Dating Rocks: a million year myth?

Science must begin with myths, and with the criticism of myths.
SIR KARL POPPER, 1957

Science is...not this foreign thing, done by an arcane priesthood.
STEPHEN J. GOULD, The Independent, 24 Jan 1980

...a most intense feeling of déjà vu. I had the feeling that I had already experienced this moment and had always known this world...waiting for me for five thousand years.
CARL G.JUNG, *Memories, Dreams, Reflections*
[Fontana Press 1995] p283

Essence

This chapter checks the thinking behind the millions and billions of years said to have passed by in a long line of time. It shows there appear to be such serious errors in the reasoning used to make those claims that they can no longer be accepted. Do we have a myth? It seems we do, because no one can prove we do not, and the top experts realise that actual, concrete physical proof is indeed missing.

All this arose very easily: an error in our idea of time was accepted long ago, and it stuck. Even this is a major obstacle to overcome...the sheer enormity in scale of this claim that our whole basis of thinking about Time itself could have been misunderstood. It could mean the entire vision of science in all key fields would be one massive mistake that gives rise to 100,000 others equally as huge.

For many, that is just too much to deal with, after over 300 years of opposite thinking. Yet if fresh facts suggest such immense changes, we have to consider the clues.

Not only are the obvious signs of billions of years in a line actually missing, but the dating method also remains unproven. The assertions used to support these concepts have a problem in both thinking and physics: they have no technical proof, because they require belief. The theory of earth and space history then becomes a matter of invention.

Even the physics does not form *any actual proof*, because the meaning of the 'dates' created is only inferred. The linear time claims lack objective proof, and thus fail all three key tests of the *Münchausen trilemma* where an idea ineffectually relies on belief or merely 'proves itself'[See Glossary for details].

The main technique to calculate the earth's age depends on thinking. This method is the key way rocks are dated. It only applies to volcanic or igneous rocks, because it relies on relic radioactive 'decay'. Despite the immense importance of accurately 'dating earth history', this method is still accepted even though a recognized and fatal flaw completely invalidates its use. This flaw is the presumption of time being a long line, an idea that fails every test of 'proof'. It is only used at all because experts lacked another option, and cyclic time had not been realised as possible.

Every degree level textbook teaching this method mentions this weakness as a problem, yet the method is accepted because science has no other 'concept' to believe in. This situation is extremely serious because the whole of science relies on it as support for the current vision of reality and all history. If truth be told, not a single person can prove it works, yet it is still in use, because the only alternative in play for 300 years has been the religious version of Creation, and even scholars find that a challenge to explain.

Not many scientists would ever imagine their long accepted method could contain a fault serious enough to demolish its results, yet it does. This finding is highly significant, because it shows the current view of earth history would be a titanic scale mistake. It allows 3,000 years to look like 4 billion years, using just a glimmer of belief.

Amazingly, on close inspection, the key dating method for rocks is unable to confirm the ages it produces. Here is how the method works, and why it appears to be wholly unreliable. The problem stems from our vivid imagination as people. Usually this is a good and amusing thing, but in science it can be a source of false results.

The idea relies on a story or theory, which claims that radioactive energy inside certain rocks 'has been decaying' for millions of years. As the experts say, if this can be shown to be untrue, then the method fails instantly to have any meaning. If no one can prove it is true, it must fail. Now that we have a provable alternative concept in our cycle of time, the long line fails the classic tests of proof. The signs of a young and cyclic solar system seem to confirm this view (F Ring of Saturn etc.).

As with all linear time dating methods, this one relies on the same set of assumptions about earth's past: that earth has existed as we see it today, and has done for millions of years going back in time. This basic thought is not actually factual, but a theory assumed to be true. Experts could see about 3,000 years of history, as we all can, and realised any ideas they had about deeper time periods were speculative, so what could they do to create a longer version? No problem, they thought, just invent one.

It would impress many with a technical name. Called 'extrapolation', this idea just meant 'extending the line' of known history, as far back as experts decided. They loved it, because it allowed those 3,000 known years to become millions, and later billions. There was no one around to disagree. Yet the concept had a hitch when it was imagined around 1900. While it fitted their feeling of a long line of time being right, it lacked concrete evidence. They felt it was their mission to produce new answers.

They searched hard for real facts to back such theories, and decided to rely on the radioactive elements present in rocks. Known as radiogenic dating, it was worked out mainly around 1905–1915, but those early pioneers had none of the data known today, such as this evidence for a cyclic 're-set' of the cosmos. The Flash Time shift mentioned here supports this idea, as does the 'flatness' of the universe[29] in space, which suggests time was not always invariable.

They had none of this information to inform their decision, over a century before spacecraft made it possible, yet we have never updated those old ideas to include the new facts we found. So how does the technique claim to fix a date for volcanic rocks?

The theory relies on unstable elements decaying over time, by losing particles and 'becoming' another element. A broad analogy of this is

---

29 Changes in density of the space medium make the flatness impossible, if the universe moves in short cycles.

like leaving cheese to become mouldy, the portion of mould growing over time. A candle leaves molten wax as it burns down, with its remaining height used as a primitive clock in medieval times. We can see how iron becomes rusty. Simply by measuring the two quantities, of the rust and the unrusted iron, and knowing the speed of this decay process, a period of time can be calculated. Yet if the 'rust' was already present on day one, the true age could not be known at all.

The same problem affects the 'decay' of radioactive elements in volcanic rocks: it is impossible to know if the decay element type has decayed at all. It may have always been in the rock on day one of its formation. In that case its presence would mean nothing. As we can appreciate, if these 'expected' decay elements are actually already present in those rocks when forming, this fact would create false data *inferring great age*. It would be like our block of cheese being sold as new with lots of mould on day one.

The significance of this one point cannot be over-emphasised: it means the age of the universe appears to have been deeply misunderstood. It is astonishing to present this challenge to current thinking, when so many mainstream experts would disagree, but it is an astounding situation we now find ourselves a part of.

The famous pioneers of old have given us a story of our origins, and those of our solar system, which cannot be true. They did not know this at the time, of course, but today's facts leave us no other conclusion to draw.

Yet the experts appear unable to deal with the failure of that old vision, and the need to adjust or scrap that outdated version. Even that is hardly surprising, but it forces us to draw new conclusions. With almost 200 years of being the key arbiters of the world's academic thinking on life and time, and effectively ruling the world of modern thought, it cannot be easy to accept the worst case future scenario they felt sure could never come true: that their entire world view was based on a series of gigantic miscalculations, and it was wrong all along.

Each key point raised here to show the reasoning behind this shocking claim is already a famous issue in its own right, and yet not one has been evaluated in how it should alter our thinking. The Cambrian Explosion is one, with *Anomalocaris* as another, and so many more as we encounter them. Any one is enough to force a re-think. They are only explainable in a cycle of events, but no one considered that either.

So what might have happened instead?

The key to resolving this issue is in seeing time's events as a circle that ties in these weird anomalies. In a cycle of events that repeat, a long linear 'age' cannot be calculated, since the 'clock' of time is re-set to zero in a regular pattern. With cycles of such events being refreshed and altered every few millennia, for example, the radiogenic content of rocks could not prove a long age. Instead of being a few billion years old, the cosmos would be *infinitely older*, if lasting forever in cycles.

If Time is infinite, then such a cyclic set of events that repeat is logical, and this body of evidence showing this answer would be correct. Most of us realise the famous 'wheel of time' can be a valid solution here, while others feel that an eternity is simply unimaginable.

The lack of an ability to visualize a concept does not prove it cannot exist.

Sir Karl Popper wrote in 1971 that '*On a scientific level, we systematically try to eliminate our false theories…*'. With fixed thinking, this is often an impossibility.

How does this work practically?

Let's check this carefully, because if the above is all true, then modern thinking needs a new worldview, and to rethink earlier cosmic 'dates' offered. How were those dates created, and could they be wrong by a factor of a million or more? The 'method' used is the foundation of all linear thinking: the decay of radioactive isotopes, currently thought to show Time has continued unaltered for millions and then billions of years. Is it truly reliable, or could it be a myth?

The answer is yes, it can be mistaken, because the meaning of those dates has been inferred, but our view depends on how we think. One thing is clear: those dates are not reliable facts since they rely on an unproven scenario being true.

Not a person on earth can prove that 'long line of time' scenario ever happened. The top experts quoted here realise this fault that deprives this method of full legitimacy, but acceptance of a new vision requires two obstacles to be overcome: old thinking, and an alternative. For some in science, the very idea of linear time being a giant error is 100% unthinkable, but few ever considered an exact cycle. When we do, the anomalies like the cosmic flatness, the lack of fossils and the Cambrian Explosion of life all fit into place.

This problem is an interesting one. Deep history had to be invented, because no-one could remember seeing it happen. To many experts in the last 150 years, their search was to find a physical cause for reality. Any idea may work, so long as a religious answer was removed from the story. Of course they hoped later discoveries would support their ideas, but they haven't.

The pioneers preferred to think Nature worked by itself. Their great idea was this: life and spacetime appeared on their own. They assumed history was simply a long line of events going back to unknown eons of time. It could not contain any major changes to what we see today, they felt: how we see it now 'must be' how it always was. If we accept this chief assumption about pre-historical processes being 'unchanged', this notion might appear to show time as a line.

In fact this would turn out to be a key error, as we see later. There were volcanoes in the past that would make even today's most colossal eruptions look like garden fireworks. The ice ages were another example. The flood from the glacial Lake Missoula cut a totally new landscape across 60,000 square kilometres of north west America in just a few weeks, raising the entire sea level of earth by many metres; just imagine that.

If we place more emphasis on the discoveries set out here, which show oddly 'young' features in Nature, then we recognise an opposite view: Time does not appear to be similar to now, as we look back, since there are signs of cycles, not a long line. That would mean, if true, that the universe's 'age' *cannot be calculated* from the signs we see today. In that case, the old method's results based on the old assumption of uniform history would be entirely incorrect.

It all depends on which facts we prefer to adopt, and which assumptions we accept as true, if any. The new thinking outlined here tries to recognise a reality without using any assumptions at all, because they can be totally false (quite possibly so, since people made them up). There is a very real problem for science here, since more recent facts have overtaken the older, incomplete set. The Saturn F-Ring's clear youth of particle size, so clearly elaborated by Prof. Chris Lintott on BBC television[30] in

---

30 *The Sky at Night* programme on astronomy since 1957, the world's oldest.

England, along with the microwave flatness of the CMB, are enough to illustrate the difficulty of seeing time as linear and unchanged. Clearly it has changed, and Flash Time offers a fresh answer.

We then have not two views to choose from, but three: one is the science view of time as a long line; another is Creationism, in which God created the world, and then there is cyclic time, in which the basic cosmos always exists. Many in science quietly hold variations of all three, so actual views are not so clear cut.

Conventional thinkers took the first view, and developed a firm belief in their concept: that the present is the same as the past. It is the key uniformity principle in geology, taught by James Hutton in 1795, and expanded by Playfair in 1802, leading to the extremist *Uniformitarianism* of Charles Lyell in 1830 (assuming geology today matches past processes, which we now find it does not). The very proposal this might be wrong was never an option to them, because the only alternative they had heard of was Creationism, and that was the very view they decided was wrong.

To those thinkers, that would be unthinkable for another reason: if time is not linear, *then every ancient date is wrong*. This they could not imagine, but appears so. Today experts now call the Uniformitarian view a 'considerable oversimplification'.[31]

It is far more serious than that, because the linear assumptions do not hold up at all.

This new list of fresh facts overturns all of the grand claims for real accuracy, and invalidates the oldest dates given. We will see examples of how a modern rock can 'appear' millions of years old, while being recent, even in the mighty Grand Canyon.

Are there signs to tell us what truly took place?

Intriguingly, there are. When we reassess them we get a radically different story. This is not surprising, since the traditional theories in science were formed when we knew very little indeed, factually speaking. Now we know more, we find there is this third option the early pioneers did not consider...a series of repeating cycles. The early thinkers never saw that coming, and neither did we. Yet when we study it, a cycle fits the facts perfectly.

Radiogenic dating requires us to accept as true that a long passage of time happened. Now, a century after this claim, the evidence contradicts it. Yet it is not so simple as that, because the actual time passed would not be measured in millions or billions of years, but a far longer period...to infinity and beyond, as Buzz would say.

The curious thing about this most famous of all scientific methods is this valid concern that reveals the linear 'billion year picture' to be an invention. This suggests we live in an 'infinite cosmos', not a small bubble that formed itself. Time should then not be reduced to such sums as mere billions of years...such periods would be too short.

Only infinity works, with cyclic phases that repeat as natural seasons.

The radiogenic dating method's Achilles heel is this simple: it assumes a list of things 'to be true', so if they are not true, the whole method fails instantly and totally.

The reason lies in how this method of decay works. As experts rightly teach, there are traces of radioactive decay in all crystalline volcanic rocks. To the professional scientist, this section will be simple if perhaps a bit disturbing. The proposal is that we appear to have misunderstood time as a line, and therefore shoehorned all our methods of dating earth and its rocks into this concept. Each misfit is set aside as an irregularity, so far unexplained. In the linear vision, they have never been, and can never be explained.

In a cyclic cosmos, each of these anomalies is not 'irregular' at all, but a vital piece of the whole jigsaw that explains our historical error of vision. All these factors set out here show why this is so, but after 300 years of thinking the linear way, it will not be easy for some to 're-think reality'.

It is not just the method itself we need to question, but how it can be misused as 'proof' to support a conclusion. When questioned closely about the word 'proof', workers in these fields are always very honest about the *caveats*, and admit there are certain constraints about how accurate the work may be, but you never hear that in a TV documentary. They are brushed aside neatly and firmly in the phrase 'we now know' this is so.

Here is one answer that works. The method is unable to confirm when the decay product entered the rock, and it could easily have been on day one, and even well before it was extruded. Result: the 'ages' derived this way would be meaningless, and time can be cyclic, not linear.

When this decay method began to show the promise of creating apparently useful dates after about 1910, the trust placed in those results took on a significance that has never gone away. It was seized on as the 'proof' of Evolution and more. The snag is only seen now, with so much more evidence, that this cannot be the right way to see time.

All methods rest on the shoulders of one accepted central concept, which is this: *earth must be old* in a conventional sense, and thus *cannot show youth*, in any sense, simply because science decided there is no way it could.

Any flaw in this starting point, as there appears to be, and these 'clocks' would not merely tell the wrong time, but can be out of synch with reality by a factor of millions or even billions of years. This appears to have happened.

This is the key. Cycles within the grand scheme of infinitely 'long' time *would show apparent youth*. Seeing the rocks can indeed be wrongly dated by millions or even billions of years, then objects taken to be ancient can then be very young. This is how dinosaur bones, as one example of many, can be claimed to be millions of years old while actually being only 3,200 years old. This could be why collagen still exists in T-Rex bones, when such a find would be impossible if time were linear (see Introduction).

We should be under no illusion that big scale science relies on belief. It is not a set of solid facts beyond question. Such science is a mixture of fact and fiction, and the process of separating them to its devotees' best ability is an open process depending upon emphasis, while the world looks on with a mixture of admiration and horror. While vaccinations and surgery are shining advances, science also contains many unknowns.

As each reader makes up their own mind, these factors will inevitably come into play. There are oddly young features in space. These upset the reliability of the assumption used to date rocks: that time has always been the same.

The arguments for linear time are well-known, yet none of them can stand without first accepting it as true. Try it and one can easily see this effect. One example is the movement of light in space, reasonably assumed to be a constant by Einstein. Yet even that assumes time never changed. The idea in Flash Time is that there is such a periodic change. We may instead be looking at a *snapshot in time* only, so that we cannot assume time has been unchanged in a line.

It may therefore be that events have not had vast eons in which to happen; then odd things start to stand out, such as the snow white water ice on the TNO[32] or dwarf planet known as Haumea, which 'should have' become covered in dark dust over the billion or so years it is claimed to have existed. This lack of dust shows Haumea *cannot have been drifting through space* all those years, collecting space dust. It does not have that dust coating, which was not the subject of an important recent article on its size[33].

Time to reconcile old thinking and exciting new discoveries

The thinkers of the 1700's could hardly have been expected to be aware of astrophysics findings some 300 years before they were found. We can see how science reached this dilemma, where old ideas became established only to be contradicted by finds from modern space travel. Who would make that announcement? It seems no one is funded to check cyclic time and how it contradicts the linear view, so no one has.

Dating rocks using radioactive decay is one key to the whole controversy. The idea of dating the radioactivity in volcanic rocks was developed as a way of assigning specific dates to specific rock samples, as everyone wanted to know one thing: the true age of the earth. Darwin's followers needed a very long age to be confirmed, for Evolution to work.

Earlier methods seemed to produce dates that were far 'too young' to fit the scientific model after Darwin, so the search was on for a way to prove a longer age. This isn't usually the right way round of course,

32 Trans Neptunian Object in astronomy, about 10 main ones, c.2300kms wide, at the outer edge of our solar system.
33 Nature 12 Oct 2017, p197, Letter by Ortiz et al. p219.

LONG RADIOACTIVE DELAY CLAIMS – 2 answers

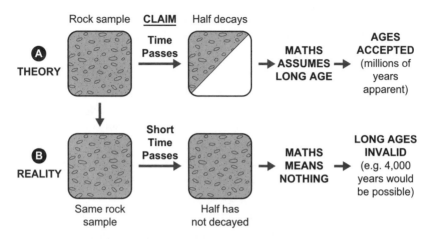

FIGURE 10A *Rock Dating Method: claimed to measure millions or billions of years, yet diagram shows how assumptions are used to do so, and such long linear ages may be less than 5000 years. All long ages affected.*

FIGURE 10B *Discontinuity: example of rock section below surface, with 'ancient' folding below A-B line of old erosion surface. Layers below the line are then eroded to that plane, forming an unconformity or 'discontinuity' when sedimentation stopped for an unknown period; layers above were laid down later and then tilted as shown.*

to find a method to fit a long date 'known' and expected to be correct, but that is what happened.

It is a fatal flaw, since it allows a finding that fits that view to be accepted. Again, no one stopped to assess time as cyclic. Their search was for a solution they favoured.

Here was the promise of doing just that, and they must have come close to howling with delight, if only on the way home. This system was to become the foundation of modern geology, and was to underpin Holmes's geologic timescale. He was a key person who helped create the first working system of rock dates based on observed maximum thickness of sediments around the world, or at least the few parts that had been seen at the time. Since the first congress of geology met in Paris in 1878, they searched for a system.

Many in this old and much respected science may be appalled at even the suggestion of doubts about such famous, foundational work. It is just not done, and all this research carried out over centuries has become more than just accepted as fact: it is no less than the very bedrock of modern thinking in both earth science and the biological principles of Darwin himself, which use geology to underpin every word and idea.

Holmes' time scale is the foundation of dating all rocks, yet 100 years later, we have new evidence to show it may be incorrect.

He and his colleagues took their radiometric[34] dates to be basic facts, with sediments fitted in between those pillars that held up their building's upper floors. No one imagined any other possibility, nor saw any reason to do so. Major finds like the six huge mass extinction events, Canada's Burgess Shale or the Cambrian Explosion of life, were still set far in the future. They could not have imagined later finds that would show earth's axis could have tilted in days, that Bermuda's coral would show 20 hour days not 24, or that 95 years later the cosmic microwaves would show their curious 'flatness problem' science was set to puzzle over.

The early pioneers saw their work as a clear-cut success because it looked so obvious. There was simply no reason to think in any other way, so they didn't.

Therefore, to question the famous geological timescale is to query

34 Radiometric and radiogenic refer to radioactivity residence time and
    measurement.

the heartland of geology itself. Yet a gigantic problem has arisen which none of those earlier pioneers could have envisaged: findings mainly in astronomy that force us to revise that earlier thinking. It is as big a change as was the discovery of quantum physics around the time of the First World War. Our own era now faces an equally huge change in ideas.

Even today, few question these basic beliefs. How can centuries of careful, sequential work, numerous Nobel prizes and great distinction in many interlocking fields of study conceivably all be wrong one day in one major respect? The very idea may be regarded as something to be rejected out of hand. Yet this is just how advances happen.

Alas science has a long and famous history of ignoring new thinking, to its great loss. A challenge has to be made when such discrepancies are discovered, otherwise these studies would never progress.

Could cyclic time help predict disasters?

Out of respect and courtesy, we have to tread very gingerly over such matters, as anyone would who has made geology a major part of their lives. This line of inquiry may seem to be going out on a limb to some observers, but the issues raised in this book seek to solve an *impasse* created by at least four centuries of linear time.

After so much work, it seems impolite to sound a note of caution, yet we have to do so about this central field of science, for three reasons. Firstly, rock dating has to be right because the clear understanding of Life's existence depends upon it; secondly, because it underpins all modern thinking about both the past and the future. Thirdly, any error is important because all our predictions about climate change, floods and hurricanes, as well as volcanoes, earthquake forces and risk areas, would be useless if time is not measured accurately.

So if time turned out to be moving orbitally, when geology firmly continued to treat it as a linear arrow going only one way, then there would be a problem. After all, if all the maths and models rely on linear time, and it turns out to be cyclic over a shorter period of orbit than any of us realised, that would seriously change everything.

As many have rightly said, if we don't ask new questions, we won't see new answers. The gifted writer Bill Bryson quotes a most percep-tive remark by the journalist Geoffrey Carr, who pointed out we have:

'a mountain of theory built on a molehill of evidence'.[35] Not all that theory can possibly be correct, but which parts may be off kilter?

Geology began formally in the 17th century. In those spirited days, geology was done by people with notebooks and pencils, walking along beaches looking at cliffs, or riding past a new canal cutting on a horse. The first discontinuity was seen this way, which is where a noticeable time gap exists between rock strata, such as horizontal layers overlying others below that are inclined. Astronomy was much the same, only later with a telescope for company after 1610 or so.

By the time the papers by Darwin and Alfred Wallace were read to the Linnaean Society in 1858, the new version of an evolved world was now perceived in a firmly 'linear' way, despite Darwin writing in the final line of his main book of how '...*this planet has gone cycling on...*'.[36]

His book, and the thinking shared by those two men, began the battle between Creationism and the Evolutionists. The differences between these two we cover elsewhere, but the issue is not resolvable without bringing in the aspects of cyclic time, which removes the classic necessity of both evolution and creationism that requires the universe to appear from nowhere, which both scientists and theologians find is quite something to explain.

So often the scientists hear themselves saying 'you don't understand', when actually the other person simply does not agree. This is taken as a lack of understanding, which is rarely if ever the case.

As we recall in Chapter 16 how Velikovsky was treated in the 1950's and later, it was not a rational analysis of his thesis that emerged, but a campaign to silence his views of catastrophism. His astronomy has at least partly been proven correct, while his evidence of catastrophic events in geology mirrors what was to come later, with the discovery of the KT boundary[37] iridium layer, and the hidden 180kms wide crater at Chicxulub. [For new terms, see Glossary.]

It wasn't about the truth so much as silencing criticism. Not our best era, many agree, so perhaps now we should examine new ideas with the aim of checking them.

35 A Short History of Nearly Everything, Bill Bryson, Black Swan 2004, p217.
36 The Origin of Species, C. Darwin, Penguin Classics 1985, p460.
37 A geological boundary, first known as 'KT' at a German site; Kriede is German for 'Cretaceous'.

Many in science's older generation have the impression there is simply no issue any longer. They say the rock dates are factual, no argument is even possible, and that is that. The opposite may now be true, but it is rarely taught in schools and universities. Yet superb university textbooks, like those of Dickin and Allègre in particular, are changing this inclination that science contains only 'self-evident truth'. Their books on isotope dating explore what assumptions have been used, which is a very refreshing approach. If the basis is false, they rightly say, the method fails.

Yet few admit the full impact of these facts.

How did these concepts arise?

Isotope geology began as 'nuclear geology', and then became 'isotope geochemistry', so it is an amalgamation of earth science with nuclear physics. To be able to give dates to rocks that were previously undateable, was a leap that made geology a quantitative science in an exciting way. To this day, few realise it can untrue.

How did radioactivity emerge, and how was it first perceived by an unsuspecting world? The arrival of radioactivity in the global awareness was an odd birth. To begin with, it was greeted with understandable wonder as a kind of alien magic power. Being invisible, with no smell, taste or touch to detect it, radiation was thus 'obviously' of immense, strange and unseen power, which 'had' to be good.

Needless to say, this concept was a huge error, and one of the most dangerous in all of science. Despite being completely misunderstood, radioactive face-creams and toothpastes were nevertheless made, on the basis that it must be 'good' for health. It was seen as a beneficial power, but they were wrong, and unaware it would kill the famous Polish chemist and radium discoverer Marie Curie. In fact the opposite was true of using it on bare skin in this way, now that we realise radiation comprises tiny particles that shoot out to damage living tissue and so can cause the cells to mutate, which is how it can lead to cancer. Meat collects these atoms via cows eating grass, which may be why it has been linked to cancer risks.

Safe it was not, but no one realised this. America even tested 30 atom bombs openly in the Nevada desert in Operation Plumbob with

K-T Event inner blast area, estimated

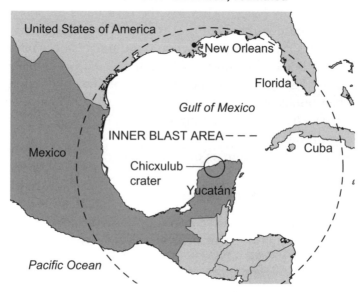

FIGURE II *K-T Impact Blast Area: diagram Gulf of Mexico local asteroid blast zone said to have killed dinosaurs 65 million years ago, yet can be timed at 3,600 years ago (for K-T meaning see Glossary).*

18,000 troops in the area, unaware that fallout was more dangerous than they realised. The UK, France and others also carried out such atmospheric tests, as they were called when not underground.

The mutation link with radiation was confirmed in 1926 when Hermann Müller found that X-rays caused mutations in fruit flies. Only later would the hazards be fully appreciated. Even today some experts play down the dangers of radioisotopes leaking from nuclear reactors, so concerned are they to preserve the prestige and use of nuclear energy. The UK's huge Windscale fire of 1957 released kilo-curies of massive radiation into the air of England's Cumbria area, so that local milk all had to be treated as hazardous waste for a long time. It was serious. British Nuclear Fuels (BNFL) changed the name of the plant from Windscale to Sellafield, and later its own company name.

Countless examples of damage exist, but one British expert was asked in 2011 what he thought of the Fukushima leaks of iodine-131, among other hazardous isotopes present in the clouds of radioactive material released, and if this amounted to a new Chernobyl. Certainly not, he replied, but days later officials admitted it was indeed a hugely serious situation of that order, among the worst. Some in science just cannot admit the dangers, but the 1976 Flowers Report set out some of them. Leaks and errors happen often, and even recently the Sellafield plant mistakenly released an entire tank of radioactive waste water into the Irish Sea, when a worker turned the wrong gate valve.

How the wave of technology rose to power

As the last flickers of 19th century light faded, there was a flurry of activity in science.

- 1879 saw the invention of the electric light bulb separately by both Edison and Swan.
- 1887 saw the invention of the first petrol-engined car by Gottlieb Daimler, and the next year found Hertz discovering radio waves and electro-magnetic waves behaving as light does. Science found other rays that defied simple description. Radioactivity had arrived, with Roentgen in 1895 finding rays so strange they were called 'X' rays, being unknown, paving the way for Antoine Becquerel to discover the peculiar nature of radiation.
- 1897 was a big year for discovery, with several major landmarks being made in science: J. J. Thomson described the electron, Diesel discovered a new type of engine, and the Curie family nnounced the discovery of radium the next year. As mentioned, her notebooks are still intensely radioactive, and seen only with safety shielding precautions.
- 1900: The scientific revolution was really taking hold by this time, as fresh and ingenious discoveries began to amaze the world. Paul Villard detected gamma rays in 1900, just before the Wright brothers launched the first powered flight into the air in 1903, and 100 years after John Dalton proposed his atomic theory of matter; all quite a leap forward since the French Montgolfier brothers sent animals skywards in their first hot air balloon launch of 1783.
- The Wright brothers' *first three* powered flights were only 30–61m long, which is less than the current wingspan of the giant cargo plane Antonov 124, at 73m.

As noted, the dating of radioactive isotopes in rock was pioneered by F. Soddy, Holmes and others in 1911, becoming possible thanks to Thomson and Aston's work on the mass spectrometer in the period 1914–18, while the First World War raged in Europe, and shortly after Einstein had published his 'special theory of relativity' in 1905.

These giant discoveries included Einstein's general theory of relativity in 1916, and Edwin Hubble discovered in 1924 there are other galaxies besides our own. These two particular finds would later be linked.

Niels Bohr described quantum energy theory in 1913, and in 1915 Alfred Wegener proposed continental drift to the world, but the scientists were not ready at all to accept his strange new proposal. These two events later turned out to be closely connected: the idea of the earth's surface having giant 'plates' of rock floating on a different density of ocean floor rocks, rather like blocks of ice in a lake, and the broadly contemporary analysis of their radioactive content. Our dispute with their ages comes later.

How the older linear thinking became accepted

Once this discovery of drifting plates had been made, it dawned on the pioneering geologist Arthur Holmes (1890–1965) that continental drift was right, and he was among its first authoritative supporters, for which he deduced 'convection current theory' for the mantle's rising magma. He saw these must contain giant upwellings of liquid rock, separated by type, heat and pressure variations, and that these currents could be strong enough to move even the continents themselves.

This made eminent sense, and especially if major cracks or 'faults' were to form in the oceanic floor areas between the plates margins, then the whole world's continental areas could begin to skate around like ice-hockey pucks. What he did not have time to explore, as we must here, is how massively these currents could change in their intensity over time, caused by the giant effects of an axial tilt of the earth.

In the cyclic model, this happened on a far faster and thus grander scale than anything we see now, today's tiny millimetre movements being merely the remnants of those massive migrations. The giant mountain chains under the waves prove that it did happen, but it all depends on two key questions: when did it happen, exactly, and was it recent or millions of years ago? [See Fig 12 of ocean floor ridges.]

The cyclic model revisits this issue with a large question to solve: could time itself possibly be cyclic, and not linear at all?

Can rock 'dates' be physically misleading?

Long-lived isotope dating methods are simple concepts in essence. We noted how 'parent' iron turns into rust by 'decaying' or oxidation. A parent radioactive material that is an 'unstable' isotope is constantly 'decaying' by losing particles. The result is that a new isotope 'daughter' is formed during this process, a new element with a new atomic number, such as potassium-K decaying into argon-Ar (K40 Ar40). This seems strange at first, since potassium is a metal, and argon a gas, yet it does happen. [Symbol key: Rb=rubidium, Sr=strontium, U=uranium, Pb=lead etc, are examples of decay pairs]

The theory is this: by measuring the amounts of each, and estimating the time taken for this breakdown or decay, an age or time gap can be calculated. This is all very well, so long as there is no doubt about the many assumptions used in reaching this 'calculation'. The key one is that no Ar40 was present when the K40 emerged on Day 1.

As we will now see, these assumptions do not stand up to the challenge of a cyclic time universe. The primary problem is that these measurements depend wholly on there being *none of the decay daughter present* at the time of eruption, but that is not certain. It is suggested that this vital constraint has never been true, and that the common decay products are present anyway without needing decay to produce them. Argon, thorium and lead are commonly found in volcanic rocks, so this may well be true they were there on Day 1, before any decay happened at all.

If so, the rock 'ages' are wrong, and cyclic time would be correct.

This is the chief objection to the dating methods that rely on this principle: measuring an element *thought to have formed* by slow decay over eons of time, when it is brand new and there already, and all ready for breakfast on day one.

All scientists will admit that there is this risk of *both parent and decay isotopes* being already present inside freshly erupted volcanic rock. Since this cannot be ruled out, it is possible. Since these 'decay' elements are commonly present in such rocks, it is very likely they were present from the start, and never arrived by decay at all, and were as new as the so-called parent elements. If so, the whole radiogenic decay method as above becomes invalid.

Since no one can prove this is not so, it remains a permanent concern.

When we examine the methods used by the radiogenic dating specialists, we see how linear time itself was the prevailing view,   so geologists had no alternative but to take the physicists' word for this long age. The long ages of millions of years created a separate problem: these ages were never doubted, because they matched what was expected by Lyell, Hutton and Darwin…an old earth. It confirmed what they all 'knew', much to the delight of the geologists, who had craved firm dates which no-one would dare to question (or had any reason to, even if they did dare).

It looked ideal. Dates showing an old earth processes that seemed to have lasted for millions of years was what they all thought 'must be true', so no-one questioned them. Science appeared to have 'won' the battle of earth's origins, by showing 'earth's true age' at last…job done. Only the job was not done at all.

Not one person thought of a reason to reconsider all this, and suggest a cyclic process of events, because the above assumptions were accepted as correct.

Why should we not all accept this answer? For one reason: it is not possible. In no way can it be correct, for all the reasons given in this study. We now have literally thousands of points that show time could not conceivably have passed by smoothly and regularly, as they had to assume it did, to arrive at the maths they used and draw those conclusions. The many signs of bizarre or anomalous 'youth' in those features appear to prove this point, but some who long since voted for linear time will not be pleased, because it means the universe is cyclic and pre-existing, and that means starting again for evolutionists. Yet to be displeased at all about this is to miss the point, since it could be the actual way reality works, and to reject reality would be a distinct disadvantage.

If the cosmos is a constant, and did not 'emerge' as some fashionably claim, then we need to know, for our decisions about both Life and science to have any meaning.

Each life would be affected in a new way. For the first time in history we have a modern view that shows why space produces such puzzling features, and favours actual facts over past presumptions. Those numerous features, such as the white snow of Haumea, the odd galactic rotation speeds and so much more, are only 'puzzling' when seen within the Standard Model of spacetime. Take them out, pop them into a short period cycle of those same events, minus the Big Bang, and we have an account of Reality where theory and fact match up. This is a game changer.

Since no-one has ever shown Time cannot be cyclic, when so much evidence suggests it is, then the universe can be a continuum. If that is so, it could be a pivotal result, because it would unlock the mysterious finds in quantum physics, geology, biology and astronomy in particular, which also point towards exceptions being the rule.

Those anomalies are only bizarre within the old worldview, yet fit neatly into the above cycle. Superconduction[38] may look weird in Newtonian mechanics, which was never designed to deal with such factors, let alone the super-atom of the Bose-Einstein Condensate (BEC), or entangled electrons of the Super Grid, but they would all be precisely predicted for a short event cycle that repeats, since without such super-fast quantum shifts at great distances, none of the events we see as real would have a mechanism to occur at all. Yet they do.

Missing dinosaurs and other fossils explained by a cycle

Geology also has such anomalies, such as the Cambrian Explosion of Life and the missing trillions of fossils over proposed billions of years; as does biology, which lacks any trace of the planetary presence predicted by linear time. Why else would there be only 1450 dinosaurs found, when there should also be trillions piled high in mounds?

We have never used science to draw all these strands together.

This new worldview of continuous cycles does match reality, and explores a fresh view of the known and unknown worlds.

Take this point from one of the sources that cover these methods in detail, from the justly famous Professor Claude Allègre, whose major work explains the equations and circular thinking behind these dating

---

38 When current transits materials without the usual resistance

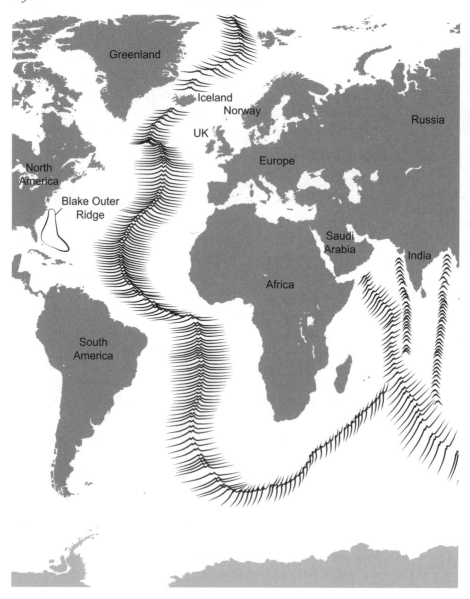

FIGURE 12 *Ocean Ridge & World Map with Blake Outer Ridge: showing earth's largest feature, the mid ocean ridges that formed when the globe split apart in as little as 5 years, not 500 million as claimed; due to axial tilt & vast volcanic eruptions on land and sub-sea.*

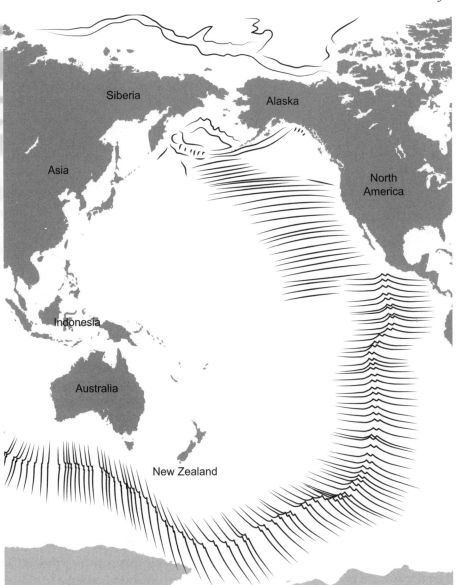

tests. His key book shows errors can occur, where periods of either intense heating could alter the apparent age of a rock, or via weathering due to water processes that could remove potassium.[39] Both these factors can alter the ratios of elements, and *create false results that still look reliable.*

The isotopes being measured may have simply been mixed over a much shorter timescale, in which case we would naturally find a meaningless mixture of both old and new material in differing stages of decay.

If so, this old method would have been entirely misconceived. Then there is no need to create the complex mantle/crust mixing models previously used as an explanation.

The important factor shows *time is taken as linear.* They just took this to be true. Since no one had any other ideas, it became set in stone. To disagree, had anyone dared, would have meant dismissal, because science in that era worked in a strictly hierarchical way, so unusual views were seen as ridiculous, and not taken seriously. Experts knew best, and that was that.

This is not as odd as it may seem, since scientists have to start with some idea, and they are not about to accept a shorter timescale as 'assumed' without good reason.

Who said time had to be linear? Nearly everyone did, except Sir Fred Hoyle and friends, along with a few others more recently, such as Professors Turok, Steinhardt, and Penrose. Hoyle's ideas had other flaws, so his whole notion of a Steady State continuum that always existed was rejected.

We tend to start with the idea that tomorrow will follow today. So far, in living memory and recorded history at least, that may have held true, but our memory is short.

Science, and its underlying maths, goes much further, and has to assume this *has always been so*, for as far back as we care to look. The top scientists, such as professors Dickin and Allègre among a few others, are fully aware of this potential weakness, and say so in their books, which is a real leap ahead of the old 1970's thinking styles that ignored the risks of relying on assumptions.

39 Isotope Geology, by Claude J. Allègre, Cambridge University Press 2008, p214–215

We must also pay tribute to the legions of scientists whose work we have seen over the last 130 years, with finds like the highly significant Cooper Pairs of quantum physics, and Prof. Josephson's valuable work on superconduction. Without their combined efforts in so many fields, we would have nothing to discuss but speculation. Sure, nuclear fission has been a very mixed issue, but the associated sciences have given us data about the world, as well as planetary and interstellar space, that is quite unparalleled in all history.

It would be impossible to analyse all their superb work fully and properly here, and so one hopes they will forgive an inevitably short and incomplete snapshot of their conclusions and methods with a view to achieving one purpose: to gain a better view, and clarify the striking contradictions in both cosmology and geology.

This has meant that a scientifically unhealthy situation has inadvertently arisen, by which the original concepts have been backed up by the later findings, by being deemed to be true. This is circular thinking, meaning the isotopic dates confirm the geological age estimations, and vice versa. If they did not, they would be rejected.

Professor Claude J. Allègre wisely remains cautious about assigning meaning in drawing conclusions, stating the concept of 'age' in rocks is 'purely arithmetic' and 'virtual' in nature.

Now for a pivotal point: Allègre points out the maths used to date rocks is not definite, and contains 'vagaries' which cannot be resolved, because the radioactive atoms found in a rock's crystals often vanish, and so then cannot be measured at all.[40]

This very honestly sets out the risk in drawing a 'meaning' from 'supposed geological facts'. It is supposition to do so. Those so-called 'facts' are actually presumptions, and so change as science changes.

Allègre goes on to say that one method is not enough, while many may be too costly, and still we have to think carefully about the foundational basis of a geological timescale, that may be flawed in its thinking.

Even the sample crystals used in such tests can give unpredicted results purely based on the heat of their formation phases. Allègre cites the fascinating example of Ar40 at low temperatures. Heat the same system to 250°C, which is no big deal as he also points out, then

40 Isotope Geology, by Claude J. Allègre, Cambridge University Press 2008, p214

the distance covered becomes four orders of magnitude greater in just 1/10th of the time.

This could affect a result by 100 million years or more. If time is cyclic, then errors may be in the billions, without anyone realising it. If results seem to fit the idea, why look any further? So they don't.

How ideas can remove meaning

So central is the 'thinking' behind the theories, that scientists have no apparent choice but to connect these results to the rocks themselves.

He describes the Rhenium-Osmium method as 'a despairing case' since it has huge theoretical ratios to work with, and the rocks do not act as closed systems, so fixing ages is tricky. [41]

In a supremely significant passage, he foresees a crisis within all this uncertainty, and warns that:

'Each geochronological result is affected by uncertainty. If we do not know (estimate) this uncertainty, a result is scientifically meaningless.' [42]

This is one of the most pivotal statements ever written in science, and one of such extreme importance in this field especially, because this is 'a concept relying on an ideology' used to connect the chemistry to the dates. The maths may look fine, even with its estimates to replace the unknowns, but if the beliefs behind the hypothesis are flawed in any way, the results will be entirely valueless.[43]

This shows all such ages truly are formed by maths *applied to estimated ratios*, and the results of isotope ratios are used to confirm the theory, and the theory confirms the ratios' value. This is classic circular thinking, well known to be of limited or zero value.

There is one aspect that trumps them all in importance, namely 'our interpretation' of the results. The meaning attached to such figures relies entirely on the presumption that time is a long line. The evidence for a Flash Time Zero 'energy re-set' is strong, and it changes everything by offering an alternative. Earlier researchers never saw this reason to doubt their figures and concepts.

Here is the key issue. If we ignore this re-set, as science currently does, then the results could lose all meaning.

41 Ibid
42 Ibid
43 Ibid, pp 215-6

Allègre then very fairly concludes that mistakes are part of this process.[44]

This means that outright errors can still be the result of careful work, but the fatal flaw of basing all of it on geological assumptions, always remains; it is the shaky basis of all these methods, and not solid at all. We can therefore see how this geophysics is *thought* to support these methods, while other factors disagree. The claim made here is that the whole design of linear time is an artificial proposal, so this error can be real.

A new concept is needed to fit the new findings

The computer models used unsurprisingly often 'fit' their own scenario perfectly, the exact one they were designed to explain. That too is circular thinking and testing.

Now we have so much more information and experimental data, we have never used it to analyse the cyclic universe option. We are still using 17th century thinking with mainly 20th century data. This may be why we can see the current 'old' model does not work, but cannot reconcile why this is so. If we look back only a little way, it will still be incomprehensible. Only by winding back the progress of modern science and mathematics all the way to Galileo, and then further back to the ancient thinking of the Greek and earlier Indian thinkers, can we begin to reveal these inconsistencies.

The central fault is such a small thing: a concept. Yet rather like a mere ¼ degree of error in a million miles, the size and extent of this small error, after so many layers of time and research, has become massive and serious. Why is it so serious? By continually using the linear format, we cannot test or analyse the future of these events. If we think they are linear when they may be moving rotationally, then our future modelling will be pure invention that will never actually happen. That fault is costing human lives.

In our short human lives of 70 years or so, we have about 50 adult years of our best scientific work. In this limited timeframe, we only see events appear to progress forward in a sequence, so many are utterly certain that all time must be linear.

44 Ibid, p216

Even the daily rotation of the earth on its axis that creates days gives the lie to this notion. Each day is like a microcosm or model of the larger cosmic circle of events. We begin each day with dawn, the sun appears to rotate across the sky in a large arc, but this too is an illusion, since the system we live in is solar or 'heliocentric', with the sun at its centre. The plant leaves all tend to face the sun as it moves, to maximise their absorption of its life-giving rays.

Slowly the light wanes as the sun dips towards the horizon, and we ourselves also feel tired, and ready for rest, only to repeat the whole scenario again the next day, as the rotation comes round to the next phase in the sequence. All this is a rotation, from our own lives, to the very air we breathe. Every part of it is rotating constantly. Sequential, it is, not linear.

This is the old chicken and egg dilemma. Which came first? You can't have a chicken without first having an egg, and of course the reverse is also true. This is a strong argument for a cyclic universe that is *so cyclic or orbital in nature* that the principle extends to time itself, and not in a random way, but in a perfectly 'complete' form of circularity: from the vast galactic spinning of stars or quasars all the way down to the tiny sub-atomic level.

This idea of a deeper principle of rotation can be seen in every part of earth and space. Therefore it is not at all odd that all the theories based on the old linear notion cannot explain these details, nor account for this actual cosmic set-up. It is therefore entirely logical that we can propose time's deepest level of motion to be circular as well.

Early pioneers had to picture their reasoning, but this process does not always lead to reasoned results, especially when much of that thinking was done several hundred years ago, when we didn't even understand electricity, or light, let alone quantum physics; and we still are not sure what light is or how electricity moves.

To be fair, cyclic time was never really on the modern agenda, because this alternative is just too strange and extraordinary to consider easily.

Now we have to think of the key challenge to linear time (and Darwin), and if both earth and space 'evolved' from nothing[45]. If this cycle is correct, then an 'evolution of space' could not have happened

---

45 We will deal with the 'multiverse' idea later, because logic disputes that is even
    possible; and it is unproven.

in so few years. There were never enough centuries in a row, with no re-set, for all that to occur; so it must always have been here. There is no middle ground on this one. Either the earth we stand on did indeed cool from a hot mass, or it did not. There are now no apparent grounds for continuing to believe the earth was red hot. How could we be sure?

The answer is simple, and has three parts. The old linear model disregards the classic concepts of the *conservation of energy law*, which states that energy may be converted to other forms, but is never created nor destroyed. This seems obvious, since not many of those in science subscribe to the idea of magic, in which things appear out of nowhere. The multiverse is not believable, because matter cannot keep appearing out of other universes we just invented to plug this yawning gap in a theory. The oceans appearing on comets, at just the right moment in history, as if on a No: 9 bus, is equally unfeasible, as noted. A continuum solves all this.

Therefore, the idea that the whole universe, along with time, suddenly snapped into existence, is straining credulity well past breaking point. Yet this is just what is called for in the old Big Bang theory, and when theorists run out of universes, as the maths finally forces them to.

Is there more objective evidence?

As Dr Param Singh, a colleague of Prof Smolin, and also from Canada's Perimeter Institute, once said of Big Bang: 'I don't believe that at all'. It seems he is right.

There is a similar law about matter being conserved, and there is the mass-energy equation of Einstein, $E=mc^2$, based on his special theory of relativity. Since this is proven in countless chemical and physics experiments, this is not a group of laws we should set aside too easily. Even though many people in the modern world, roughly half, accept the idea of the universe springing into being one day, the other half don't. So who is right?

Perhaps the universe exists all the time, and only needs to change levels of order.

We would therefore no longer need to insist on vast time spans for all these events, for which time period the fossils and bones are conspicuously lacking. The intricate and complex systems we see in nature need not have formed slowly over the long periods claimed, but can instead have always existed, and provably so.

This may not fit in the mind of a linearist, but the very long linear model of billions of *uninterrupted years* can now legitimately be questioned. The CMB is strong evidence that time has changed recently, via such a quantum re-set.

We are now bound to reassess the whole idea, not just a small part of it.

Gravity is a wonderful thing. If something is high, it will tend to fall to a lower place. The conservation of energy law means that energy exists constantly. We don't tend to see giraffes or spaniels springing out of bowls of soup. The world would be a more complex place to live if they did. So why should we assume Matter did this? Claiming it all sprang out of a parallel universe is the same thing, because the maths does not allow such magic. The multiverse, as this idea is known, is then an extreme attempt to shore up the old notions of linear time, but their basic failure to respect physical laws leaves us unconvinced.

Many astronomers have noticed a very significant fact. The more we find out about the universe, the more these new findings show how little we know. They do not prove we were right at all, but quite the opposite. The galaxies are *accelerating*, as we saw, not slowing as firmly predicted. Inventing dark matter does not solve this, as we will see.

Now we can see the problem must lie very deeply indeed in our psyche as a fixation with the linearity of Time's arrow, when it may not be an arrow at all.

When we add the notion of a 'repeating' cycle to the mix, we can ask the 'unthinkable' questions. Do the latest methods of fixing dates for rocks, now a century old, still work? We can all perceive radioactivity as real enough, especially if you lived near a nuclear plant like USA's Three Mile Island in 1979, Windscale in England, Fukushima in Japan or Chernobyl in Russia, which all suffered massive radiation explosions. We can measure it, while not able to see it, but the atomic bomb is enough proof for us to accept its existence as a certainty.

Igneous rock has similar radioactivity. The isotopes are unstable, and so they give off particles at a more or less constant rate, or so we think. Scientists then calculate its 'Half Life', or how long it takes for an element to lose half its radioactivity.

All this seems reasonable enough, but it relies on the assumption that no situation could affect this process, which is not true. As Prof Allègre pointed out, we cannot know the number of such atoms that were there at the start.[46]

Further evidence

Having looked at the basic idea, we can now consider specific examples. Radioactive decay is said to begin when rock cools.

When igneous (Latin: fiery) rock emerges from a volcano, it is also assumed that it has none of these decay type elements *already present inside it*. One example of these is Argon-40, as noted, which is the 'decay daughter' produced by the degrading of Potassium-40. Another decay product is Calcium-40.

If the rock did start with some of these decay products, the method fails to have any value. As scientists know, not a person on earth can prove it isn't so.

As we have seen, this turns out to be a real flaw. Argon-40's mere existence in that rock does not guarantee that all that Argon-40 we find in this volcanic rock *'must have'* formed from this process of decay. As everyone now knows, it could easily have been present in the rock on day one. The assumption that all the Argon-40 has formed over huge periods of time may not be correct, if volcanic rocks already contain such decay isotopes before eruption.

Horror of horrors, this does actually appear to be the case. Volcanic rock was taken from a specific eruption *of known date*, which was seen taking place in 1801. Samples of this eruption at Hualalei in Hawaii were used in dating tests to see what their 'radioactive age' would be, if checked by this decay method [47]. The answers were a shock, to say the least. Some samples came out of these tests as being from 160–3000 million years old, which would be in conflict with their actual eruption date of 1801.

Such anomalous results may be evidence that this and similar methods have a fatal flaw. This leaves us two tantalizing options: is the

46 Isotope Geology, by Claude J. Allègre, Cambridge University Press 2008, p30
47 Funkhouser & Naughton 1968, Hawaiian Institute of Geophysics. Quoted in The Facts of Life, R. Milton, p66, Corgi 1992.

anomaly just a small error that has no big significance, or does it show the entire theory just became meaningless overnight?

Yet this is no small error, with a range of 160 million *to 3 billion years*. As we can see from the eruption date of 1801, on an island with constant eruptions, any date over 216 years would be wrong. This major method flaw explains how errors happen.

The situation appears to be this simple: once a theory is accepted as true fact, then the questioning stops, and we get on with proving it right, and rejecting any trace of the very idea that it may not be. [We have also heard of the *scotoma*, a concept in psychology where a person can be unable or unprepared to recognize a particular issue. This may explain the inability many show of 'seeing' another point of view, no matter how valid it may be. Alas we cannot know if this is true or not, since we all regard our opinions as clear and valid, so we only note this. This is why science tries to be objective, yet cannot remove the subjective.]

Prevailing thought is the most powerful influence of all, and even 'solid evidence' can appear absolute fact one moment, whereas later work can show it may not be factual at all. Several cases show this is true. Recent studies show our memory can be selective, even in one survey of soldiers, when test people were given false information and encouraged to believe they were factual; 50% did switch their view from false to true, while being clearly wrong (such as saying there was one man in a room when they had noticed two). They were convinced to change. This may explain how accounts of real or imagined events often vary so dramatically.

In short, even in science, we usually see whatever we want to see, and believe a theory or idea because we prefer it to be true.

Some people start demanding a cherished theory must now be treated as 'fact', and lose the title of being 'merely a theory', in an attempt to stamp out the speculation that still surrounds the thinking, which can become tiring after 1½ centuries or more. This is exactly what has happened to Darwinism, as we see.

Naturally this attempt to blot out any further discussion can never succeed. Science should be like the blindfold of justice, that no matter what our preferences, the facts should be allowed to prevail. The real snag is this: how can we tell which part is fact?

There was the case in 1906 when Rutherford carried out the first radioactive age test. It was a time of uncertainty, since helium was often confused with nitrogen (which behaves inertly like the noble gases[48] that have complete outer atomic shells, and so do not readily combine). He measured one rock sample to be 'a billion years old', while Lord Kelvin was claiming a date of 100 million years for the age of the earth itself. Their judgement was based on totally different methods of isotope decay rates and heat loss respectively, and this is how science works.

If the senior scientists vote yes, it becomes treated as fact. We may now suggest neither was right, because they were utterly fixed on time being a line, and so they would never agree it could be a fault. To admit such deep errors after a lifetime is never easy. Few of us are ready for that, hence Planck's comment that old ideas only fade out with their holders. Here is another example of accepted wisdom affecting results.

An interesting graph can be seen in the superb book of Prof. Allègre[49] which shows a model of the earth's 'core growth', meaning how the central liquid-metallic part of our earth might have developed over time, perhaps with nickel (hence the old term NiFe – like knife – for this core zone). The inner core is said to be a solid sphere. [See Fig 13]

Naturally it is based on a linear timescale, in keeping with current thinking. This shows the iron content moving smoothly upwards from zero to the present, and the caption suggests that 6% may still be contained in the mantle that swirls with convection currents of magma that rotate below the crust. The magma's viscosity is controlled by the amount of SiO_4 tetrahedra it contains, as its chains and rings get in each other's way, to speak liquidly for a moment. This is why the slow and heavy, thick lava of Peléean and Strombolian volcano types differ from the fissure ones (Iceland, Hawaii, India etc), as we have seen, and every geologist knows. If we adopt the cyclic time version for a moment, this graph may show only an idea. The chart is a hypothesis, and accepted ideology.

This metallic core will become even more important later in our chart of the progress of a cyclic earth, since it comprises a fairly humble 16% of earth's volume, but a massive 32% of its mass. Shifts in the

48 These are: helium, neon, argon, krypton, xenon and radon-222.
49 *Isotope Geology*, by Claude J. Allègre, Cambridge University Press 2008, p459.

rotation of this dense metal sphere at our planet's centre allow several things to take place, *including polar reversals* and even assist with massive tectonic changes, as noted above.

This core growth graph also gives us a fascinating window into the thinking of the whole theoretical basis of linear time. Once that was established and accepted, many things rested squarely upon it. This is why very few scientists would be ready to set aside so much earlier work and research, now that the edifice it supports is so huge.

These values are of the 'residence times' of magma containing the isotopes in geochemical reservoirs, such as the rock of the upper mantle, the oceans and atmosphere, meaning the amount of time they have sat there, while decaying. These locations, which include rivers and lakes, each contain different amounts of isotopes to be compared.[50]

In this way a statistical map is drawn up, and test results are then plotted, to demonstrate how the data look as dots on a graph. Again, where the line is drawn through these dots on the graph, is a statistical decision, and may not be an absolute certainty.[51] The isotope amounts *may thus not be due to decay at all,* but only seem so. The isotope amounts are assumed to have resulted from long decay, but can actually arise from a short period cyclic process of those volcanic rocks. In this case they may instead be 'infinitely old', and not the 'smaller figure' of billions claimed. This is very simple to understand, because it shows that decay may not have occurred over long periods.

No one had any reason to disagree, until now.

Every expert would admit this is a possibility, because it cannot be denied. Another assumption used is that chemical mixing and separation or 'fractionation' happens over a long time. This also assumes that continental drift has been pushing some areas of rock back under the crust (subduction) and deep into the mantle to be re-melted, which is assumed to have happened over billions of years. In the cyclic model, we do not need to invoke this claim at all. It is again presumed so, because they never considered a short cycle.

Some processes are very fast. These subduction zones are geologically violent areas where plates are destroyed as they sink to a depth of perhaps 700 kms below a continental margin, as in the case of

50 Isotope Geology, by Claude J. Allègre, Cambridge University Press 2008, p467.
51 Based on establishing 'a mean, a dispersion, an asymmetry etc'. Ibid.

Japan's eastern coast, and the Andean Pacific Rim, creating Andesitic volcanoes. These processes can happen in sudden steps that create earthquakes of immense force at the key friction points, and often resulting in tsunamis, as in 2011 and in Alaska, or Chile. Such events are so huge, the whole earth rings like a bell, which scientists only detected recently with modern seismic stations.

Now we can see that, just by employing a new way of thinking, the same data can be interpreted in an entirely new and totally contradictory way. This is central to any attempt to separate fact from fiction: to run the counter exercise that tests the results according to wholly new and different parameters.

When we do this, the results fit the cyclic version.

More science detail

This melting process within the earth's mantle tends to equalise or 'homogenize the isotope ratios of the source zone', i.e. the mantle. These two forces are therefore in opposition: one blending towards equality, the other separating. Thus, depending on which types of rock we subject to testing, the results can be very different, even though their true ages may be identical; hence the isotopes present may not show the correct age at all. Finding argon does not prove it derived from potassium, inferring long age.

The calculations are not plain sailing, as Professor Allègre wisely points out, and 'adjustments' have to be made in equations, because the maths is affected by the dispersion ratios used, and the effects of fractionation, as in basalt, for example.[52]

This means researchers have to *manipulate the maths*, by literally having to *create estimates* for various 'unknowns', simply to reach any answer at all. This may sound fine, but if any one of those estimates is wrong, then we have a problem. Even maths can therefore be totally mistaken, by inventing values to put in the equations purely to make them turn out as expected. The results can then be wrong by a factor of millions or billions, just by using assumptions that are false. As noted, if these artificial values are wrong, the results would be meaningless.

This is how the 'age' results using maths can cease to mean anything.

52 Isotope Geology, by Claude J. Allègre, Cambridge University Press 2008, p470.

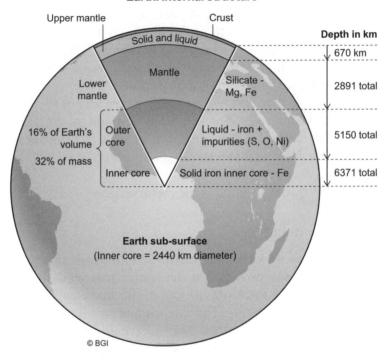

Earth: internal structure

FIGURE 13 *Global Earth in section: showing interior of earth with solid core that generates our magnetic field.*

In one university test question Allègre uses, we get a revealing example[53], since the calculation uses a value of a billion years for the residence time, as this basaltic rock sits in the mantle, ready to burst out from below the Atlantic Ocean as Mid Ocean Ridge Basalt (known as MORB). In this case in point, the equation uses this value to give our test rocks a 'mixing time' of 530 million years (Ma). The assumption used is that 'this did take place'. It may not have.

This has been used in Professor Allègre's book as an example for students of isotope geology to work out, but the example is carefully chosen to show the methods and thinking behind the maths in use today, and it gives us a window on how linear time is taken as the baseline to start assigning ages to volcanic rocks.

53 Isotope Geology, by Claude J. Allègre, Cambridge University Press 2008, p471.

His book is all the more impressive for the error sources he has described, and offered ways to overcome, but they all rely on linear time, as does every scientist.

In another Allègre book exercise, the basis of the thinking is set out in a way that may sum up the premise of radiogenic dating: that since earth once did not exist at all, as in linear models, then neither did these particular decay products. They had to form from other processes, so by setting out a hypothesis, a date for earth's atmospheric or mantle (sub-crustal hot rock between crust and core) age can be calculated, yet how do we know it is correct? The mantle forms 84% of earth's volume, so it is an important consideration of bulk.

Another example of this battle between 'new versus old thinking' lies embedded in the presumption that Earth began with a start date. There is no evidence this happened. It may seem strange to some that the cosmos might exist forever, merely changing instead of forming from nothing (or a parallel world), but no other answer fits what we see.

The usual story is that earth formed, then became hot and liquid, and then much of the iron fractionated to the core, leaving the boiling mantle magmas above to fizz, bubble and lose some of its gas in a process calling 'degassing'.

This account may be untrue, since there are other technical hitches in this model.

Professor Allègre goes on to point out that the upper and lower mantle have separate levels of degassing, in which the gas argon's ($Ar40$) different isotopes have been separated or 'fractionated' by heat conditions at earth's formation. He suggests no $Ar40$ was first present, but only $Ar36$ and $Ar38$, being forced to state this by the convention of linear time.

This final clause would be logical, if earth formed in the linear model. Did earth have a beginning? It seems not. All the dates are undermined if this premise is true. We can see how central the linear theory has become. Take it away, and instantly the many 'unexpected' results can be moved into the 'expected' category. A cyclic model changes all the theory, suggesting time has no start or end, and exists forever.

The $Ar40$ balance mentioned in the above quote relies on this 'degassing' model of 'a long primordial period' in which $Ar36$ and $Ar38$

decay into Ar40. What is really significant about this is that the Ar40/
Ar36 ratio has been measured at 40,000 for the upper mantle, but
4,000 for the lower mantle, and a mere 296.8 for the atmosphere. This
is the hub of the whole issue: when these measurements are interpreted
under the assumption of the linear 'long time' history of earth, then the
results are totally different, and, it is suggested, incorrect.

It is usual enough to create ideas as hypotheses, and then develop
mathematical equations to see how these ideas pan out. The key
problem with linear time is that the results continue to be 'unexpected'
or 'astonishing'. The reason for this appears to be puzzling scientists
today, but not those aware of the Flash Time answer.

The results [54] of such tests on deep ocean rocks can be seen. What
do they show?

They show values that do not accord with linear time, but with a cycle.

When we look at the oceanographic maps of the deep ocean floor of
the north and south Atlantic, we don't see any obvious reason for the
rocks extruded to be 2–300% different in the north and south areas,
or why the Indian Ocean should be 692% older in the south-west than
its central area. Even using plate tectonics theory, the movement of the
Indian continental plate from near Madagascar and Australia would
indicate these areas were both affected in similar ways. They clearly
were not, and only a cycle would explain this. Look at a map of the
ocean floor…the huge ridges show the plates did move.

What is not widely realised is that an axial tilt could be a more recent
event than judged by these above methods, and that would create such
imbalance that broke up Pangea quickly. These plates could have
moved *very much faster* than many advise.

In the cyclic model, the ages of the faults on this area of the deep
ocean floor would be directly related to this same movement of India
to form the vast Himalayan mountain chain, and the Tibetan Plateau,
when India as a 'tectonic plate' pushed up the sediments by moving
north; so these giant ocean floor fault systems could not be considered
as entirely separate formations of such hugely different ages, as above.

Yet the cyclic version can challenge the linear notion with this
concept: the formation of a global continental split in one very violent

54 Ibid p507

era of earth's geology that sees each plate moving rapidly to its new, current location. What could cause such a split? A shift in the earth's axis as noted, forcing Pangea to break apart as already accepted, and then each continent to move to a stable place for earth's new spin regime. This could be why Australia and India moved north east, and may have done so at high speed. This is not only possible, but much more likely, because there isn't the depth of sediment to account for any long periods of calm deposition.[55]

Many areas have no sediment at all, implying very recent formation.

Instead, what we see is a truly mighty system of transform faults that stretches from the Nansen Cordillera in the far north of Iceland, south past the Mohns Ridge, through the centre of the Atlantic, along the mid-ocean ridge that lies hidden far below the surface, as an invisible yet giant mountain range, and right round the Cape towards India to join the Amsterdam Fracture Zone, and on into the Pacific. [See map in Fig 12].

This global feature is truly vast, yet its scale was hidden...until science found it.

Although entirely unseen from the air, this is the longest and largest single connected feature on earth, taking up nearly all the deep ocean floor area, and thus dwarfing even the largest continents. Its shape, nature and 'freshness' are highly significant, because they show a marked lack of weathering and the expected sedimentary or detrital build up, if earth was billions of years old. This lack of sediment would only be possible if it formed recently, so these ridges must be much younger than was ever thought possible. This vision of reality must shock some experts, but not all.

Only this option fits the facts we see.

Here and there along the length of this vast fault system, lie clues to its existence in the form of immense volcanoes that rise from the deep ocean floor and whose tips not only break the water's surface, but continue to stretch far above it. Examples such as Ascension Island, Tristan da Cunha, Gough Island and St Helena, rising from plumes of hot material that become Ocean Island Basalts (known as OIB's), and these are just a few in the Atlantic. The Pacific Ocean is full of

55 Deposition rates are based on theoretical models that fit long age assumptions: linear thinking confirming itself.

many more, all the same depth, suggesting rapid deep abyssal plain formation.

This same titanic ocean floor fault system becomes known as the Pacific-Antarctic Ridge, then the East Pacific Rise, and continues all the way to California's highly active fault system on America's west coast, as far as Alaska. These vast and faulted mountain chains do indeed circumnavigate the entire globe of the earth. We will examine the suggestion that this system, big as it truly is, could still have formed much faster than geologists are used even to considering, let alone accepting, and yet there are valid conditions that do appear to have actually happened to bring this about.

Bearing in mind the earth's axis is tilted over at 23½°, it is entirely possible that this massive system could have formed during a resulting global upheaval which shattered the old continents of Pangea and Gondwanaland very much faster than we imagined. What might have initiated such huge forces? The answer could be a passing asteroid, or a planet, some of which are still wobbling on their axes, perhaps as a result of this recent event. Many share such opinions, but it is a very different way of thinking from the norm, and the facts do match this new way of seeing history. [See Fig 14]

Naturally enough, when we look at today's rate of continental plate movement of 1–3 cms per year, and apply the standard linear time model to this rate, and then calculate the time elapsed, we get the usual result of 10's to 100's of millions of years. If we apply the cyclic model to the accepted existence of these crustal plates, and to the ocean floor geology on which they rest, the result is vastly different, and could happen in 100 years or less, as we will explore later. That would explain the lack of sediment on ocean floors.

To many, the linear sequence of time looked likely to be one element in all science that would never be overturned. One may predict that it will be, and soon.

[*Science extra detail*: In 1886 Henri Moissan isolated fluorine, and was later to discover and give his name to a man-made crystal he naturally called *moissanite,* which is used to simulate diamond. Luckily for gemmologists, it is not too close to the real thing, and has a higher dispersion of white light, which gives it a colourful 'dispersive' appearance. It is heavier than diamond, far less hard of course, but its most important

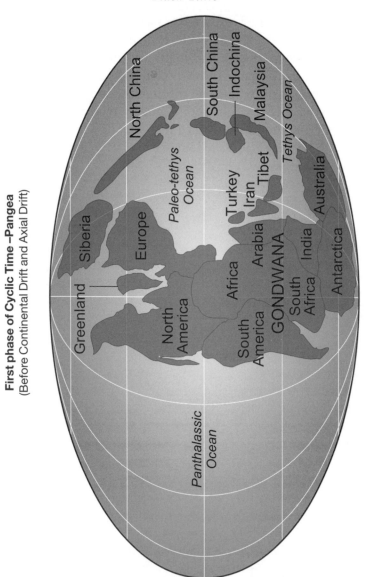

First phase of Cyclic Time –Pangea
(Before Continental Drift and Axial Drift)

FIGURE 14 *Pangea Supercontinent: diagram showing how present land masses once fitted into one land area, later to split apart very rapidly when axis tilted and polar ice formed, lowering oceans by 110m and exposing sea floor areas such as Sahara, USA, Australia, Brazil etc.*

property is its double refraction when seen from any angle except the long 'c' axis...often the top view. The way to detect this is easy enough with a 10x lens. Since they are normally cut with this 'c' axis at 90° to the table facet, by looking at a suspected *moissanite* gemstone from any angle except the obvious one through the top, one can see every speck of dust or facet margin with a ghostly twin beside it, which is diagnostic of a non-diamond, since real diamond is singly refractive (isotropic). They may also have long parallel flaw lines inside, seen in the side view.]

CHAPTER 7

The Weird Fossil Record: why it doesn't agree with evolutionary claims

Discovery consists of seeing what everybody has seen and thinking what nobody has thought.
A VON SZENT-GYORGYi, 1962

It is undesirable to believe a proposition when there is no ground whatever for supposing it true
SIR BERTRAND RUSSELL, 1920

Essence

Now for a quick look at a controversial subject....the fossil creatures we find. It is of course a huge subject with many aspects, about which many books have been written. Have these books missed anything? It seems they have, so here is the essence for you to judge for yourself.

There is a problem with fossil quantities found, and the lack of altered forms needed by his theory, which Darwin predicted may not exist [56], and that there may not be enough found to prove his theory right.

As Darwin wrote: 'We meet with no such evidence, and this is the most obvious and forcible of the many objections which may be urged against my theory.' [57]

This is an astonishing and honest admission, but he was right, and there are not enough *by trillions upon trillions*. Orthodox thinkers say they 'must have' existed, but the reality of this situation is that they do not.

Each transitional form would require millions of versions to create a species that worked well enough to walk around even for five seconds,

56 *The Origin of Species*, Charles Darwin (1859), Penguin 1985, p 457.
57 Ibid. p 438.

let alone years. Add to that the vast complexity of living things, with complicated ear bones, cones and rods in eyes, bone collagen to form blood cells, neat teeth, tongues and taste, fingers and toes, hair, stomachs, intestines, hepatic portal veins, valves within veins, lungs for gas exchange, precision heart valves, the glomerulus in kidneys to purify toxins, the endocrine system, blood flow, the hypothalamus in brains, tendons, muscles that work in pairs, vast genomes, body mirror symmetry, cell reproductions, DNA, RNA, a central nervous system, a mind with spatial awareness and the cunning of a hunter for predators and prey, and this would require an incalculable number of forms to make just one that worked, and that's just 0.01% of what humans use. The three ear bones are amazing: the smallest bones in the body, and yet they exist in mirror opposite shapes in opposite ears in each of our heads. How could they have 'evolved' into opposite shapes in that way without any intermediate or 'in between' forms? Much of the human body also exists in mirror opposite in a similar way, as in countless other life forms. Did all that evolve without leaving the required trillions of mutated forms claimed by Darwin? The evidence shortage suggests they did not, and logic compels us to accept that fact. What did happen instead? A cycle of time provides the best credible answer that works.

Evolution is said to be about as likely as a tornado tearing through a junkyard and producing a ready for take-off brand new jumbo jet, with crew and fresh lunch. This amusing analogy carries a serious caution which Darwin recognised: *a clear lack of both* fossils and the altered forms that 'should exist' in vast quantity. They are not found.

Where are those 'in between forms'? We are short by trillions and trillions needed to fill the claimed sequence of billions of years. Everyone agrees on one thing: they truly do not exist. The question is if they were invented to fit Darwin's theory. The answer 'yes' is supported by the facts. The lack of fossil intermediaries is still the problem Darwin predicted it could be, only worse now that humanity has dug up so much of the earth, and looked in nearly all the caves. What did they find? They found evidence for a cycle, but never realised it. That was never an option all those years ago, but Darwin hinted he knew with his key book's 'cycling on' final line.

This lack of fossil forms is crucial for long linear time, yet they are not there.

Some missing forms have been called 'hopeful monsters', meaning the failed creatures 'evolution' is said to have tried and failed to make work. Each creature would have needed their neural system and brain to run everything perfectly. Each mammal would have needed a blood system that correctly metered and pumped the fluid around the arterial and venous networks with precise balance, varying constantly according to exertion rates. The veins have non-return pressure valves that stop the blood flowing the wrong way, and the heart/blood system can never 'partly work'. They cannot be 'half' alive with half a blood system, or no lungs to oxygenate the cells.

We do not find these monsters. After all, if life was busy arranging itself into workable models of different species, there must have been countless changes that did not function well enough to stay alive. So where are they? They too are missing.

In a cyclic universe, they would never have existed. That may be why they remain absent. When even soft tissues leave stains in sediments, to suggest trillions of tons of bone and biomass simply vanished without trace should strain anyone's belief. Yet an entire world view has been built up, piece by piece, on the premise this really happened. With evidence being essential, this lack of it is the biggest single problem in science. We used to be taught that soft creatures could never be fossilised without hard shells, but that turned out to be untrue (eg in the Ediacara rocks, with 30 genera of jellyfish etc). The real reason for all these errors arose from the two choices people had over a century ago: linear time, or Creation. Now we have a cycle that explains both, it all fits. This is our story too, so let's check a little deeper.

What is the thinking behind such claims?

First of all, what are fossils? They are the remains of dead creatures that lived in pre-history. Some think their whole existence has been made up, but they are real. It used to be thought they slowly died and were covered over by mud or sand, so that any soft parts would be destroyed by decay or scavengers. Yet this is not the way it usually happens. Most of the fossils found around the world show signs of fast mass burial, and so rapid that soft bodies were buried too, in seconds.

As we noted, recent tests with crustacea showed even a 30 minute time gap between death and burial caused considerable and obvious deformation of the creature, so it was nearly instant. This key fact shows these creatures were often covered by mud or sand in seconds. One moment they were alive, and the next they were buried under layers of sediment. Only major catastrophes can do that on the global scale we see. That gives us a picture of a once calm world that, due to a major cause like an axial tilt, became turbulent and chaotic very suddenly indeed. Examples are too numerous to list, but fish found entombed in Wyoming are one, and groups of dinosaurs are another. This high speed of much rock formation, once thought to be slow, is also strikingly evident in the acute lack of fossils in many sediments.

Fossils form in rocks of one main type, so let's glance at how that happens.

There are three main types of rock on earth: volcanic, sedimentary, and metamorphic. Volcanic rocks begin as red hot material beneath the earth's crust. Sediments are either wind blown or aeolian, as in sand dunes, but usually form via water, as in seas, rivers or lakes. Metamorphic or 'altered' rocks are formed by later heat or pressure, such as when continents collide to uplift mountains. Alpine folds are caused by such forces as these that can distort vast areas of rock.

Only in sediments do we find classic fossils, because both volcanic and metamorphic rocks require colossal temperatures and pressures during their formation, (occasionally strong enough to produce diamonds [58], rising to 100GPa at the core-mantle [59] boundary), a fraction of which would melt or otherwise destroy any fossil.

Even the very definition of a fossil has evolved over the years, as scientists realised the old one was too narrow to accept. It also ignored another false assumption. Soft and delicate creatures could indeed be fossilised, as the Ediacaran and Burgess Shale finds have demonstrated [found in Australia and Canada respectively, include jellyfish, annelid worms and soft corals in the former, and creatures so weird in the latter formation that they are unclassified, along with our fossil friend *Anomalocaris*].

---

58 Diamonds crystallise in the mainly liquid hot rock of the mantle, below the surface 'crust' of the continents.
59 The mantle is where lava originates before emerging as volcanoes, being 84% of the earth by volume, and 65% by mass.

Ichthyostega

FIGURE 15 *Amphibian: drawing of Ichthyostega, claimed to be an ancient ancestor of mammals, hence having 5 limb digits, later found to be an error and actually to have 7.*

It showed these were very rapid deposits, formed in moments for such soft organic matter to be preserved at all. These, and many others, were not the slow, gradual, millions of years' long strata once expected, proving instead that a huge number of such geological events were very swift indeed.

We all agree there are fossils, but we are not agreed about how long the rock strata took to form with them trapped inside. The old claim of millions of years of sequential history is simply not supported by solid facts.

Let's pause a moment and see what the fuss is all about. The convention accepted by Darwin theorised the earth once cooled from a hot sphere. He took this from natural philosophers like James Hutton, who invented a system in 1795 of earth's continental formation that curiously relied on cycles. This 'hot earth origin' immediately ran into the major obstacle of explaining where the oceans came from, if it were true the earth was once entirely red hot, and why no other planet has oceans of water. Even the massive planet Jupiter had only traces of water vapour detected by the Galileo spacecraft, which orbited it for over 6 years. As we noted, this is indeed odd if the oceans truly did have as their source the wonderfully named 'Late Heavy Bombardment'.

Yet this is what scientists claim did happen, as noted, because all this water arrival is meant to have taken place inexplicably and conveniently soon after the earth cooled down enough to receive it, all neatly splashed into place, and ready for life to begin forming single-celled organisms after breakfast, as required by the theory. This is not credible for these reasons, and that this story requires belief to accept it. Without the proof it needs, this inventive notion just becomes a big story. It does lack any proof.

We are also told the Primeval Soup formed in this water, then CH_4 or methane emerged at the right time, despite being highly volatile and explosive as every student knows. This had to be invented very quickly in the story, since it was required to provide carbon, assumed to be necessary, as were heat flashes to break a few bonds and create a few amino acids, so what better than eons of near constant lightning to do all that? This was science: if a theory needed water or anything, it was often proposed that it 'flew in from the sky'. Seriously? Such unprovable ideas became popular props to linear theories for just this reason: not as actual proof, which they could not be, but as a sort of answer anyway. Even the oceans are among these 'sky theories', as we have seen.

Here's the thing. Life doesn't tend to work too well after being hit by a million volt smack of lightning hotter than the sun. Yet the theory needed heat, so lightning 'arrived'.

MEGA-EVENTS	Pre-Cambrian	Cambrian	Ordovician	Silurian	Devonian	Carboniferous	Permian	Triassic	Jurassic	Cretaceous
Volcanics	●	●	●	●	●	●	●	●	●	●
Mass Extinctions	●	●	●	●	●	●	●	●	●	●
Floods & Sea Level Changes	●	●	●	●	●	●	●	●	●	●
Anoxic Events	●	●	●	●	●	●	●	●	●	●
Ice Ages	●	●	●	●	●	●	●	–	–	–
Continent Shifts	●	●	●	●	●	●	●	●	●	●
Cyclic Strata	●	●	●	●	●	●	●	●	●	●
Hothouse Shifts	●	●	●	●	●	●	●	●	●	●
Carbon Changes	●	●	●	●	●	●	●	●	●	●
Sediment Turnover	●	●	●	●	●	●	●	●	●	●
Climate Change	●	●	●	●	●	●	●	●	●	●
Magnetic Reversals	●	●	●	●	●	●	●	●	●	●

FIGURE 16 *World Mega Events table: showing major disasters in every geological era within half of one short cycle, not as one long assumed line, or just in extinction eras; all these events fit into 1600 years.*

Among all this theory, there is no indisputable proof that any of this happened at all, or proof of any kind. The old chicken and egg problem is never solved by the Evolution version, because you cannot have an egg without a chicken, and vice versa. Only a universe that always exists solves this knotty enigma.

The problem for evolution is that it relies on the fossil record, meaning the creatures *actually found* in the earth's sediments. They are missing: the required fossils to prove life 'evolved' are still missing, and the fossil record shows no such process.

One example is the fish, which is claimed to have transformed into amphibians via many millions of other shapes as it did so. We are told it emerged victorious from the ocean it once called home, learned to use its pectoral fins to walk on the beach, and set off across the land to start a new life, transforming into mammals like ourselves, the human beings of earth. It was even taught that these amphibians had 5 'digits' that became our 5 fingers, until it emerged the first fossils of these creatures had more than 5 digits. One researcher even counted 5 digits when he was in fact looking at 7.

Yet these very amphibians, once claimed to show this wonder of evolving 'our limbs' before we had them, proved not to be five-rayed or 'pentadactyl' at all, having 7 or 8 lobes on a recount in the fossils [eg *Tiktalik, Icthyostega, Acanthostega, Rhipidistia* etc.] This revision by later scientists is of huge importance, because it showed the old assumption that amphibians marked the evolutionary half-way house between fish and mammals, all with five-rayed fins or limbs, was simply not true. [See Fig 15]

The huge significance of this mismatch has largely been ignored.

As a highly imaginative idea, it suited perfectly what they wanted to see, namely a neat link between fish, reptiles and land mammals. It sought to describe how life was restricted to the oceans, only to burst onto land and take over the very niche to which it could once never aspire: earth outside the sea. Anything was possible with this idea of fish colonising dry land. It explained how fish could become mankind, and then rule the world with great skill and brilliance…only with less of both than we would have liked. A brilliant idea, and the only fitting history and outcome for a clever and ingenious species such as ourselves, or so they thought.

Only one small problem remained. It appears to have been entirely made up, as all this later evidence now shows, hence why evolution was seen by some in the 19th century as humankind's hidden origin, even though Darwin himself was among many who doubted it could succeed without the fossils required to support it.

So, can evolution be true or not?

There is no evidence for it, and so much against it, that only belief can make evolution look like real history. The fact is that science cannot find proof, and has resorted to relying on theory for what it claims 'must be true'. Now that cyclic time resolves the issues of the missing intermediate forms between species, and why they do not exist, evolution truly does have the exact problem Darwin foresaw. It lacks the fossil numbers, and ignores cyclic time, for which there is evidence. The answer is for you to judge. Indeed our geologists and biologists have often admitted, to their great credit, that it takes a high degree of faith to believe the disputed story of evolution.

Hold on a minute, now we need faith to believe in science? They promised and assured us it was a faith-free zone, being so well-supported by solid fact that mere 'belief' was wholly unnecessary. This is also where science has been called a religion of its own, because it is true the physical proof of evidence is lacking, and it requires faith to cross those gaps and still believe. Many find this faith too much to ask of our trust in human thinking, and prefer one of a few alternatives. Cyclic time is one, and it was never even considered by the evolutionists, because it never occurred to the ancestral thinkers as being remotely possible that Time was rotational.

What does all this mean?

Now there is wider agreement time can be rotating as a cycle, and this solves the remaining issues of where everything came from, meaning not only life, but even the solar system and the universe too. It is clever to think up new ways the 8 planets may have formed so differently if they really did all solidify from the same dust cloud, but few people who study this aspect are convinced by it, because of so many features of different composition and magnetic variation.

Evolution still has these massive problems it has never overcome, and we should not leave out the powerful evidence that appears as a fossil in the form of *Anomalocaris* noted above. It is not only one of the oldest claimed at over '540 million years', but a shrimp with the most complex eyes ever found, while also being presented as a fossil from an era when 'only simple life forms' could ever have existed.

Yet here it is found in the exact era that began with the claimed 'simplicity'. This is another false assumption that cannot be overstated. To say this is a problem is to miss the point of this vital find, because in one single creature we have firm proof the fossil record disproves evolution. If evolution was reality, this would be impossible, hence its Latin name meaning 'strange shrimp'. It is also part of another enigma geology cannot explain, which is this very era when life bizarrely 'appeared' without ancestral forms: the Cambrian Explosion. This 'instant' arrival of complex forms supports a cycle of time, not a line. We will return to this later on.

Now a quick look at the 'ages' of the rocks, some with fossils.

How long did many types of sediment take to form? The usual radioactive dating methods do not apply here. They can only be used for non-sediment rock types, because they alone contain original radioactive isotopes. There is no reliable way to date large vertical masses of rock, except by fossils as claimed, and by another curious idea: that each year could create 2mm of vertical rock. This 2mm figure is simply an estimation, a guess to you and me, and an inaccurate one at that, because it was deeply necessary to prop up the story, and thus to provide a figure that seemed to prove 'long age' for earth's rock formations. This assumption is so arbitrary as to defy belief it was ever proposed. Yet science loves a guess to work on, and this one suited them fine.

As we have also seen, the biggest features on earth do not even match this idea. The Grand Canyon is one, and nearby Monument Valley another. Both are connected, but they show clear signs of rapid formation in 1400 years, not the 1.2billion claimed.

Looking at the numbers of fossils in many of the world's deposits, there are either far too few for such vast ages claimed, none at all, or too many at once for them to be laid down slowly. This massive problem has never been overcome.

Even the ICS, the *International Commission on Stratigraphy*, has been unable to put this right. Its experts meet often, publishing the GTS2012 report in two volumes, covering their giant task of trying to resolve these issues, commenting very reasonably that they could be accused of 'circular thinking' in some of this.

This is highly significant that around 35 of the world's top experts in dating rocks should make such a vital and honest admission. It means the current 'way of seeing fossils as having evolved' over time is used, rather than 'absolute' proof, which they agree is a perception that does not often exist physically. It is *an interpretation* of what is seen, and one that cannot solve the above problems.

As top experts in trying to support evolutionary thinking, they are acutely aware that the basis of it all relies on philosophy, and they say this too: depending on how one sees the data, one can reach a chosen conclusion which is bound to be subjective, because even they

Monument Valley strata names

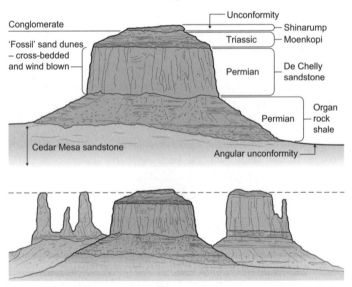

FIGURE 17 *Monument Valley, USA: diagram showing famous formations with identical height top sections marking old sea floor level; evidence of very rapid erosion as oceans drained from this area to cut the Grand Canyon.*

cannot agree why evidence is not found. There are serious areas of disagreement found by the ICS, as one would expect with so many contradictions to deal with, so the issues go unresolved. The linear time model appears unprovable.

Part of their task is to choose which strata are older, and match up rock exposures around the world, and often find they cannot decide which are earlier and which later. Why? The rocks are not just set out in neat layers like stacked napkins. The conditions of formation often changed every few miles, hence why pioneer Arthur Holmes once noted that placing the scattered pages of earth's geology in order 'is by no means an easy task'. Assuming time as a line, not a circle, it becomes an impossible one.

As we will see later, the whole of geological time can be reviewed as fitting into a very small period, even with all the complexity we see, and the 5 key mass extinctions show there were vast events. The experts know not why, since linear time does not suggest reasons why those disasters arose.

Seeing the table opposite, we can see there were such disasters in every age. The suggestion here is that these issues point to a crucial error in viewing Time.

Then there is the 'record' or list of fossil numbers actually found entombed within the layers or strata of the world's rocks. Fossils are claimed by Darwinists to be quite rare, because there are relatively few of them. Vast areas of the earth, such as sandstones, glacial tills, and a fine sediment called Loess, are lacking in fossils. For Loess, a fine wind born sediment covering huge areas of Russia, China, north Europe and central USA, it remains a mystery as to how it formed so widely around the globe…especially without time for soil or animal burrows. This must have been a very speedy sediment forming event, and almost global in an era that could be described as 'post-apocalyptic': slow, gradual and ancient it was not.

Actually there are many areas globally where fossils are rare or wholly absent, with no signs of biological activity required by great age; this is a serious problem for one vital reason. After all, if it had been slowly laid down, there must have been eons of time for many different creatures to have burrowed into it, either looking for food, or a home. Such signs of animal or insect life are entirely missing from these deposits, which logically means they were formed with such extreme speed that no such activity *had time to happen*. This obvious shortage can be seen all over the globe.

So where are those missing eons of time? The answer is very simple: they never existed. If time moves in short cycles, they cannot have done so. It is impossible for relatively soft sedimentary material as this to escape the attention of the world's animals and insects when every other similar habitat would have been home to entire ecosystems. This is another key point; eons of time passed leave signs of that history.

To find nothing is a powerful sign of youth in itself, because life would have lived there if the sediments were available for the eons claimed. Even the parched sand dunes of Namibia and the Sahara are full of life forms, from insects to lizards and snakes, which hide from the hot sun by burrowing below the surface. If there were even tens of thousands of years of such 'bioturbation', the traces would be clearly visible.

This is strong evidence of extremely short duration sediments. It is just not possible that all those moles, rabbits, gophers, lizards, birds, beetles, bees, snakes, parrots, monitors and other burrowers all walked or flew past a perfectly good habitat. Did not one leave any washing in the sink? Would ants turn down an ideal habitat like this? Never, they seek them out. If there were creatures around, they would have fallen on this area like locusts. Yet they didn't, so it appears certain that few individuals existed to burrow at all, suggesting a short passage of time lasting only centuries.

This is the only explanation for such huge areas of fossil-free sediments with no signs of biology. Moles like worms, so soil is their usual habitat, but over any period of time, there would be soil formation at the surface of damp sediment. This too is often missing, so those sediments must definitely have been laid down too recently for any such humus to build up, or even vegetation.

No plant finds means only one thing...that no time elapsed, since even deserts support quite a varied range of life. Quite a few desert or semi-arid types of similarly rapid wind-blown [aeolian] deposits show this kind of life signal. No bio zones means no bio forms, and so very rapid and life-hostile condition changes prevailed, just as we would expect where both the land surfaces and the atmosphere were not good for life to gain a foothold.

This is just what we would expect after an axial tilt, and consequently massive climate changes. Surface geology and geomorphology do show such huge physical changes, and their cause *has never been explained*. Linear time cannot offer one.

These finds contradict the basic thinking in geology, that nearly all deposits of sediment happen slowly over long spans of time. There are obvious exceptions, like the Loess, flash floods, deltaic formations (river deltas e.g. Nile, Ganges, Mississippi), or glacial till, which is rapidly laid down as glaciers melt, forming chaotic and unstratified detritus with boulders and fine grains all lumped in together. Needless to say, they don't contain many resident fossil species either. With rocks the size of Buicks barrelling out of glaciers amid tons of muddy slurry moving at speed, it is hardly the place for Miss Piggy to set up home. None did, it was all moving far too fast.

The Loess examples of lifeless deposits show something rather important. The geology of the earth did not all happen slowly as first thought. Even the parts that did form gently, such as chalk and limestone, were *nowhere near slow enough* to prove that millions of years passed by. Should that have been the case, then the fossil life variation and basic numerical extent required would have been truly vast and spectacular. It is not found.

We find nothing like that at all. Darwinism therefore has the exact problem that Darwin himself predicted it might one day face. If evolution really did take place, then we would have to see the immense numbers of 'fossil changes' he realised were necessary for his theory to be proven correct. We do not find them.

Even chalk shows a huge lack in fossil variation, compared to the billions of forms we should see if it took as long to form as claimed. Chalk even shows those interesting black nodules of chert, which were soft clumps of algae that were entombed in the rock. Many more fossils should be there if time were as long as claimed.

There should be literally trillions of intermediate forms, and they are not seen. The key fact is this. There are a few thousand, not the trillions required. Even so, modern scientists find it unthinkable, after 150 years of evolutionary thinking, to imagine any other option, despite the contradictory evidence. To their minds, it has become almost impossible for them to think the line of time could be mistaken. The scale of the error is also what worries them, because the idea of time as a line is tied into everything, and taken as the foundation for all modern views.

If that is wrong, it would be by far the largest and most serious mistake in all human history. They feel that is impossible to imagine. Some experts have started to consider a cyclic continuum as mentioned, but are still thinking of long cyclic periods in the billions of years. The evidence only seems to work in the short cycle scenario.

Without the fossil record to prove that millions of years have passed, we are forced to consider it never happened. The past geological eras amounting to 545 million years of claimed fossil accumulation really can be a miscalculation. How else can we account for so many inconsistencies, such as the Cambrian Explosion, where life just appeared from nowhere without any fossil ancestors?

Only the continuous existence of earth, and its original life forms, can account for this striking 'explosion of life' in the fossil record. It is easy for scientists to claim there were ancestors' forms that were never found, but with so much research in so much of our globe's surface, this 160 year old claim is no longer credible.

We cannot fail to sympathise deeply with those who have spent their lives working in fields that may be affected by this finding, but in some ways we all are, since all life on earth has been defined by science using linear time. If that story has been incorrect in any way, then we are all affected, and need to find out.

So what is the source of this central error? James Hutton was one of the first writers on geology, and both he and William Smith set out the ideas used ever since in geology and of fixing 'bio zones' by fossil content.

He described two 'laws', the first of which we cannot disagree with, where one 'bed' or rock layer overlying another would be the younger, if not moved since of course; beds of sediment are often turned upside down, but he was making a basic point about undisturbed strata. The second law of William Smith is accepted by nearly every geologist who has not studied cyclic time as set out here. This law claims that strata can be identified by the fossils they contain, known now as biostratigraphy; literally the study of biota or life forms found in strata.

This is deeply contentious, since it assumes time was a long line.

We should note two things here. One, these bio forms are not sequential in their 'shapes', implying less time passed before they were entombed as fossils in that rock. Two, and so importantly, it is assumed by authorities in this field of geology that the correlation of these life forms *guarantees* they lived at the same time, and are of the same age. This relies on evolution being true, and relies on circular thinking as noted, meaning that the one proves the other to be so: idea A proves idea B, and vice versa. Not ideal, but we remember that no other ideas were on the table. Not one of them was aware of the contents of this book, which relies on the last 100 years of advanced science, particularly in astronomy, to prompt fresh thinking of time as a cycle instead.

Geologists then used methods to date the rocks independently, but hit a problem with sedimentary rock, which cannot be separately dated. No problem there, they felt, because the fossils took care of all that. It all seemed to work, or did until someone questioned the whole fabric of these assumptions. Modern geologists cannot do that, if they wish to keep their jobs, because Evolution has become an accepted belief, rule or principle of geology: discussion over. Naysayers were ignored, and with some reason, because without an entirely new world view, such as a cycle, no other idea worked.

No one had a new world view, so the old version became the modern one too.

For the rest of us, these assumptions must be questioned constantly, as new facts arise that cause us to re-think these issues. Not one geologist uses cyclic time in their thinking as suggested here, because they have never heard of it, let alone studied it carefully, thus many never doubted Darwin was right, period.

These two laws have been accepted ever since, because they all took it for granted that time was a long line. What else could it be? They wasted not a second on any other option, because no one could think of one, so they used it. Darwin published 50 years after Smith's map sections, Einstein was another 50 years after that, and still cyclic time was not considered a serious option. It is now.

They scented success at last. It all looked so obvious time was a line, and new geological thinking was just the fuel the scientists wanted to find in their battle with the religionists, who had ruled the world with very mixed results for millennia. So they set about creating a geological timescale in earnest, and soon had a linear form, all ready to receive any fossils that appeared. None of them paused for a second to wonder if the whole idea was pure fiction, except Darwin, so they carried on. 'Index fossils' were judged to 'fix' their local strata, wherever they occurred, and were named for their wide global occurrence. It looked perfect, and the history of the world was in their hands at last. They had rewritten the whole earth story to suit the linear plan.

Handshakes all round, it seemed a success, or so they reckoned. This was their grand plan:

- Trilobites were seen as the oldest and thus placed in the Cambrian era (540myo)
- Simple or no fossils before that (Burgess and Ediacara as yet unseen)
- Graptolites 'fitted' in the Ordovician and Silurian (500–400myo)
- Ammonites in the Jurassic (190myo)
- Foraminifera in the Cretaceous at 100myo
- Chalk 'must be' very old taking a 2mm/year estimate
- Dinosaurs could be found around the world lying on the surface, but they 'must be old' too, so that decision was easy, and thus fixed.

We will see later how these dates were arrived at, but largely the figure of 2mm per year of most sediments laid down gave a rough age to work with, and more time was 'added' where needed.

The snag was that experts found errors in all this. Fossils like echinoderms just did not exist in evolved layers as so confidently predicted. Such key issues have never been resolved even now.

Fossils were quite rarely found, so it was assumed many were not fossilised at all. We now realise this is not credible, since even motion traces leave clear signs of their presence, often as mineralisation with calcite or pyrites. A huge rock in Scotland shows the drag marks of a Eurypterid or sea scorpion crawling over what was a mud flat. The surface must have been quickly covered over, or it would have been washed away.

No-one ever stopped to wonder if all these forms were rare due to a shorter time period, because they saw no need. Rock exposures remain quite rare, so no one had studied more than a few limited areas of fossils by the time Darwin went to print in 1859, so the real evidence would only emerge much later, when the mindset was well established; sadly few would even want to listen.

Neither had they any reason to do so, because they were now in charge, and science had just claimed the territory of earth in all its glory, so they were not about to share doubts, or give it back. This situation has existed more or less unchanged to the present day, backed up by the method that seemed to prove it all right...the radiogenic dating of rock. It should remove all doubt, but it actually cannot.

As we can see, this hi-tech method looked to scientists so wonderful and fantastic it might have been minted in heaven by flocks of laboratory angels, but it would be a false dawn.

Fossils were given a central role in defining and 'classifying life on earth'. No one doubted it, because the cycle was never imagined as feasible. Evolution relies on one notion above all others: that a fossil fixes the age *of any deposit in which it is found*. A widespread fossil is then used to indicate a whole biozone around the globe, so if there is any reason why this may not be true, that would destroy the whole idea.

No one could think of such a reason to doubt it. For many years, this was the only game in town. This idea led to the concepts developed by Darwin and Wallace that became Evolution theory, but they extended these same global problems.

Local strata may be linked by fossil content *locally*, as William Smith decided in central England seeing cuttings for canals; but to roll out the same concept to cover the globe with equal certainty is to make a large assumption: that life on earth *did* evolve, full stop. It makes the claim that there is no other way to account for life's various species, and since no one had ever studied another version of how life may exist on the earth, this became the agreed view of science. The idea in Creationism that God created life had long been the widely held view, so these two concepts took their separate paths. No-one had thought of the cyclic view of time to explain these differences; it was never seriously considered.

Darwin himself realised fossils were the key for his theory, and a lack of them being powerful proof he could not be correct. He wrote this in his famous book, yet that central point has been dismissed by modern scientists, who accept these problems despite not resolving them.

The fact is that the fossil record does not match the Darwinian claims in some very famous examples, such as the 300 metre high chalk cliffs

168 *Flash Time*

of the southern England coastline, beside the English Channel. These cliffs contain species of echinoids, but the progressive 'succession' of 10–15 species that were expected does not exist there, nor anywhere. They do not alter shape vertically as they 'should', but lived instead as separate species, so the required changes were expected, but absent.

Micraster is one species of Cretaceous echinoid, along with some others, all much written about (Rowe 1899), but there is not the predicted sequence of changes seen in them by natural selection, with species lower down seeming to vanish and then appear higher up in younger strata. This should be impossible, since even Darwin himself claimed that no species could continue over long periods of time without evolving into new shapes or species. As we'll see, the 'Lazarus' species also defy this claim.

The same problem of missing zonal fossils, or 'vanishing and reappearing species' exists everywhere, including along the same English coastline in Kent, where the Gault Clay appears or outcrops near Folkestone. Several species of ammonite can be found in this clay, popular since Georgian times for brick making. Three examples are found in great profusion there, but once again they refuse to show the predicted vertical pattern of change from one shape into another. From *Mortoniceras* to *Euhoplites* and *Hoplites*, they show features that vanish and reappear as samples are collected in different vertical layers. They do not 'evolve' in higher layers as predicted and claimed. Other ammonites can also be found, but they all share this same lack of change, with features like ridges, bumps or coils in their shells, failing to follow a sequence of change, but instead appearing or vanishing in anything but a sequence: the opposite of evolution.

The Lias clay near Gloucester, England, has a similar story with the case of *Aegoceras*, which Hyatt made the oldest (in his view of 1870), only to have the decision reversed later in 1938 by L. F. Spath who decided it was the youngest of 3 key species.[60]

Now a quick glance at those Lazarus species, which seem to 'rise from the dead'.

These are creatures that appear as living species for us to see *today*, millions of claimed years out of order entirely. Some are even *half a*

60 The Facts of Life, R. Milton, Corgi 1994, p135 for more details.

billion years out of place. Only a cycle explains these amazing facts. Linear time just passed its sell by date.

These Lazarus species should be completely impossible, according to Darwin himself. To quote Darwin:

'Judging from the past, we may safely infer that not one living species will transmit its unaltered likeness to a distant futurity.'[61]

Here is the problem. This is simply not true, and we do find such species, although he did not know it in his era of the 1850's. The above statement he wrote suffers from three problems of its own, which he would also not have known about. The past record would be carefully studied for the next 150 years, but without the findings needed for his theory to succeed. Inferring fossils to exist is not the same as finding them, but science need only consider cyclic time to see the alternative of a cycle works well. He was also incorrect to say each species 'will' mutate with certainty, and to accept that time had been long and linear, as Hutton and Lyell had also assumed and suggested.

Darwin rightly pointed out that the earth's apparent past record shows this marked lack of evidence to support evolution, because the rocks do not show what they wanted and expected from them, namely to support the obvious fact of linear time. The rocks refused to oblige, and showed the opposite, causing Darwin to lament: '... Geology loses glory from the extreme imperfection of the record.'[62] Imperfection only in terms of what was expected, when in reality the lack of expected fossils may have been showing the scientists a narrative story they simply could not recognise as matching their linear theory overlay. To this day, that remains the case, because non-linear time is a new idea to most people.

Charles Darwin reckoned the problem was ignorance, including his own in that, saying in 1859 that 'Only a small portion of the world has been geologically explored'[63], which was true at the time but not now, after literally millions of us have searched the earth for rocks and fossils to analyse for many reasons.

His concern for their lack of facts showed in his worry about his

61 *The Origin of Species*, Charles Darwin (1859), Penguin 1985, p 459.
62 Ibid, p 457.
63 Ibid p 437.

theory being true at all, what with the rocks seen already disagree-
ing. He appreciated his era knew very little, as we noted above when
Darwin wrote:
   '...we are confessedly ignorant; nor do we know how ignorant we
are.'[64]

This is a hugely significant thing to say, because even Darwin cannot
claim in one breath to 'judge the past' with precision while confessing
to having no details of it, and those he did have proved his idea to
be impossible. Yet he felt totally certain that not one creature could
live for millions of years without evolving. He was incorrect purely
because linear time has no evidence to support it, and such spans of
time can now be shown not to have passed as a sequence, and he was
also wrong about the species always changing over time; curious proof
of this appears in the appearance of many 'ancient' species remaining
unchanged.
   Darwin suggested vast periods of time had elapsed, over 450 million
years he thought, in which life had blossomed, yet he was puzzled[65]
why they had eluded discovery. He wrote a very telling line:
   'To the question why we do not find records of these vast primordial
periods, I can give no satisfactory answer.'

His era simply never considered a cycle, and acted accordingly. Modern
experts have their own answers, yet they too stop short of accounting
for the potential of a short cycle to explain what we see, because it is
only now we are discovering a quantum physics link to Time, and that
the Flatness Problem, for example, shows how fresh astronomy sheds
new light on geology; to such an extent we need a new timescale.
   No expert on Earth has ever considered a repeating short cycle as
outlined here, nor any of the evidence presented here to that effect,
so how would they derive an answer? The facts gathered here simply
cannot be explained without a cycle.
   As to 'vanished species', there are now many cases found of fossils
that still live unchanged, one 'extinct' 'Devonian' fish turning up 80

64 Ibid p 440.
65 Ibid p 313.

years after Darwin's book came out, 415 million years out of place (if the timescale was correct).

We see many examples of this fact, five that spring to mind being the Coelacanth fish [*Latimeria chalumnae*] from the '*at least 50 million year old*' Mesozoic era, which very famously turned up in a fishing net off Mozambique in 1938, alive and well despite being fully extinct in the eyes of science, for all that time. It wasn't, and just lived in deep water at 1200m and more, so few caught one. London's Natural History Museum now proudly displays this fish species in a cabinet, with few realising how profoundly it changes science, almost disproving evolution all by itself.

There is also the Ginkgo leaf from the same era, seen in central London and globally, and the bivalve *Lingula,* unaware of being extinct *and unaltered* for the claimed 480 million years since the Ordovician era, along with Nautilus, and the *Sphenopsid* or Horsetail, which formed vast areas of coal in the Carboniferous era: all are alive now. Darwin was wrong about these claims, even while realising his era 'did not know of their own ignorance'. He even noted that Lingula and Nautilus looked unchanged over this claimed span of time, yet not realising he would later contradict this being possible[66], and not visualise this was evidence for a cycle.

It seemed obvious to think of time as a line, rather than see a cycle as the answer, in which species already exist in a cosmos that always exists. That can seem weird.

Yet all these points seem to disallow any other conclusion.

The key point is that claiming life's species 'evolved' is not proof that they did, without the physical evidence of their fossil remains. Ideas have to change as finds grow in scope and accuracy. Often we find this counter-intuitive, yet believe our own thinking over physical reality. Aliens are an example: not one found, yet many believers feel they are real, known as the Fermi Paradox (since lives examples should exist if they are real).

Fossil finds have new definitions. As noted, it was first taught that soft bodied fossils would never be found, because only hard shells or bones would be encased in mud or sand.

66 Ibid p313

Darwin declared[67] this to be a firm fact when he wrote: 'No organism wholly soft can be preserved.' He was mistaken.

His era's experts simply had not found any, which is quite a different matter.

Then the exciting Burgess shale was discovered in 1909 by Walcott in the Rockies' British Columbia state in Canada, which upset many of those early misconceptions. The fossils were not only soft, but so bizarre as to be largely unclassifiable to this day.

The oddest fossil of all time was found in this outcrop, known as *Anomalocaris*, which had more complex eyes than any creature ever discovered, as noted. Such strange finds look awful for the evolution story, because this level of complex life forms was claimed to appear much later...not at *the beginning* of life's history as Darwin said. This was thought to be a Cambrian deposit, when every fossil 'should have been' simple and basic, yet here was a highly developed predator with compound eyes containing over 16,000 lenses, each very advanced.

Geology has never solved this enigma, and cannot do so using linear time.

These are truly huge problems on their own, but when combined they show the flaw that Darwin suspected from the outcome: the fossil record does not contain the proof he needed, just as he predicted. It is no longer good enough to claim they lived around the world, but were inconveniently erased from history in each location.

Not a single location confirms evolution's claim of the missing millions of fossil forms. This is one such fatal flaw Darwin expected may prevent his theory's acceptance.

Conventional science is therefore obliged to reconsider its position, in the light of these details, which show the theory is untenable. These examples all show long linear time has not passed by, and the lack of transitional forms alone is evidence enough for the standard timescale being a 'million year myth'.

What we must consider is the way Nature actually is in reality, and then be prepared to reject the 300 year old conjecture we added on.

Wider exploration of different sedimentary strata around the world has built up a more complete picture. That exploration has largely been

67   Ibid p298

Fig 18 a. Chesil Beach: recent post Ice Age shingle beach stretching 16 miles north west, as seen from north Portland; can have formed rapidly in 3,000 years.

Fig 18 b. West Bay sandstone East Cliff seen near end of Chesil Beach, showing regularly spaced seasonal harder bands that project out, where each layer can form in 1 or 2 years only; Portland on horizon.

Fig 18 c. East Cliff base with 28cm hammer for scale, showing 6-7 softer sections covered by harder layers, suggesting seasonal extra clay content, with fewer fossils implying rapid deposition.

Fig 18 d. Same section close-up to show clearly the hard & softer phase layers or 'cyclothems'.

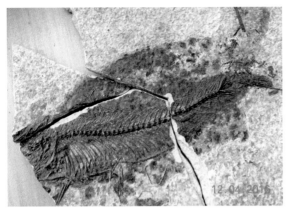

Fig 18 e. Rapid burial of fossil fish with no decay or predation; commonly seen in such fossils.

Fig 18 f. Fossil ammonites showing cut and polished sections with calcite crystal infill of spaces.

Fig 18 g. Small fossil ammonites shown beside clip for size, common yet not enough for claimed eras.

Fig 18 h. Stalactite of 26cms growing on concrete in London car park, showing recent 45 year formation.

Fig 18 i. Fossil mass of chaotic ammonites with wood branch: rapid burial & no time for wood to decay.

*Fig 18 j. Petrified tree
trunk section of 65 cms:
no decay, cells intact =
very rapid anoxic burial.*

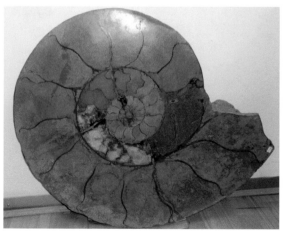

*Fig 18 k. Giant
ammonite fossil
of 68cms: infilled
interior & large size
may be due to higher
oxygen levels.*

Fig 18 l. Slice of petrified wood polished to show fine cell formation, rapid burial, minerally replaced.

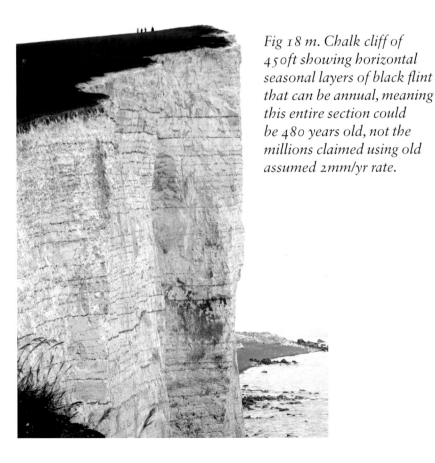

Fig 18 m. Chalk cliff of 450ft showing horizontal seasonal layers of black flint that can be annual, meaning this entire section could be 480 years old, not the millions claimed using old assumed 2mm/yr rate.

Fig 18 n. Same chalk cliff one mile east showing seasonal flint laid down in bands; UK south coast.

Fig 18 o. Flint nodules showing chalk contact layer; breaks like glass and used in axes/tools; rapid deposit.

Fig 18 p. Flint nodules above flint layer: derived from seasonal silica gel, forming in both deposit shapes.

*Curved Earth [A]:
ship seen from shore
at 14.21hrs with
small part of stern
below horizon, small
boat visible.*

*Curved Earth [B]:
Same ship seen
veering seaward at
14.34hrs with stern
and deck partly
obscured.*

*Curved Earth [C]:
Same 35m ship seen at
14.46hrs half below
horizon with no stern
or deck visible &
only mast and funnel
clear (camera at 8 feet
above sea level, calm
sea state, with no
alteration of sea/ship
photo composition).*

carried out, 150 years after Darwin, with millions of geologists and amateur rock hounds scouring the rock exposures in every country, including the Polar regions, and even other planets and moons by means of robots, telescopes or more advanced remote sensing.

The results are not in favour of evolution, to put it politely, and can often be interpreted in several ways. Not a trace of life has been found in any other place in space; this result would be expected if time is cyclic, since there is never enough time in a cycle for it to develop by itself, even if that were possible. The fact that no life is found elsewhere in space is powerful evidence for earth being unique, and part of a cyclic time sequence that lasts only a few millennia. If time is a cycle, then earth would be unique in this way, because of insufficient time for any other outcome.

Some deposits are claimed to be very old, such as chalk.

Chalk is full of microscopic shells, as are many rocks, but not more than could be formed in this short timeframe. Even 1200 vertical feet of chalk (360m) only requires 300mm/year to exist, or 25mm (one inch) per month, which could occur in a $CaCO_3$ mineral-rich marine environment; so the Cretaceous may be 12–1400 years long, and need not have been 65 million years ago.

This is shocking to any conventional geologist, because it suggests the whole idea of the chalk sequence needs revision. Having spent one's life working on the old linear solution, that cannot be easy for a scientist to deal with, hence why this study required nearly 40 years to check a cycle was even feasible.

We should remember something else. Nowhere on earth is chalk being laid down. We do see the ultra-fine-grained *calcareous ooze*, the most common ocean deposit, being slowly laid down at certain depths, less than 3500m, because they would cease to exist at greater depths, thanks to depth variations in dissolved CO_2 [*known as* CCD *or Carbonate Compensation Depth*].

Yet there is no current example to confirm how quickly chalk could form in highly carbonate-rich seawater. Since we see chert or flint forming frequent bands in chalk, such as on Britain's south coast, we can propose a situation where the process is rapid, since chert is a soft algal mass, often of silica, that may well never have been preserved at all. Yet there it is in neat lines, perhaps showing seasonal changes caused by the rapid oscillations of an axial tilt. England's south coast white chalk cliffs do show this, with flint lines every two feet or 6ocms at the top [see picture on page]. This may be evidence of very fast chalk layer formation, if the sea was rich with CO_2 as above. Chalk really need not have taken millions of years to form.

This fresh conclusion may solve the mismatches still puzzling the ICS (*International Commission on Stratigraphy*)[68] to this day, such as the trilobites: they appear all over the globe, suggesting they may not have evolved in those locations. Since the lack of fossils agrees with this version, it becomes a viable if contentious alternative. This may counter the ages old presumptions of William Smith and others, the bedrock of geology, but it fits the facts.

Many of these ages could all have been forming their characteristic sediments at *the same time*, such as chalk in one area of Britain and France, while coal and limestone, for example, formed in others. The existence of cyclic sequences of mud, sand and coal, known as *cyclothems*, in many widely separated parts of the world gives strong credence to this scenario of giant catastrophes as a series, in which massive forests globally can be covered by large waves, possibly of 100–300m in height. This association of mud and sand with coal seams, often interleaved, shows rapid deposits took place so fast that decay was prevented by such anoxic/oxygen-free conditions.

Let's see if this could have happened in reality, and the possible causes.

The existence of coal with strong cellular detail proves those plant cells had not even days in which to decay or rot. Leaves, and cells such as *mesophyll*, have been superbly preserved after what must have been intense pressure and high temperatures that drove out volatiles and moisture, while increasing carbon content towards the anthracite end of the scale; plants found in *sapropelic coals* are one example among many. This could not have happened slowly, while the common presence of mud and sand layers in close proximity paints a picture of similar events all occurring at the same time, possibly even within months or a single decade. Eras in millions of years are not needed for

---

68   Under the 1960 International Union of Geological Sciences (IUGS) & with many
     ICS sub-commissions

this, and the presence of lenses with mud and sand in huge quantities, with grain sizes indicating very rapid speeds or rates of deposition, persuades us to agree they could not have formed slowly.

The suggestion is that these are axial shift signs of very rapid formation.

As noted above, *a rapid shift in the axial tilt* of the earth could produce such extremes, along with climate change on a prodigious scale, and another effect: the break-up of the original *supercontinent* known as Pangea. If we set aside the dating of rock for now, there is no impediment in this radically different version of what happened, because the geophysics is simple enough. If a minor planet or asteroid did come very close to earth, and in doing so created the marked axial tilt of 23.45° we still see today, and pulled earth into its current elliptical orbit, then that supercontinent would no longer exist in that form, since centripetal force would throw the continents outwards to become the landmasses we see now, centred on the current equator.

This splitting of Pangea could have occurred in 5–50 years, not millions. Taking the lowest figure of 5 years, North America would move west at the rate of 145 yards in one hour or so, and the Atlantic could form as it did so. Bearing in mind the huge centripetal forces suggested above, it would most likely be a much faster process than this. Even the poles have moved from where they were, hence why coal is found in Antarctica.

If this did happen, we would also see very rapid oscillation periods creating 'apparently ancient sediments', such as glacial varves, producing 'seasonal' sediments in weeks, not years. We would also see magnetic effects from the earth's solid sulphur-iron core (2440kms diameter; 32% of earth's mass) moving separately from the rocky outer core and mantle, with changes in the magnetosphere and cosmic ray production (thus changing atmospheric carbon levels used in carbon dating). We see just these effects, with 'varve layers' in Japan as an example of additional banding of light and dark material. So intense was this astronomic event that the earth's axis is still oscillating to this day [Milankovitch also estimated his cycles last century, using linear time]. We will return to this shortly.

Equally dramatically and tragically, the continents show proof of this great lateral motion because they are still moving, albeit much more slowly than when they began their moves away from the earlier stable configuration. One example is India, which is still moving north into Asia at 25mm per year, thus uplifting the Himalayas, having moved from its position beside East Africa and Madagascar.

The huge cracks that opened up in the earth's crust when Pangaea broke apart also caused several other gigantic volcanic events to coincide with the axial tilt, with Flood Basalts in India's Deccan traps, Siberia and Columbia River in America's Pacific northwest, as well as Mid Ocean Ridge formation, which all combined to speed up the motion of the land masses to their present locations. The sulphur dioxide emissions alone from such huge events, which even made Krakatoa and Tambora look minor by comparison, would have been sufficient gas and dense particulate clouds to alter earth's climate globally forever, an effect increased and made permanent by the axial shift's forcing of the continents to new shapes and positions.

The Sahara Desert shows such a giant climate change from lush savannah to hot desert, with its famous rock carvings of temperate region fauna, signs of ancient lake beds and rivers, trapped water, and as radar waves below ground level have shown. The Mediterranean Sea also shows intensely arid/heat phases before it flooded in the post Zanclean era, evidenced by the salt domes found by drilling sub-sea floor areas.

Without the fluidity of the volcanic activity at the crustal margins of the plates, such speed would not have been possible. The existence of those huge areas of outpouring magma in those locations, as well as much of the ocean floor areas in between, provides a credible alternative to earth history; this version is reinforced by a lack of sediment at the shelf margins, and near the mid ocean ridges.

The Blake Outer Ridge is just such a 'rapidly laid down sediment' to have formed during this huge upheaval, being fine grained and unstratified, which is evidence of rapid formation from the chaotic ocean state of the fast-forming North Atlantic. No other explanation accounts for its formation and huge size, at 700kms long on America's eastern seaboard [See Fig 12]. The current slow movement of earth's tectonic plates has been reasonably taken to be the norm over history, but that conclusion ignores the evidence and effect of a rapid axial tilt as above.

This new solution specifically aligns earth's history to cyclic events of this magnitude, which appears to be entirely necessary to account for the lack of fossils, and the trillions of transitional forms required by Evolution.

The ten classic geological time periods were invented because of evolution theory, and to accommodate the linear time vision. Yet nowhere on earth does this full sequence of Cambrian to Cretaceous rocks or fossils, and beyond, *ever occur in reality*, or join up one with another era. The whole structure of the idea has been suggested as a theory by successive generations, 300 years in the making.

The GTS 2012 report of the ICS even called the timescale an accepted 'convention' fitted into an 'arrow of time'.[69] This shows the timescale has limitations by relying on the circularity of assumptions, and only rarely do the fossils seem to demarcate the zones as expected, even in the view of the 70 top experts who lead its author committees. No one thought of a short cycle because they felt certain the convention of a timeline seemed to be so obvious. Yet they found impossible obstacles that required 'rubber-banding' of events to give an appearance of fossils fitting this linear framework, when they do not.

The lack of the fossils and their changes needed remain unsolvable problems.

More recent discoveries also agree, such as the mounds of mammoth tusks in Arctic Russia, suggesting major waves swept those tusks into piles. Some other recent finds were superbly preserved. Mammoths have been found in Russia still frozen so quickly in the permafrost that wolves were eating them centuries or millennia later. The Beresovka Mammoth reportedly had buttercups in its stomach, all snap frozen within the animal, indicating a climate shift of such speed and intensity that the animals froze where they stood. Smaller mammoths were found more recently in Siberia, some with soft parts like trunks and fir, all in place and yielding DNA, suggesting recent burial. Other warmer climate animals such as lions were also found in Alaska's famous bone beds, reportedly also swept into frozen mounds, which again indicates rapid burial and instant climate change in hours.

The tar pits of La Brea, in the heart of the giant city of Los Angeles,

69 A Geological Timescale, page xv, Elsevier 2012

preserved every creature that fell in, so fine a medium is tar for preserv-
ing organic matter. It was found to be full of impressive dire wolves and
sabre-toothed tigers, and an exceptional sight at the La Brea Museum
on Wilshire Boulevard, central Los Angeles.

Of course not every location is that superbly set up to preserve
organic matter, but there is another point to note about shell fossils in
rock strata. Even if the calcium carbonate is leached away or replaced
by other compounds present in percolating groundwater, as often
happens, there then is a 'pseudo-fossil' that forms in the same space
within those rock strata, all neatly preserved to be found years later,
such in the case of ammonites around the world. These may then be
'replaced' by calcite or iron pyrites (*aka* fool's gold, formula FeS), as
each atom is 'swapped' in this process, yet the creature remains easily
identifiable, with every bump and line intact. They do not just disappear, not by any means.

As noted, a great place to find these is on the south 'Jurassic coast'
of England, made legendary by Mary Anning's 1811 finds of extinct
ichthyosaurs found there. Let's see what materials fossils may be made
of, and how even that may change.

A working example is aragonite. Many shells are composed of this
carbonate substance, which formed when the creature was alive, as
in the case of bivalves. Over time, this unstable carbonate changes
into calcite, but the shape is maintained in great detail, ideal for later
classification. Even though these forms are soluble in dilute acid, the
space they would leave behind has often solidified into that shape, set
within the void or shape it made by lying there for some time, which
then became enclosed by the rock particles surrounding that animal or
plant. Even rainwater is a dilute acid, picking up CO_2 as falls through
the air, to form H_2CO_3, which is corrosive to carbonate.

Over the course of further time, other solutions present usually
deposit material inside these cavities, whether formed by fossils or not,
which is why so many are preserved, some as *geodes*, where fine crystals of amethyst, smoky quartz, fluorite or calcite often form, pointing
inwards from the walls of such hollows.

Vast periods of time are not needed in this process, so it is fair to say
that much, much more of those 'presumed to have existed' past species
should be present than actually are. This remains not just a hurdle for

evolution theory, but a major failure of the theory's basic predictions, since so much surface deposition has been studied.

Here are some truly unusual finds that counter the linear view of time, one example being those strange nematode worms found in deep mine shafts 1.3 to 3.6 kms down, in South Africa's Beatrix gold mine. They should not be there.

To explain this astonishing and pivotal finding, these tiny worms of the phylum Nematoda, such as the new species *Halicephalobus mephisto*, named after the underworld lord for their location in complete darkness, were found in deep mines of the Cape area, where no such creatures 'should have' been able to live, even in mild conditions. These waters were so deep that the temperature was a blistering 48°C, and yet they were present. Some pathogens can survive in even hotter places, such as *H.gingivalis*, which can live in 61°C.

This creates a major problem. How did they get there? Also, since the rock is much older, *how are they still alive*? No one knows how, at least not in a linear time frame. Clearly they have not sat there for the millions of years claimed. This answer is easily understood if we use a cyclic time frame, in which these tiny 0.56mm long worms were cut off from the surface in a more recent overturn of sediments, not long ago. The claimed age of their ancient or 'palaeometeoric' water is 3–12,000 years, but that is quite different from the host rock's age estimates, which is claimed to run into millions of years. It is not claimed the water just percolated or trickled down to these extreme depths. By any standards, this finding is very odd indeed, and with *hypoxic* water to live in, meaning little or no oxygen, and no surface contact, even odder still.[70]

Not only are they strange for living at the high temperature of 48°C, but they cannot be living so deep underground *for millions of years*. If they had been, there would be generations of dead worms, and there aren't. Let us not forget these are not worms that caught the wrong bus one day, on their way home from the office, nor parachuted in from up above. There is no access to these deep layers, except by mining, which worms do not tend to attempt, and could not do so through solid rock. They were trapped in the rock itself, and literally entombed there, when it formed.

70 Nature, 2 June 2011, vol 474, pp79–82.

The fact they are still alive, means it was recent…but when, and how? This shocked the scientists who found them, because they were forced to conclude they were millions of years old, when common sense told them it could not be so, in which thinking they were of course correct, yet they lacked a reason how this came to be. Those worms can only be there from the overturning of the sediments in an earlier event, and an extremely recent one, since they could not conceivably remain there for millions of years without leaving the proof of such antiquity. It is pointedly lacking, so their age appears incorrect, and by a huge margin. They can be a mere 3,300 years old: the era that fits these facts. This is the only feasible answer that seems to fit.

Evolutionists never imagine how this may be possible, and so never propose such a young date. They call such ill-fitting finds 'intriguing' and move on. We should discuss and notice the contradiction. Any one of the thousands of such examples is enough to show the error that evolution ignores, which is the lack of time passing that is proven by the maths. A simple calculation of the 'active biomass' required for millions of years to have passed shows a huge tonnage, literally, of creatures that *should have lived and died* within that rock space…and it is missing.

Like the missing cavemen, 137 found and 600 billion skeletons missing, this is really the end of the theory. Is there any concrete proof of such an apparently wild assertion? It seems there is. Either dead or alive, there are too few worms for great age.

As some do comment, such odd finds are 'totally unexpected, and incredible'. That is a nice way to avoid saying what many realise: the sediments are clearly young because the worms are still alive, and far too few in quantity for their claimed age.

We have to admit the old notion of time is not working. These worms should not be there at all if time is linear and long, but can only be explained if those deep sediments have recently been overturned in huge geological events. There is no escaping this outcome, but it does contradict conventional geological thinking, and so it was never even proposed. When asked if such recent catastrophes may be the answer, geologists often reply that 'would mean nearly everything is wrong'.

They appear to be right…nearly everything does appear mistaken.

How did the classic ideas arise?

Like any theory, their origins lie in simple human ideas using presumption.

Just one wrong assumption could invalidate the entire edifice of ideas it supports. It could only work as a theory if the physical world continues to back it all up by existing as predicted. The problem is that the modern facts proving actual reality no longer support any of these old ideas.

We can make a short list of ten such presumptions.

1 The earth 'must have' formed from dust and gas drifting in space [not so, the ionic charge is usually negative in dust particles, so they would repel each other, not stick together as suggested]

2 The other planets must have formed the same way [if so, they should be similar, but are very different as noted in the astronomy section; some rings of Saturn show young age as widely noted, and so would be recent or 'new']

3 The earth was once red hot, and then cooled over millions of years [there is no actual evidence for this stage, and amounts of helium and lithium etc counter it]

4 The oceans then must have arrived after this era via watery comets [there is no evidence that such vast amounts of water could have arrived like this, when the other planets would also have been so showered, yet have not been]

5 That spacetime has never altered its quantum state [the CMB shows it has altered]

6 That Neanderthal Man lived for 750,000 years [only 137 found, with at least 600 billion missing, shows this appears to be a gross age range overestimate]

7 It is assumed that the species, all of them, have evolved from others [if so, then species would always differ over time in rock strata; the data show they do not]

8 That they did this over a long period of time, i.e. over 600 million years [the dating methods use the same linear basis of time, which is not reliable]

9 Chalk and sediment depths are assumed to grow at 2mm per year [various factors show this is not correct, such as carbon quantities

allowing for greater amounts of CaCO3 and thus far higher deposition rates]
10 That there were continuous periods of good conditions that allowed for life [this is also not proven, and the vast time required appears not to have existed for the above reasons, showing the big events in earth history are recent, not ancient]

As many now realise, these vital and assumed pillars of the linear time version of earth history are simply not met. Geology relies on time being supported as linear both laterally and 'vertically', meaning that across the globe each place where rocks are exposed, called outcrops or exposures, must also be seen to 'overlie' others that can be proven to be part of an older period or era. This was never demonstrated globally, hence why Prof T. van Andel found a 'claimed 15 million year gap' that did not exist [Ch.12].

The fossils 'should' show evolutionary changes upwards in each stratum. The snag is that they don't show that trend, and nor can it be proven that those strata are even near old enough for that to be so. This may be a revolutionary way of thinking in these fields, but that was before a constant cycle had this weight of evidence behind it.

The fossils found in the ground are frequently 'out of place' and strange, and often disagree with what 'should be' there. One clear favourite we have noted is *Anomalocaris*. This is a crucial problem in what is known as *'Problematica'*, which are species found as fossils that do not fit claims for vertical linear time, and so are given an amusing class of their own...the 'don't know' species that defy all logic (in linear terms, at least). Examples are *Spriggina* and *Mawsonites*, as well as *Paraconularia,* which do not seem to fit into any group; the first two may be either jellyfish or burrows.

Further fossil 'errors' and oddities

Now we can examine a few final puzzles hidden in rock strata.

The lower Jurassic was an exciting era to find in the early 1800's, and the layers were named as they looked, often by colour. They named strata as they saw them, but without uniformity, leaving a legacy of confusion for later experts. In Germany's south west it was known as the Black Jura (by geologist von Buch, 1839), while in England's south coast the same dark clay-rich layers were known as the Lias (Conybeare and Phillips, 1822). To this day, stratigraphers struggle with standardisation, and find many a sediment that defies clear classification. The variation is near endless. In cyclic time terms, this era's vast age is another estimate, not a fact.

It was only in 1878 that the first *International Geological Congress* (IGC) was convened in Paris, that an attempt to find order was made. One famous English sequence in Dorset, the Kimmeridgian Stage, was even named by a Frenchman called Alcide d'Orbigny, who firmly got his teeth into studying similar rocks in Bologna, Italy, between 1842 and 1852, without ever coming to England. We will go into how he achieved this feat later on, and not so easily from a desk in another country using fossils.

As recently as 1964, an ammonite called *Sonninia sowerbyi* was used to define the base of the Bajocian strata. All went well for 8 years until the reference (holotype) creature for this species was found to be only the nucleus or central section broken off a larger and quite different species known as *Papilliceras* from the overlying *Otoites sauzei* Zone[71]. This is an example of uncertainty in forms, which is easily done, and shows how difficult is the task of classification, let alone the use of such forms to fix a layer or stratum age.

These reference species are easily mixed up, which is awkward for a creature used to define whole geological sub-strata. Another holotype species that was also misidentified was one known as *Strenoceras bifurcatum*, at least it was, until in 1981 it was re-classified as a *Garantiana*[72] from an overlying and thus younger zone, thus making the whole zone invalid. There are many other such errors and revisions. This is the use of fossils, clearly not easy to identify, as pegs to fix such ages and links all over the world. Yet this is the business of fixing ages in strata, and prone to snags.

The big problem is that they do not actually prove evolution, but take it as accepted, and then use this as a 'fact' within geological history, so that if a species is found in two widely separated assemblages of fossils, they 'must be the same age'. This is an example of circular thinking, the bane of palaeontology. Logic tells us this is not proof,

71   Westermann & Riccardi 1972
72   Dietl, 1981

but conjecture reliant on supposition. Yet it is an accepted method of 'proving' evolution, even though it relies on the circular presumption that life 'did evolve'.

All was not well, when later work showed that many fossils are in the wrong places from where they should be. Echinoderms in the chalk cliffs of south England are one well known example noted.

Once again we alight on Alcide d'Orbigny, who did much useful work, but is also said to have wrongly assigned ages to strata, and unwittingly reversed ammonite species between the Bajocian and Toarcian Stages, as reviewed by modern experts and standards; but there are much more serious problems with the whole concept of relating rocks by their fossils. Such errors are only now being realised.

Again, it is these assumptions that are the pivotal weaknesses.

If long linear time did happen, there would be no clear method for species to avoid predicted evolutionary changes. Yet they do this often, and refuse to fit this presumed process of slow change over long eras of time. This anachronistic factor fulfils one of Darwin's primary fears, namely that the fossil record would later show he may have been wrong in this central tenet of his theory, that species could not possibly avoid change over time. Today, now that scientists have found such evidence that fossils do not do this after all, they have altered Darwin's premise to say that they can avoid such change, but it is unconvincing to say Darwin was wrong...when it suits.

This led to the illustration of 'trees' of branching flora and fauna that gave life to the idea itself. They could see this idea was really bizarre, that all this variety of apes, birds, giraffes, fish, insects, rhinos, mice, frogs, bats and bears could have evolved out of one life form like the *stromatolites*, a sort of bacterial equivalent of moss still found in W.Australia for example. An inventive idea, but it relied on transitional forms and eons of time, neither of which we see physically, or proved without assumptions.

The search was also on for a way of explaining it all more plausibly, at least in the eyes of the science officials bent on success. They had to succeed, because this was not a calm, gentle swapping of ideas among friends, but an angry battle for the hearts and minds of Victorian England, and then the whole world after that, so giving in or conceding were not on the menu for those bent on world domination.

Another idea arose: a 'series' of leaps from one form to another was proposed. Then there could be just smaller jumps from one animal to another.

Then came a global group of marine creatures called belemnites, that might link strata to a date; classed as cephalopods, these were creatures that floated about in the ocean, a sort of straighter ammonite, as well as the *nautiloid*. All of them would be used, yet still no one stopped to wonder if millions of years had really passed at all.

So the Jurassic, for example, has been 'set in order' according to the ammonite successions of Europe, and these have become the 'global primary standard' for dating each stratum. If these 'standard' species did not descend one from the other, then the whole system is undone. When the duck-billed platypus was first seen in Europe, albeit a rather dry looking and rather dead one, no-one believed it could possibly be a real creature, and must have made up as a cruel joke to play on scientists. It was real, but just very strange to their eyes and minds. Until then, they thought they had a good, solid grasp on what was real, and what was not. The platypus fooled them: too odd to be real.

Often the variation is so massive, that it has been called 'adaptive radiation' as the different ages have been combined; good idea, but the same problem persists.

The fact that there are strikingly different fossil ammonite groups in different parts of Europe[73] including Russia, shows that mere local differences do not solve these problems. This marked difference means they just do not match, and at this junction between the Jurassic and Cretaceous eras, many of these creatures being in the same Tethyan marine area [bordering the ancient ocean known as the Tethys seaway].

Bound by the straitjacket of linear time, these troubles could only be glossed over. Everyone moved on, yet they remain unsolved to this day. We can almost get a hint of how desperate the first geologists were to lighten the mood amongst all this, naming one ammonite *Zigzagiceras zigzag*, which just may have had hint of a suture line with a zigzag or two, if we are not being too bold. Perhaps it was the same sense of humour that helped name the sabre-toothed tiger *'Smilodon'*, which rushed round biting things about as much as it could. Smile it may have

73 The Geological Timescale 2004, ICS Report, Cambridge University Press, p 326.

done, but not so we would sit down to tea with one, without losing limbs.

One day cyclic time may be accepted, but these old principles stem from Hutton and Lyell as far back as 1795,[74] as we have seen. A key one is the old idea of the 'Uniformitarian' concept of earth history, which the superb *Oxford Companion to the Earth*[75] regards as outdated and should be 'rejected' for several reasons, as noted.

The ghastly truth is that even science has to be selective. We get to choose what we test, how we test it, which results to use, how we tabulate them, as every scientist has to pick the tests they use. Any research must do that, or waste valuable resources on being too broad in approach. So called blind tests are designed innocently enough to check the results, but there is always a degree of choice and selection at every stage.

It is said that almost anything can be proven using statistics. The get-out clause is always this: with the number of tests we made, this was the result. Those tests may have been abnormal in some obscure way the tester missed, or too few to be realistic, so the conclusions drawn could mean nothing at all.

This is the awful truth about science, and when a majority agree with a big idea, the dissenters may face ridicule, while perhaps being right all along.

The *scientific method* relies on us questioning everything until the questions receive proper answers. So we cannot stop questioning and checking, until all this fresh probing has revealed some truth. We become so in awe of science's major successes, it is easy to have too much trust in it.

This method is good in theory, but in practise we often overlook it.

Some may even claim a great finding while using wholly incorrect evidence or a hypothesis of total fiction. One example is that of Felix Pouchet, the French scientist who in the 1850's developed a 'body of evidence' that convinced many it formed an unassailable proof of spontaneous generation of life, which we now realise is impossible. Where did he go wrong? The difference between fact and fiction is often

74 The Theory of the Earth, James Hutton, 1795
75 Edition printed in 2000, p102.

a subtle one, and he could see microbial growth 'just beginning' in a sealed jar, so that was that. At least until the famous Pasteur showed a packed theatre at the Sorbonne on 7th April 1864 that Pouchet was wrong. History was changed that day as a result, but even Pasteur was not right all the time.[76]

Sometimes an advance can be warmly received with scenes of delirious excitement, while in reality being totally mistaken, and misleading generations to come.

In fact he was wrong too, they both were, since their methods did not support the conclusions they drew from them. Both had preconceptions, and as Dr Waller observed, Pasteur did not leave his ideas at home each day.

Pasteur was a great scientist who made truly famous and vital medical discoveries we all use daily, such as the process of pasteurisation that bears his name, but science historians have shown his record was not ideal. He suppressed negative data, and refused to replicate key experiments that could have cast doubt on his own work. This in no way diminishes his huge achievements, far from it, but it shows even our greatest achievers can simply get things wrong, or be far too forceful in championing a cause they like, and producing the deeply desired outcome of reaching the 'right' results. They were being human.

One fact is clear from all this. Results are often 'wrong' for a reason, and are trying to tell us we are wrong; yet we may so want one outcome over another that we set aside the whole purpose of doing the experiments at all: finding true reality.

Selection of data is normal, and we call it analysis. A bunch of dots on a graph can be truly derived, but where we draw our line through them is bound to be affected by our beliefs in what 'we think' it all means. Even placing the dots can mislead.

Every scientist may favour some outcomes over others. Ignoring key data we know could affect our own results is a very different thing, but that happens too.

We have been educated to think linear means logical. It doesn't. Yet even though all this may sound logical as the currently orthodox explanation, it is still a concept rather than observed fact.

76 *'Fabulous Science'*, John Waller, Oxford University Press, 2004. P18.

Not all geology is fast, nor all slow. Some deposits are laid down in hours.

Imagine a major airport frozen in time for a moment. What can we see? Planes, people, and buildings with shops full of goods are there. Now we may visualise a large rain storm in nearby hills causes a massive flash flood that rapidly covers the whole scene in mud and sand, many metres deep in an hour of debris dumping. Such tragic scenes do happen[77]. Cases are seen each year in Brazil, the Philippines, Italy, and England's Lynmouth disaster of 1952, the 1953 storm surge of East Anglia and the Thames Estuary, the Weymouth disaster of 18th July 1955, and many others. Back to our airport scene again. Then 100 years passes by, which may be unlikely with search dogs and rescue teams, but go with this one for a moment.

The land has moved in height by now, after the consequent earthquakes, so we have uplifted strata containing our fossilised airport. A river cuts down to reveal the layers, rather Grand Canyon-like, known as an incised meander. We can now see the flattened scene of destruction preserved for future analysis in 100 vertical feet of now fully dried sand and mudstone.

Suddenly seeing this, and without any knowledge of what took place, this is not as easy a scene to reconstruct as it may sound, for a non-expert at least. Did it happen fast, or slowly? In addition, if we start with a strongly held preconception of what we are seeing and how it arose, it is even harder to see the truth of it.

Let's start with the people: where did they all come from? We do not know from science, so we can only estimate. We could never even hope to sort out the arrivals from the transit passengers, who have no detectable link, and thus no physical connection, with that location, and so our idea of this story begins to take shape *as we make it up*. After all, a theory is only a grand word for a story that is meant to fit facts we propose, and very often they don't fit at all.

Our hypothesis is taking form. We can see the similarity in the finds in each layer of the strata, and so would be bound to feel certain they are connected. They are, in the sense one overlies the other directly,

---

77 This did happen to a town called Nevada del Ruis in Colombia; tragically they had to build a new town.

but any deeper link is speculation. It is a simple step to progress to the conclusion that the contents of these higher layers evolved slowly over time from those lower down, which we know are older.

Only if that flood happened rapidly in one day would this idea be impossible, but we do not know if it did. The fossil record is much more complex, yet similar in some ways. Picking which layers were floods is not easy to see, even for a sedimentologist.

After a few months or years of thinking over all this, we have constructed a huge and carefully prepared scenario of how all the fossils are linked over millennia or longer, and our new theory is dusted down and rolled into view before the audience. Some might like the new idea, while others may be incredulous at how we reached such odd conclusions. This is pretty much what did happen when observers began to find fossils and record them in the 17th century. Even the word fossil only first appeared in a book by Lovell in 1661, but is said by Dr D. L. Dineley to have been taken in its modern usage around 1800.[78]

Can all this help us decide between the two views of the above flood?

All that splits them are two primary aspects: the mechanism of the evolution of unseen amoeba into the people we can see, and the age of the rock strata or layers we walk over. The first one is beyond simple proof either way, while the second is also difficult to date, if we have never seen the speed and power of a flash flood, still less such a huge one. What are we to make of it?

While the few fossils found are indeed real, our idea may be incorrect.

Similarly, while we can see fossils in rock, we cannot say with scientific certainty that they evolved from others we see elsewhere. It is our idea, *but not yet a fact*. The age of the rocks does offer a key, but our methods show flaws, so even this is not actual 'proof' their resident fossils evolved slowly over a long stretch of time.

So are the rocks old or young?

The race was on, mainly in the 19th century, to 'find' the long expanse of time they needed. When Dr. Velikovsky wrote his controversial books in the 1950's, such as *Earth In Upheaval* (1955), showing evidence for a series of catastrophes that had clearly happened very fast indeed, he was greeted with disrespect and other unsavoury reactions.

---

78 *Oxford Companion to the Earth,* page 68; OUP 2000.

One publisher was even pressured into refusing to print his book at all, but he succeeded in the end.[79]

His challenge was immense, but the evolutionists refused to accept defeat, and resurrected an idea from 1795 to sum up their 'slow geology' worldview. Scottish naturalist James Hutton had called it Uniformitarianism as we noted. So when we find giant catastrophes in a short span of time in sediments, this concept breaks down.

The idea of millions of years arose, because they were needed to explain so much change. Darwin mentioned his own amazement at such long periods, and how impossible they were to imagine.

Nearly every top life science professor in the last 50 years in the Western world has been a committed evolutionist, and would not have been appointed if they thought otherwise. Indeed to think otherwise would have been a career end. So why should they look for flaws they feel don't exist? They regard their premise as right, so flaws are just accepted, but still annoying.

Now back to our example in Japan, where there is a sequence of 92,000 tiny layers called varves which are 'thought' (i.e. believed) to be the annual layering of sediments from nearby glacial melt waters. As the glacier melts a bit each season, there is a difference in the colour and type of the fine grains laid down in this nearby lake.

The proposal is that during the course of each year there is variation in deposition, creating a nice, neat pair of sediments, one dark and one lighter layer, so we just count them and there we have the age. This may not be true, for this reason: there are several factors that can cause this to happen many times in one year, not just once, so the whole concept would be incorrect. Annual climate variation can cause this same effect, and may have done so during the periods of extreme fluctuation in earth's seasons. Axial tilts and oscillating poles could also cause this abnormal result of several such layers in a few weeks, not years. This axial tilt was never imagined as a cause of these layers.

We don't see that pace now, so it has been reasonably assumed it never happened in the past either. Yet old coral layers in the Bahamas have shown the day lengths may have altered in an irregular way, so

79 *Worlds in Collision*, 1950; *Earth in Upheaval*, 1955, V. Gollancz, Sidgwick & Jackson, Abacus & other publishers

it is equally possible there were anomalous effects on glacial melting rates and thus sedimentation as well.

This is the huge danger of having a concept that relies on 19th century thinking, which later proves to be unreliable. Virgil used to say, around 40 BC, that 'We can't all do everything', which is so true, as there are so many subjects that need to be combined over decades to reach an accurate conclusion.

In 40 AD, Seneca the Younger used to muse about comets 2000 years ago, as we do today. We know what he did not, which is that the solar 'wind' of ions quite quickly wears them down by 'ablating' their surface of frozen gas. This means they have a short shelf life if we are seeing a 'short period' comet, and so they should no longer exist if time had been unchanged for millions of years. Yet they do, showing a short cycle.

When Alfred Wegener published his theory of continental drift in 1915, it was treated with total derision. The English version of his work only came out in 1922, but they howled with laughter at his idea, which was, of course, actually correct. It became a mainstay of geology. He was a meteorologist, so what did he know about all that, they thought? Yet he was also a physicist, and never lived to see the proof of his great work, sadly disappearing on an expedition to the dangerously unstable Greenland ice cap.

It was nearly 60 years later that magnetometry totally proved him right, as ships sailed over the Mid-Atlantic Ridge and found parallel and symmetrical lines of magnetised rock 12,000 feet below their sensors, showing the polar reversals that are still studied to this day. Think axial tilt and a magnetic core for the answer.

Science is chiefly the study of knowledge, not knowledge itself, as we often forget.

A fascinating type of slime mould called *Dictyostelium* was studied by Dr Bonner, and then observed by Einstein and others in the 1950's, to be moving in rotational pulses which showed this mass of single-celled organisms 'acting together' in perfect unison, as one connected group. This should be totally impossible, yet it happens.

How is it possible? If there is a 'rotational rhythm' to the universe, then this slime organism may simply be responding to that hidden motion. Einstein said it was the most amazing thing he had ever seen, as he watched the slime forming concentric rings with perfect waves that repeatedly ebbed and flowed like a tide, or formed spirals. The Super Grid could also explain this hidden connection the cells respond to in this 'dance'. Being only one cell, they cannot be conscious. Some deep-sea life-forms, copepods, also pulse in a way. The research was done at America's Princeton University, where Einstein was based after the war, and you can see it on the net, but remember it is speeded up.

Having seen this slime motion on film, it is really spell-binding stuff, and another natural 'impossibility' which science is wholly unable to explain...without cyclic time at least. How could these tiny cells with no brain or even a nervous system, act so exactly in harmony as one coherent mass or object, like 1000 dancers on a stage after years of rehearsal? In terms of Darwinism, they certainly could not. So it is reasonable to say that Cyclic Time could be a rhythm of repeating events, perhaps so apparently and precisely mirrored in that intriguing slime.

All matter can be rotating in time.

Numerous leading scientists like Sir Roger Penrose, Lee Smolin, Peter Woit and others, are ready to voice fresh opinions, and the body of new evidence is growing into new thinking. It takes great courage to voice new ideas as they have done, and their influence continues to be very significant indeed.

Physicist Professor Lee Smolin vividly explains we have a problem '...*because of the incompleteness of the 20th Century's scientific revolution*'.[80] If the 'science' doesn't work, then it remains theory, not knowledge.

The more we learn about the world of sub-atomic physics, the more we find that the quantum world of energy does not appear to function in a linear way. Going back over some of Einstein and Dirac's work, along with Schrödinger, Bohr and Rutherford, we find this linear thinking formed the basis of their conclusions.

As we can see, changing this level of maths is a revolution we seem to need.

CHAPTER 8

Volcanoes and Ancient Cultures

... if it was so, it might be; and if it were so, it would be:
but as it isn't, it ain't. That's logic.
LEWIS CARROLL, 1872, Through the Looking Glass

Wait for that wisest of advisors ...Time.
PERICLES, 450 BC

Essence

Volcanoes, quakes and tsunami waves show giant events can happen in seconds. The lesson that big things can happen very suddenly is a tough one to learn. Some have assumed our past is full of long, slow periods of ordered calmness. Geology was built on this primary assumption, yet we now see the reality is that it was not like this, as the cyclic time evidence shows. The rocks hold the key evidence, and they show just how fast huge events can happen. We have imposed ages on most events in human history that cannot be right. As we can now see, the artificial dates we gave those events may be totally incorrect. All this may be easy to see now, over 200 years of research later, but Lyell and Darwin had none of this modern information at their disposal.

Ancient cultures are another enigma. They produced almost identical symbols and art, and yet never met to share those signs. This amazing fact points to a uniquely plausible conclusion, that they may recognize those signs from a past cycle of time. No other answer fits these facts as well, so it is possible this is evidence for such a cycle. They lived in an era of vast changes and disasters we are only now finding, like the tsunami that hit Crete around 3000 years ago, and the Thera/Santorini volcano. We will also consider how these features fit into a short cycle in which even the continental split of the old Pangea supercontinent may also be recent.

The poles are extremes in every way, and so those living in Iceland, the South Poles, Greenland, or Spitzbergen for example, will have around 3 months of near constant sunshine, and later 3 months of near total darkness, but for a glow of blue light as the sun's rays never quite break the horizon. Try growing roses in that.

We can see there have been huge mega-volcanoes in the past, but scientists have judged them to be of great age that happened millions of years ago. Not only will we see that they could not have happened so long ago, but we will also see evidence that they are not extinct at all, but will return sooner than most of us suspected.

Vulcanologists like Prof. Bill McGuire of University College London have been saying this for years. There is great value in knowing about cyclic time events before they happen: it gives us valuable months or years in which to make vital preparations.

When something major is about to happen, as most of us can see it is, then it is time to realise that such awareness is like a gift, since it gives us those precious few moments in which to react before the event, not when it is too late.

The people of Pompeii or Herculaneum in AD 79 did not realise the significance of the rumblings that came from Vesuvius, their nearby volcano. Tremors had occurred before, and nothing much took place. That was their first big mistake. The past is not a good sign of the future, but acts rather like a soft blanket of false security that everyone believes to be reliable. It so is not. Their second error was to think they could outrun an eruption. When the 200 mile an hour cloud of burning ash did arrive later, it was too late even to make for the sea shore nearby. Actually they did get a warning in the form of earth tremors, but these happened quite often, so few people reacted.

An equally extreme example can show just how vital time can be in dealing with nature. The natural world can look peaceful enough most of the time, but appearances can be deceptive, as ships passing near the Tonga Island's Pacific Ocean trench found out in 2008. This was a rare deep ocean floor eruption that suddenly began to billow smoke at the Pacific Ocean's surface as a new island began to form.

There is a Caribbean example, just to the south-east of Florida. One summer morning over a century before, far from Tonga, there occurred an explosion so fast that no-one even had time to move away. The hospital clock was to stop at the time of eight minutes to eight on May 8th in 1902. Nature can move very fast when pressure builds.

A crack had formed on the south west flank of the mountain's peak, as the pressure rose with the highly viscous molten rock forcing its way upwards from deep below, yet cooling at air contact to form a plug which allowed pressure below to increase far beyond dangerous levels, until it split the rock. This sent a near frictionless cloud to one side at very high speed, as the fine particles released the hot gas they contained. On this day, the same kind of *nuée ardente* (burning cloud; hot ash, now called *'pyroclastic flow'*) event happened in the French Caribbean island of Martinique on 8th May 1902, when nearby Mt Pelée erupted under extremely high magma pressure.

Sadly Nature had chosen the side that faced the town below.

Out of the eight main types of volcanoes, this Peléan type is one of the most explosive, and it destroyed the town. Since the villagers from the local area had come into the port seeking its protection, the population was sadly much larger, at about 29,000. The blast was so intense that it flattened metre thick walls, and set fire to 25 ships at sea, all in about 130 seconds. The heat was so intense and arrived so rapidly, that even clothes did not have time to ignite, with food and drink left intact on tables.

Only one person is recorded as having survived this appalling devastation of the port of St Pierre. He was a dockworker named Louis Cyparis, and it was thanks to the fact he was in a tiny windowless prison facing the sea, and thus safely pointing away from the mountain. When rescuers arrived four days later, he was found and released, on the understanding that he was somehow meant to be free, if he alone could live through that lot. He will certainly have needed a rest and a lie down.

He had survived with a bowl of water he had in his cell, and lived for many years to become a celebrity in a circus where he recounted his happy story with understandable enthusiasm. The volcano was not finished. Twelve days later, a crack in the south east flank destroyed a smaller town in a similar way, and the world became aware of this dangerous Peléan type of volcanic eruption. A repeat event even occurred in August, about 12 weeks later, which destroyed what was left of St

Pierre. Luckily no-one had decided to move back to the town, so there were no losses at all that day. The town and port were never rebuilt, now that Nature had shown it was not quite the safe place it seemed.

It is clear that events can happen very quickly indeed, far more rapidly than anyone alive had been able to witness personally. Today, the area looks very calm.

There was one eye witness to the above scene in St Pierre, and he was fortunate enough to have been watching the town, for no particular reason, from a vantage point on another flank of the same volcano, and luckily emerged unscathed from that particular eruption. He was an astronomer, so his description was helpful in piecing together the sequence of those terrible events, for the benefit of learning how fairly quiescent volcanoes are not reliable signals of safety.

Cyclic time should be a piece of cake to evaluate. If it is wrong, there will be no such signs of it ever, ever having happened before at a time in the past. If, on the other hand, it is correct, then we should find a whole mass of such evidence.

We find such signs in all of history, and in every science you can think of. One powerful example in biology is the humble strand of DNA every one of us carries. We have all heard of DNA since it became useful in convicting criminals. One particular type of DNA is nuclear, and then the circular form (found in 1964) present in the mitochondria carried by the female line. Scientists speak of a 'bottleneck' that we can easily calculate and see how the total number of human beings 'narrows' towards an origin point. Oddly, this point appears to be in an unexpected place: in the recent past, about 4,950 years ago.

If so, the entire history of humanity has been misunderstood, because this shows our present population of 7.5bn could have grown in under 5000 years.

The idea is simple: each generation shows a tiny change in this form of DNA, so by counting the changes or mutations, you can work out how many generations have lived on earth. This largely ignores the size of the population, and just deals with these generational alterations, which is very useful indeed.

When we look at the date of the bottleneck, at just under 4,950 years, this would clearly be an impossible date for the start of *Homo sapiens* in the normal thinking of earth history. Unless, that is, our thinking is in error in some way. In that case something amazing happens. The impossible becomes possible.

The *Oxford Dictionary of Earth Sciences*[81] states that an early male ancestor is 'postulated' for all modern humans. This gentleman is said to have 'lived in Africa between about 100,000 and 200,000 years ago', and is known as 'Adam'. These estimates are artificial, since we need only 4,950 years for today's population.

The above long time span arises from the claim that our population 'must have' been larger before this. For what reason, are we told? Because any other interpretation is too short in time period, so this seems to be the answer. We will come back to deal with 'mitochondrial Eve', who was the 'postulated' female ancestor of all modern humans... an archaic human living in Africa about 140,000 to 280,000 years ago.

This dating estimate is based on the idea of linear time being long, and is just made up to suit that idea.

The dates above for the postulated 'Adam and Eve' are theoretical. It is part of the linear conjecture that there was such a 'bottleneck', before which the numbers of people were much greater. For this to be true, we shall see the evidence in the dating of rocks and artefacts, the methods for which could fairly be described as having more holes than a Gruyère cheese. There is no actual evidence for this claim, so it appears untrue.

A much quoted study is one by the late Dr Allan Wilson from the University of California at Berkeley, who studied 147 people, and gave us the date of 140,000 years mentioned already. As Bill Bryson reports, 'doubts also soon emerged about the assumed rates of mutations'.[82] Soon the study fell out of favour.

There is that word 'assumed' again, so we can see how dangerous it is.

There are many incidents of finds which have been misunderstood when first seen, only later to be changed completely by someone else. One is Neanderthal man, which is named after the Neander Valley in Germany, and first thought, or rather 'assumed', to be simian, i.e.

81 3rd Edition, 2008, page 7
82 A Short History of Nearly Everything, B. Bryson, page 555, Black Swan, 2003.

ape-like. Only later did a palaeontologist working in the Sahara realise the error, but there were more errors to come.[83]

One look at the heavy brow ridge and limbs naturally made the observers form instantly the image of a crude, brute-like creature that *must have been* sub-human, deeply stupid in essence, and definitely ape-like. You guessed it: They were plum wrong. They were not ape-like, yet even to this day we cannot fully classify them, even though many Europeans now find 2–4% of their DNA is Neanderthal.

When that walker first wandered into this cave in 1856 and found a strange skeleton, there was confusion among antiquarians. This first finding of Neanderthal man in Germany was one example, with some observers saying it was either 'an idiot', or a new species unknown to science, while other 'experts' said the skeleton in the cave was just a super-cranially heavy-browed soldier from the Napoleonic retreat of 1814, who, no doubt badly wounded, wandered in to die. Nice story, but totally invented. It was rather older, but nothing like the huge ages claimed, as we have seen. In our cycle, these 'cave' tribes would only live for 250 years at most, which may explain why only 137 have been found.

The advanced nature of these cave people would only be established much later.

Purely thanks to later finds of jewellery, albeit basic in their design, and flowers arranged in the graves of their dead, did everyone come to know the simian epithet was wrong in all ways. These were no near-apes, but people with special ritual ceremonies used to honour their dead family members, which are aspects of religion and human ritual, and not something apes really do these days.

We may see chimps dressed in clothes and even drawing pictures, but we don't tend to see them discussing finer points of the Socratic dialogues so much.

Another shock for these beings thought to be so stupid was their brain size. Instead of being much smaller than our own, as they should be if the thinking of their primitive nature were at all true, it turned out to be the opposite. Their brains were closer to 18–1900 cc, as opposed to our own smaller size of 1500 cc. Others claim this 13% larger brain

83 Ibid page 551

size is not true, but not having reliable recent data, it has yet to be confirmed. Actually brain size has nothing to do with intelligence, as women prove very ably, with a smaller skull size than men, and yet currently achieving higher scores in exams than the men as a rule. We don't even know if cave people could speak, so we aren't exactly a mine of information about them. What we do know means they can fit into a cyclic universe. None of that was known before, so some took to inventing finds to suit.

A famous favourite in hoaxes is Piltdown Man, which is curiously absent from one science dictionary, and became known as the worst fraud in archaeology. 'Discovered' by Charles Dawson in 1912, and hailed as the eagerly awaited 'missing link' between apes and humans, it was duly given a special Latin name, *Eoanthropus dawsonii*, and made headline news around the world. Later, and much to the horror of the scientific world, it was found to be a hoax perpetrated by Dawson to mislead the British Museum in London. It turned out to be, on closer examination, half the jaw bone of an orang-utan linked to a few skull parts from a human, and then all 'aged', perhaps by being soaked in strong tea, to look realistic as the 'missing link' between apes and humans. It fooled most people in the world for a long time, but not all. Some looked deeper.

Forty years later, the story of the hoax reached the press on 21 Nov 1953, but no one ever admitted it. It later emerged the infamous Dawson had carried out 38 other such frauds and clever hoaxes, in which he used his social position to fool experts he knew. When rechecked, the tricks were found.

He died in 1916 aged 52, never admitting a word, but on that record it seemed certain he was the likely hoaxer of the Piltdown finds. He lived in Sussex, right beside the dig location, where he was perhaps the man who also left flint arrowheads for diggers to find, along with hippo teeth to add realism, although these 'additions' were never found in context, in the hard ground, but on the spoil heap waiting to be sieved. The skull was later said to be medieval, from 1400 AD or so, so not at all linked to the ape jaw. A strange thing to do, which wasted much time, since over 700 academic papers were written about Piltdown Man before it was realised Dawson had played a trick on the world. Experts wanted a missing link, so Dawson made one.

It seemed to fit, as Dawson knew it would. Yet when exposed as a hoax, it so filled the need in this field of study, even though it was not authentic in any way, that it was still being quoted as genuine evidence decades later.

Another favourite, this time an error, was the finding of a tooth in America that was instantly dubbed 'Nebraska Man', dated at a million years old (having guessed it *surely* must be) and given the scientific Latin name *Hesperopithecus haroldcookii,* and hailed as another missing link, an idea which is still intensely controversial to this day. A picture was quickly drawn of this fully upright man-ape specimen, with long hair, fur skins and all; a reconstruction so real it drew gasps from many who saw it, carrying a club and looking thoroughly primitive. Here was the perfect combo of ape and human being, and it was so welcome that it at once appeared in the Illustrated London News of 1922, and in an account by Dr Henry Osborn in *Science* magazine in May that year. Harold Cook must have been very proud, for a while.

The sound of great congratulations could be heard everywhere, until another fly in the ointment appeared out of nowhere, just when it was all going so well. Another very annoying scientist put up his hand and declared that it was the tooth of a peccary, a type of pig, and not even a biped, let alone a 'missing man' anything. Not everyone had believed the claim, to be fair, and *Science* duly printed a retraction in 1927 (Wolf, Gregory) to say it was neither ape nor man, but pig.

Equally embarrassing was another American find, reported in Time magazine in 1927. This was the 'find' of *Southwest Colorado Man,* also fully reconstructed in drawings as a 'primitive man', was created from one or more teeth. Yet a picture of a primitive man was duly drawn. This time the teeth, taken as human by some, were actually from an *Eocene* horse, so that was the end of that missing link.

The claimed difference in ages was 55 million years some said, so it shows how easy it is for experts to be so mistaken in both osteology and age. Much more electrifying even than this, is a much deeper issue about how such extreme errors occur. The real underlying problem is our apparent misconception of history itself, as long and linear, and the examples show this.

There are finds that show older cultures to have been far ahead of our European based culture that has grown to prominence since the

Romans left England and France in 410 AD, the same year the Visigoths under Alaric sacked Rome, ending Rome's dominance. In Britain, the usual Roman troops controlling the north and west regions were withdrawn in 383 AD. By 402 AD, coins were no longer minted in any numbers. Since Rome began in 754 BC, so the claim goes, their Empire became over extended, and doomed to fail finally by 410 AD.[84] Now we switch to Greece to look for clues.

One famous find clearly shows the ancients were much more advanced than anyone realised in the modern era. It is known as the Antikythera (search Antikythera Mechanism Research Project and see details). This is a uniquely unusual find made in bronze, found in pieces on the sea bed during an archaeological dive in the Aegean Sea, south of Corinth, Greece in 1901 by Valerios Stais.

It has widely been called history's most amazing object, because it is so clever.

Yet the famous Antikythera mechanism from a Roman shipwreck caused no stir when it was found. Heavily encrusted with salt corrosion, it looked unimpressive. Eighty years later, it was scanned using the magnetic waves in MRI tomography to create a sharp image. This revealed strange glyphs and sophisticated clockwork that astounded the scientific world, and still does. It was a kind of geared computer.

A report appeared in *Nature* and explained it was 'technically more complex than any known device for at least a millennium afterwards'. According to Professor Mike Edmunds of Cardiff University 'When you see it your jaw just drops'.

Dr Michael Wright, of Imperial College in London, spent three years making a 72 gear copy, having to deduce the function of extra lost gears that were never found, but it was clearly able to calculate eclipses and other data; more still remains undeciphered, but for a workshop to have made this around 230 BC or before, is quite staggering. It is not surprising that more parts were not found in the area, where the wreck was found. There have been many earthquakes in that area, which arose as 'swarms' as the shocks released pressure along an entire fault system that traverses Greece and the Turkish coast. There have also been some major tsunamis as a result, such as one that struck Crete in that ancient era.

84 *The Decline and Fall of the Roman Empire*, E.Gibbon, 1776–88.

Finding such a device is a serious shock to conventional chronology, akin to finding a fully functioning petrol engine in an early Egyptian tomb, as some say.

Often called an early computer, working by cogs not electricity, this is a reasonable description of the Antikythera mechanism, since it does enable complex calculations to be made as the cogs turn and interact together. Dr. Wright also believes the device was not a single chance piece of machinery, since the idea of chance at this level of maths is very unlikely. He went on to say the machine's maker had a clear aim to create this device, with great ingenuity and expertise, making no mistakes, adding that it must have been part of 'their everyday stock work.' The device draws together many disciplines such as maths, physics, astronomy, spatial geometry, engineering, metallurgy and trigonometry among them, so it was not the work of one person; although the vast skill used, the location and time period, have been credited to Archimedes (287–212 BC).

It is very likely no other person had the vision and brilliance to construct it, nor the trained technicians to draw and assemble the parts of so unique a concept.

Therefore, it seems certain this same workshop would have made other sophisticated items before this one, and was used to producing highly innovative astronomical machinery, of which this may be but one example. This must have been the culmination of decades or centuries of collaboration, and almost certainly with India, bearing in mind the known links between the cultures, and ancient India's famous advances in maths and astronomy.

The Indian metallurgy is also famous, and to this day we are unsure of how they managed to make an early stainless steel version of a column in Delhi which defies rust. Not only is the method of its manufacture not known, it has also proved tough to analyse, yet make it they did, about 2000 years before the West.

The Antikythera is perhaps the most astonishing ancient relic ever found. This deduction is entirely logical, since no-one else had produced the ancient equivalent of a precise calculator at a first attempt. It has been compared to being the space shuttle of its day, so how on earth did the ancients manage this feat in an era when Britons, for example, were living in mud huts, and while the fearsome Picts further north on the Scottish border were still wearing woad (a thick blue plant dye)?

Their most sophisticated inventions were stone circles aligned to the moon, and fire, or a piece of stone lashed onto a length of wood, or a shard of flint chipped off to form a surprisingly effective blade. Clever of course, but hardly in the same league as a device used to predict eclipses and the planets' positions. Yet still earlier, in Neolithic times in Orkney, we have noted the existence of under floor drainage systems, which are entirely out of place and age, with Pakistan being their possible origin, since the Celtic tribes show DNA, language and cultural ties to Asia.

What is truly incredible is the Antikythera mechanism of a 'pin and slot' machining, which creates a precise variation in the degree of turning the cogs perform, altering the number of teeth in effect. Was this linked to a Metonic 18.6 year lunar cycle by its makers? It was. This puzzled researchers as to why, and still does, yet they found this tiny variation matched the infinitesimal changes of the moon's wobbling orbit...the above Metonic cycle. Without accurate clocks, how could they possibly have measured such tiny changes, let alone built a machine to factor all this in to achieve accurate celestial calendar prediction? We are never likely to know, but it is amazing they could do it with such skill, when Europe was thrilled with inventing mud huts.

All we do know is that they did it, and did all this maths in an age when they should not have been so clever or astronomically well informed to have any hope of doing so. We can present another explanation for all this 'out of time' brilliance, which is a cycle of time. In this scenario, those ancient thinkers were using understanding that could have been derived from earlier cultures that were lost in the giant shake up of the 1650 BC quakes and associated volcanoes. Is this possible? It is an idea contrary to the accepted thinking of today, but still it is possible all the same. If there were earlier advanced cultures in India, as the Delhi steel pillar implies, we can derive a different version of history that explains these inconsistencies quite neatly.

If the world is cyclic as shown, then there would have been a world of order and sophistication before the Stone Age era, with very clever people in it. It was clearly brilliant to make the Antikythera around 220 BC with only basic tools.

One factor of this amazing machine's existence shows its makers were well used to careful measurement and celestial observations over a long time. We can deduce this since the Metonic cycle of the moon's phases takes so long to recur, which is an example of the longer repetition of a sequence of events. This is similar to the 11 year solar cycle which increases the sunspot activity from the Maunder Minimum to the 'solar maximum' with large mass ejections of force which we detect on earth, and which can even knock out electricity power systems by energy overloading.

This activity is thought to be due to the increasing complexity of the sun's invisible lines of magnetic force which draw out those vast 100,000 mile long arcs of plasma, as they flash between pairs of sun spots. The lunar cycle was discovered by the Greek astronomer Meton as early as 433 BC, who noted by observation that it took this many years for the moon's phases to recur once again on exactly the same day: another cycle within a cycle.

They must have spent many such 19 year periods observing this sequence to have any hope of seeing its recurring cyclicity; an amazing study to make. Only after decades would it become obvious.

What is clear is that these people were not the simple-minded ancient ancestors they are often taken for: rather quirky, brilliant at oratory, with a bit of serious maths thrown in, if we look at the ancient Greeks like Euclid and Pythagoras, but also engineers of genuine genius. Their brilliance must have been extreme to achieve all this without telescopes and the finely calibrated measuring graticules we have today.

Europe in 220 BC was not enjoying this level of advanced technology at all, which is a revealing fact in itself. The Greeks are credited with these advances as if they occurred without external help of any kind. In fact there had been close ties and a strong exchange of maths and information with India, which was a much older civilisation that was already well aware of cyclic time, and indeed knew it as the central pivot of all life, and still does today.

Similarly strange to these oddly clever advances in ancient Greece, which seemed to arise from nowhere (yet hadn't), are the Neolithic tribal people. Located to the north of the Picts, were tribes dated at over 1000 years BC, yet as we have seen, used under floor drainage systems, similar in concept to those of the Indus valley civilization in the same period. It is reasonable to suggest that they brought this technology and solutions from elsewhere. The linguistic links take Celtic and Gaelic directly to Pakistan and India, so there is a close connection.

Their corbelled stonework, which gradually insets each successive layer a few inches until it meets at the top ready for a capstone, was a brilliant construction also used in the pyramids, such as the Great Pyramid of Cheops in Egypt. It can be seen often, such as at Maes Howe in Orkney, and in the large burial chamber of the Newgrange 'temple' near the River Boyne in Ireland. Although in separate countries, these sites of ancient ritual stonework are very similar.

Both sites have corbelled stonework covering long passages, and are aligned with the winter solstice of December 21st, and both have used a 'letter box' opening through which the sun's rays could flood the interior of the tombs with light, either at dawn as at Newgrange, or at sunset.

This method isn't something one thinks up casually after breakfast one day. They must have learned it before, and we do see the technique in other parts of the world, suggesting earlier connections from an eastern point. This corbelling is a type of loose stone engineering of a high sophistication even by today's standards, and is still used in modern buildings to spread loading laterally.

Classic pyramid square

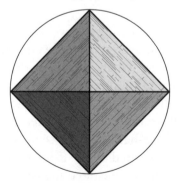

FIGURE 19 *Pyramid within a circle: classic cyclic time symbol used globally in pyramids of Peru, Mexico, Guatemala, Honduras and Egypt etc.*

These geographically far distant cultures were not to have had any connection with each other, yet it is well known that the languages of Sanskrit and Celtic Gaelic are actually closely linked by both vocabulary and grammar.

Famous in some quarters, yet little known globally, the superb work of the late Prof Myles Dillon, between 1918 and his sad loss on 18th June 1972, demonstrated these profoundly significant Indo-European links, as he travelled between Dublin and Simla in India. A brilliant scholar, he lectured in four languages, and explained this link with Sanskrit in his final book *'The Celts and the Aryans'* [published by the *Indian Institute for Advanced Study*, Simla 1975]. This shows the Indus area must have been the source of Celtic and Western cultures, and to this day one can see the red hair characteristic, and even porcelain white skin, in both locations (eg North Pakistan and Kashmir), quite contrary to what is taught in schools.

This finding is also at odds with modern thinking, since we read in one dictionary of religions an entry for the 'Celts' simply as a 'northern European' tribe. In fact they must have been the later living ancestors of the Indus Valley people (known as a 'Founder Effect' gene pool), but as Prof Noam Chomsky would say, we will return to this later on.

We tend to think we are very modern with our concrete structures and under floor heating laid in our super modern homes made of steel. In fact the Romans made concrete 2000 years before we did, and it set under water, which our early attempts at concrete could not manage at all.

Our modern under floor heating is clever of course, but not modern. The Romans had also discovered that as well, with a hot air ducting system called a *hypocaust*, which ran under the main floor itself, as well as diverting the heated air along separate vertical chambered flues running inside the walls of their villas. Simultaneous sub-floor and internal chamber wall heating already existed 2000 years ago. Even modern houses rarely have half that degree of sophistication, or with such superb insulation provided by the Roman 'wide gap air brick'.

The Romans were keen on plastered internal walls, just as we are, and so they had their craftsmen roughen the surface of this ducting before the damp clay was fired, so that the wet plaster could 'key in' rather than slip off, exactly as we still do to this day. With one small difference...we didn't think of doing that for very many centuries afterwards, using instead the old wattle and daub method of making huts by smearing mud, literally, over woven stick fencing: essentially a glorified sheep pen.

Their beautiful mosaics were also full of cyclic time symbols, as we shall see, with the four part disc that is the most common symbol globally. They also used the Hindu symbol of the cycle of four ages, the *swastika*, and incorporated it into their wall and floor work. As we will see in later sections, there are indeed deep connections with earlier ideas of cyclic time that span the entire globe, and that literally all the ancient cultures knew of it, and used the idea in their cultural and religious iconography.

It is a curious idea, but we of the modern 21st century world could be playing catch up with the ancient way the cosmos actually works... as a continuum.

Some Key Dates in History

TUTANKHAMUN CI350 BC

HESIOD 8th Cent BC

HOMER 8th Cent BC

ROME FOUNDED C753 BC

LAO TZU 60–531 BC

BUDDHA 563–483 BC

CONFUCIUS 551 BC

HERODOTUS 484–425 BC

SOCRATES 469–399 BC

PLATO 429–347 BC

ARISTOTLE 384–322 BC

EUCLID 300 BC

ARCHIMEDES 287–212 BC

ERATOSTHENES 276–194 BC

GITA written c2nd Cent. BC

JULIUS CAESAR 102–4 BC

HORACE 65–8 BC

CLAUDIUS invaded England 43[–410] AD

VESUVIUS volcano 79 AD

GALEN 129–199 AD
KING ALFRED 871 AD
VIKINGS in Canada c910 AD
ALTHING, Icelandic court c930 AD
MAGNA CARTA 1215 AD
COLUMBUS 1492 AD
L DA VINCI *d*1519, 2nd May
GALILEO c1630 AD

CHAPTER 9

Tree Rings and the Dating of History

I cannot give any scientist of any age better advice than this: the intensity of a conviction that a hypothesis is true has no bearing over whether it is true or not.
SIR PETER MEDAWAR, 1979, Nobel Prize winner

Essence

Tree rings should be the annual growth rings of all trees, but there are many cases where this expectation is not met. Carbon dates are famously unreliable due to migrating groundwater or airborne dust which can contaminate the samples. Ice cores and volcanic ash have also been used for calibration, but there are problems in doing so. As we see here, attempts have been made to use each dating method to back up the others. Few experts look any further, if the results support their theories.

Here is why one should, with examples of how it can all go awry.

Time interests us far more when we assign dates to finds in the ground. We have all noted the tree ring dating method, or 'dendrochronology' as it is called, a word taken from the Greek for tree and time. This method is closely linked to radiocarbon dating, and has been used to confirm the carbon dates, while carbon dates appear to support tree ring ages: a circular system.

This situation is not sufficiently objective to allay concerns held by many, and so requires a reappraisal. The advent of the cyclic time model for time itself poses another interesting question: is it possible that our entire view of history and pre-history is one large misunderstanding of how time passes? The evidence shows that there are indeed serious systemic errors in many other methods for dating remains, to justify such a claim.

We now have to challenge these methods *en masse* to answer this new question: do they account for this possibility of there being a repeating cyclic universe in which history may have been very much shorter? Could history fit into a few thousand years instead of many more as we are told? If the errors are real, then it could.

Now that claims for the span of tree ring dating have increased, where some ages of over 8–10,000 years are suggested, we have to wonder: are they correct? To decide, we have to check how these dates are arrived at, and it is quite a revelation when we do.

Some years do show a wonderful link to major world events, but they tend to be recent, not ancient. One example is that of the giant volcanic eruption of Tambora in 1815, which showed up in Irish bog oak tree rings in 1816 as a cold, dark summer with thinner than average rings from unusually slight growth. This example of Tambora, an Indonesian volcano, shows some effects are truly global in nature, since fine ash can blow right round earth's hemispheres.

Another global event was the Black Death or Plague, which killed roughly half the population in Europe over several years in two events, and effectively stopped the building of wooden houses, and thus the felling of large trees to build them, and thus created gaps in the available tree ring sequences, following the outbreaks of 1349 and 1665 AD. Other plague or pandemic events could have been in 540 AD, and according to Colin Burgess, also c1200 BC, perhaps due to a giant volcanic effect that created such loss of life that conditions could have allowed global disease events, and may have coincided with a Mediterranean Dark Age from 1200–800 BC. It is also possible the world was in a post-apocalyptic period at that time, after an earlier period of calm and order, as in the 'cyclic time map' shown above.

There was also the 14th century building hiatus that apparently occurred in Europe from Ireland, through Germany to Greece, which has been linked either to the 1349 AD plague itself, or a similarly giant scale collapse in society, or both.

How do tree rings tell the time? Usually, but not always, trees grow radially over time, and add a layer of extra cells of a different colour in winter, on all parts of the circular outer surface where growth takes place. Often this layer is not regular.

As we will see, this is not true in every tree, and even trees in the same wooded valley can show different numbers and depths of tree rings. This would make matching tree rings open to serious errors. Trees are naturally very vulnerable to the small and large changes in the tiny micro-climates they live, quite literally, unless trees learn to walk.

At night, the cool air tends to collect in the valley floors of higher regions. These local climatic effects can create abnormal growth patterns even on different sides of the same tree. This means that the core sample taken on one side of the tree may be entirely different to one taken on the other side, depending on the prevailing wind side, and where in the forest the tree was living.

The oldest tree type in the world, appropriately named *Pinus longaeva* in Latin for its great longevity, called the bristlecone pine, has some ages claimed to be over 3,000 years. Found growing in areas like northern California and the Rocky Mountains, these trees' ages are debatable, and not the certainties that were once assumed.

Assumption, as ever, is the source of nearly all the difficulties in establishing firm dates for events, even when the items under study seem to function as apparently regularly as trees. We see these natural systems as annual, and tend to regard them as reliable, but the facts would dispute this very human concept. Do they always conform to this neat and tidy yearly layering of one new ring? They do not.

In reality many a cold snap can fool the tree into thinking winter has arrived, and add another layer as the frost kills the outer cells, stopping growth. How would the tree know if this irregular cold snap is winter itself, in one burst of cold days and weeks, or just a wintry snap among colder autumnal? It would not, since it just reacts.

The answer is that it cannot make any distinction, and when it gets colder, it lays down a wintry layer of cells that is the same as if the winter had come only once. Therefore, there can indeed be more rings in one year than the one we assume to have occurred. This means the tree ring dating methods can be unreliable, since the width and number of rings in any tree may be very different. Local variations are therefore infinite, creating ring width variation round each tree group, by area within any forest.

There are other snags to deal with. Some of the dates of trees have been connected to others found at distant sites, called Stepwise Correlations, and this is done by matching the ring thickness sequences in each location. Researchers hope the ring matches are real, and not coincidence, but they can never be totally sure. In this way a long correlation of over 2,000 years may be unjustified. The longer the claimed age, the more the potential for error increases.

Bearing in mind the variation noted above, it is impossible to be certain that similar sequences reflect the identical period of years expected. Another real difficulty also comes in the form of trees that may have been cut far from the site, or brought in from a distant country. This creates a problem for researchers in modern times who find a house or ship's timbers, often many centuries later. It may appear to be one item made from only local wood, and yet may not be from locally sourced wood at all, which is not easy to detect. Sometimes, it has been possible to obtain a match with distant chronologies that might seem to resolve this issue, but one cannot trust the reliability.

Since the population of people on earth fits a short period cycle, it is possible the older dates claimed for various methods, such as tree ring, could be in error.

There are many struggles with the tree ring dating method noted above, so here are a few of them in a list, as a quick look at the complexity involved:

1 there can be different thicknesses, ie gaps between rings, on different sides of the same tree trunk, giving different sequences that may not match
2 even where matches do seem to fit quite closely, it is not certain they are linked as the sequences may suggest, for the above reasons, and others
3 the differences in tree ring widths can vary due to local micro-climate changes that produce odd variations that can also not be matched reliably
4 these variable thicknesses are then translated into a graph of time on one axis vs ring width on the other, in an attempt to relate these squiggles known as 'wiggle-matching', intended to relate one tree to others as a sequence; it cannot be reliable
5 this is partly done by eye, but is not expected to be an 'exact' match, but just a general one of trends, which is also done by computer, with room for errors3

6 computers are programmed to seek matches in *any location* in a long sequence for *any possible chronology overlap*, allowing the possibility of serious error

7 a site sequence may differ from other sites, or may appear to match quite closely, but these international links, the 'stepwise correlations', can be less reliable with greater age

8 there is the problem of differences in working practises and laboratory techniques, since human judgement is part of the process, which cannot be fully standardised

9 the proportions of heartwood to sapwood have to be estimated using 'sapwood allowances' according to distance from the Atlantic (decreasing heading east). This means adding a sapwood 'estimate' and a 'standard deviation' range, which leaves room for compound error over time, with little chance of detection or correction

10 there are changes in annual solar activity, and this produces differences in radiocarbon residual content in the atmosphere, and thus in wood that absorbs it

11 when scientists are 'certain' of a year derived from these methods, it is agreed to be set as a 'control' year, and is used to calibrate other methods, including radiocarbon dating, which is a method prone to error as we can see; this means that each of these methods supports the other, so if either are wrong, or both, the results would be in error

12 some trees may be cut elsewhere, imported to a foreign site, and are thus no longer *in situ*, which changes the site chronology, and may produce unknown errors

13 Bog oaks are trees found in swamps or 'bogs', while others may have been washed out of river gravels and carried downstream, ie not *in situ*; such trees come without stratigraphic and other dating signals to ensure origin

The reason that these measurements are considered true and reliable, to the best of their knowledge, is that they are replicated in various parts of the world. These areas include four zones of Europe, and America, and included German sequences developed in the 1970's by Hollstein and Huber-Giertz, and an Irish sequence.

Some dates appear to be corroborated by chronologies that show a good match in many areas, and these linked samples (chronologies) may stretch back around 1,900 years. A Scottish sequence ran back to 946 AD at that time, the Irish to 1001 AD.

Beyond that sort of age, the use of radiocarbon dating can make the results so suspect that the matches are open to question. This is purely due to the use of radiocarbon as the chosen method of calibration. Why should this method be so unreliable?

Some tests have shown river clams alive today can produce 'age' dates of 2–3,000 years, when they were alive days before the tests were made, as noted.

The reason carbon dating has been so susceptible to failure is due to the ultra high mobility of the radiocarbon content; it can be either leached away by water, or added to by other sources that can contaminate the samples, and ruin any attempt to date them accurately. Carbon dating only works with organic materials that absorb carbon in life, such as plant material or bone. Charcoal forms when wood is burned, and it is famous for absorbing elements contained in water that touches it, which it soaks up like a kind of unique 'chemical cleaning sponge', hence why it is called 'active charcoal' and used to filter and clean the water in fish tanks.

One Oxford dictionary sums up the method of radiocarbon dating as follows: 'It relies on the assumed constancy over time of atmospheric $C14$: $C12$ ratios (now known not to be valid)' *and states that* '...the cosmic-ray bombardment of the outer atmosphere that generates the $C14$ varies'.[85]

This really upsets the apple cart, since the primary assumption no longer holds true, and no-one can estimate with any certainty just how much this variation has been in reality. Enter tree rings again, because the rings of the long-lived bristlecone pine are used to 'confirm' the ages of, you guessed it, the samples tested by carbon dating, which in turn confirms the tree ring dates, and so on. Try as we might, we cannot call this a fair confirmation of a method, being 'circular', like twins confirming their own stories.

The circular thinking in carbon dating calibration is well known

85 Oxford Dictionary of Earth Sciences, 2008, p474; 3rd edition OUP.

to scientists, but because the results fit the expected ages of both so neatly, it is still used and still relied on as a dating method. In reality, dates derived by this method can be in error by thousands of years, or 10,000+ years. With the arrival of the cyclic time model of history, there is a new reason to reassess these techniques since they no longer fit the trend of historical or pre-historical events, which may now be seen as much shorter than we ever thought remotely possible. It is now not only possible, but highly likely that these error factors show we may have made some major mistakes in the dates produced.

Tree rings cannot be confirmed by carbon dates, for the above reasons. It is naturally prone to mobility of carbon from other sources. Rain even reaches bones below ground. In this way charcoal, and any other organic carbon material, can even absorb radioactive carbon from atmospheric atomic weapons tests, which were prevalent in the 1950's to 1970's, before being mainly underground, since the nuclear test ban treaty. Not every nation signed up to that treaty when they were asked, so tests continued.

This carbon absorption effect also affects tree ring samples in some cases, since the radiogenic carbon fallout from those original atmospheric bomb tests, carried out by at least five countries in the world, has a half life of roughly 5730 years. If you thought this was universally agreed as the norm to use everywhere, you would be mistaken. The old standard derived by Libby in the 1950's is still widely used, and rather less at 5568 years.

All this radioactive carbon also enters the carbon cycle in which carbon atoms combine with oxygen in the atmosphere to form CO_2 which we breathe, and which is incorporated in plant matter as plants respire, and in trees too of course.

This variation in testing results can happen simply by adding or taking away some of the radiocarbon content, which can be transported by water particularly, and this would produce ages that are either far too young than is possible, or far too old. The results are therefore not reliable, which affects every branch of archaeology and tree rings.

Such a warning has been made before about radiocarbon dating, and we cover it in more detail later, but it was brought to the world's attention by the well-known director of the Oxford Archaeological Laboratory, Dr Teddy Hall, in his 3rd Nov 1974 article in England's

Sunday Telegraph newspaper, in which he questioned the validity of such dates because of contamination. He was part of the team studying the Turin Shroud at the time, using radiocarbon dating, and when the results gave a date around 1200, it was thought to be too late to be the true original.

Later studies have suggested that the small corner area chosen for analysis, and given to several labs for testing, could itself have been a repair section, which would also give a date which had no bearing on the main areas of the shroud. The debate continues, and is not helped by the fact there are three other versions of cloth claiming to be the real shroud.

This shows how radiocarbon dates can be deeply unreliable. The method has less value as a result, since one cannot tell which dates can be trusted. Science therefore requires we use caution with all of them.

Some tree ring dates even claim to confirm the month of felling, which may be possible in some recent cases. Now we must embark on a wholesale re-evaluation of our dating methods, especially the thinking that underpins these foundations.

The acceptance of long linear time as a possible reason for additional and still more serious error has never been considered at all. It has always been thought that the unchanging passage of time was perhaps the single most solid given underlying any method.

Carbon dating has not always proved valid in comparison tests used to connect it to tree ring dates. In the words of one top expert and author who has devoted his life to tree ring dating, Professor Mike Baillie of Queen's University, Belfast,[86] it is ironic that tree ring chronology was meant to calibrate carbon dating, but has instead showed up radiocarbon's weaknesses and thus inaccuracy.

The trouble is that all these methods are engaged in a mild battle with each other, since they do not agree with or support each other. This book on Flash Time suggests the methods themselves are using incorrect linear assumptions as their foundations, which could invalidate all the principle conclusions at once. Baillie writes of 'soft information', referring to these disparities between different subjects, which illustrates that: '...we know almost nothing about the past...'[87]

---

86 A Slice Through Time, M Baillie, p11; Routledge 1995.
87 Ibid p10

He goes on to mention the Great Cycle of the Maya Calendar that suggested a final phase of the cycle on 23 December 2012, with a start phase of 3114 BC, which means nothing special in tree ring or ice core terms. It is interesting that the Maya noted a 5,100 cycle to explain Time.

Here are a few of the other problems associated with tree ring dating, and its connection to both ice core and volcanic eruption dates, which created results that do not fit the preconceptions of nice, regular years of tree growth that were once believed probable. It is interesting that words like 'belief' should even come into the realm of science, but they do, because we have to believe something to make any kind of hypothesis. As Baillie writes, the fallibility of carbon dates led to variations in dates that '...were inevitable when the principal dating tool was radiocarbon.'[88]

All this becomes quite tricky when estimates have to be made, meaning a direct annual age calculation has ceased to be possible, and some error has to be accepted. In shorter term dating by this method, there have been some triumphs, such as the dating of wood from a historic cargo vessel known as the Skuldelev Ship, and some wood picture frames which have helped resolve dating issues for the rare old master paintings they contained.

A great success too was the dating of 17th century oaks used in building, or the lack of them actually, during the Irish political unrest of the 1641 Rebellion, and the war for succession fought between James II and William III which produced the 1688 Revolution.[89] This study showed felling dates that stopped from 1631 to 1655, and between 1675 to 1690, which is interesting.

There can be snags with trying to link much older events with tree rings, via ice layers. Three such examples are seen in ice core dating suggested by the glaciologists who drilled the Greenland Ice core Project, or GRIP for short. Three higher acid signals in the ice, almost certainly caused by 2000 year old volcanic ash, have been given dates of 49, 1646 and 2050 BC, and another at 1390 BC in an earlier core (Dye 3), related by some to the huge Santorini (or Thera) explosion.

88 Ibid p13
89 Ibid p122.

The first three do appear to coincide fairly closely with three bris-tlecone frost events, but not exactly. As discussed, the reliability of ice layers for dating is seriously upset by many concerns, even for short range dates.

The Santorini eruptive explosion is said to have created high acid levels in ice layers for five years, and yet another ice layer acid peak said to date to 1595–1599 BC is only 30% of the 1390 BC level, or so it is claimed. The debate continues as to when this eruption actually took place, with some saying 1520–1650 BC.

Within 200 years or so, it could have been in that era, with some doubt existing due to several arguments put forward by different groups of experts. Each group claims priority for their work over the other results, so tree ring and ice core and volcano groups do not agree.

This is why there remains intense disagreement between experts on every conceivable aspect of this large event, including which volcano produced the acid detected, and thus where it was located, how much sulphur was produced by it, the frequency of eruptions, the dates of the acid layers in the ice cores. It is also possible that several huge vol-canoes were active at the same time, with different sulphur emissions, which would confuse results.

In some estimates it was 27–30 cubic kms for Santorini, in another it was 42 cubic kms, while a third made it 39; a huge difference. It seems it was far bigger than the 1883 eruption of Krakatoa in distant Indonesia, but the other details are in almost total disagreement.

These results are interesting in showing that dating and materials measurement are not exact sciences. Yet radiocarbon dating still has obstacles.[90]

This is significant, since if a sample has been miscorrelated or con-taminated in some way, it will not become 'right' with more tests of the same material. What researchers may have been trying to obtain was a better range of results to support their theory, which is common practise.

As Baillie points out, this may be a useless effort. Much was recently made of a new computer method of redefining several peaks showing a range of dates at one site, so that it showed one main peak, implying

90 Ibid p111

greater accuracy. This is no better than averaging out the information received, which may be imprecise at best. Using computers to make it 'look' better is just misleading, because it infers the new peak is real, when it is not at all...it has been manipulated to look that way. We should not be fooled by that.

As Baillie says, we need to know the source of the timbers.[91]

This factor is spot on, since it changes eastwards from the Atlantic, in Europe at least, in a line extending east from Ireland to Germany. Tree rings are complex.

Baillie adds that workers often have to try and 'rescue' the accuracy of dates, meaning the results were not as expected, and need 'helping' or adjusting.

'Rescuing date accuracy' is an odd idea, but he adds an honest warning that even these 'allowances' are not always reliable statistics to trust, not least because they are subjectively determined, *and averaged.* [92]

Can there really be estimates that are 'skewed' or distorted in some way? These are estimates, not direct facts, and are used to average out errors that creep into statistics. Estimates are not the same as trusted precision.

The biggest problem with tree ring dates is when they are claimed to extend beyond about 1200 years, longer than any oak used actually lived. It involves deciding which tree ring sequences overlap with earlier and later data sets, and this leaves room for major errors, as the experts admit. Sequences do not often match exactly, which is very risky, since there may then be no correct match at all. Long correlations are very vulnerable to such averaging and subjective judgement; a weakness of the method itself, and the rings.

So how is a species, such as oak, chosen for these statistical analyses? They have to be long-lived to have any chance of overlaps with other areas, and have to be a hardwood, ideally, to be able to survive centuries in rivers or swamps without deterioration.

In Ireland, one oak used only dated back to 1649, but that was before the bog oaks were found, which provided a new source of wood to test. In Scotland some trees were found to date to around 1444,

91 Ibid p25
92 Ibid p25

while in England, some dated to 1425. This was all very well, but the great aim was to go back much further, and it became a real quandary to find trees from the tenth century, and remained so in Ireland for many years.

It was also a problem to bridge the 14th century, due to the Plague problem mentioned above. Another gap in the archaeology in Ireland occurs around 648 AD and lasts for around 70 years, but no-one knows why, or if it is a real occurrence or an apparent one. The trees grew normally in this period, so the usual suspect of a volcanic eruption would seem unlikely, and perhaps another plague period may have ensued. Some historical records do say that plague did reach Ireland in the year 664 AD, so these two periods of change may indeed be related, and closer than the apparent 16 year gap might infer.

Other anomalies remain largely unexplained, such as the 1331 AD frost ring detected in numerous foxtail pines found in America's Sierra Nevada Mountains. It is often suggested that volcanoes are the usual suspects for such effects. A large volcano may be global in reach, if it has the backing of huge sub-crustal magma chambers. The climate change caused by volcanoes is due to the cubic miles of dust and gas ejected into the atmosphere, blocking the sun's rays…a mini winter in effect, or a major one perhaps.

Some large volcanoes, such as Yellowstone in America and Laki in Iceland, and so many others, have giant magma chambers hidden beneath their flanks. In seconds, or hours, these giant chambers with cubic kilometres of fluid rock, can empty their contents into the atmosphere. We should all be prepared for disasters with fresh water supplies.

A small version of this happened early in the spring of 2010 when a volcano in Iceland spread ash all over Europe and beyond, grounding all aircraft in the airspace covering Europe and Scandinavia, and spreading a thin layer of the ash over everything.

Nearby lies Laki, a volcano that erupted on a much larger scale in 1783, creating a major famine in all Europe via yellow smog cloud of gas and ash that caused the crisis, and was blamed for the French Revolution six years later in 1789.

Professor Baillie has some wry observations about the methods of dating volcanoes, which have not impressed him as very reliable. He points out that it can be difficult, and sometimes impossible, for vulcanologists to be sure if one eruption, or many of them, have happened at the same time.

Given the strongly rotational patterns of the world wind system in both hemispheres, and the west to east pattern of the northern hemisphere's jet stream, it can be a tough task indeed to pin down the source of even one large volcano, let alone lots of them.

The result can be a nightmare for the dating methods' aim of sorting all this out and ascribing ages to layers of ash deposited in largely random spots around the world. Some claim they can now identify specific eruptions, such as the huge Toba volcano of Sumatra claimed to be 74,000 years old. As we will see later, it is possible this eruption was very much more recent than this, at 5% of that age. No firm proof counters this claim.

How does this relate to tree ring dating? Volcanoes do not just throw out ash. They also produce vast quantities of gas, and steam if water is present. In short, volcanoes upset the atmosphere in a titanic way that makes even hurricanes look like nothing.

As the pressure is released within the fluid rock, which happens when it emerges from its natural gas canister under the earth's crust, via the volcanic vent, these vast quantities of gas expand rapidly to occupy cubic miles of space. This is often SO_2 and with some CO_2 as well, and these can combine with water to produce acids, which upsets tree growth, and anyone planning to build an extension that day. The result is a signal in tree rings in various parts of the world, but again it varies vastly.

A problem can arise when carbon dating is used to set dates for such events. As Baillie points out, dates suggested can be impossible to pin down, and so can appear spread over centuries.[93] He added another interesting observation of the Santorini eruption, that major volcanoes might tend to occur in groups within one era.[94]

This may signify a link to cyclic time, since an axial tilt would create a global unzipping of continental plate margins. There are also links to ancient historical records of this period. The Egyptian dynastic records are a case in point, with dates failing to match the theories.[95] He adds

93 Ibid p115
94 Ibid
95 Ibid p116

that there was a large storm recorded in the reign of Ahmose, but that would cast doubt on the dating of that reign in Egyptology.

Baillie also points out the precision difficulties of carbon dating, since the results don't point to one date particularly.[96] He is also rightly concerned about the dating of the earlier Greenland ice cores, some of which were later degraded after recovery, and there were reports of 'bad core quality'. It is worth noting that cores can degrade for various reasons.

Tree rings sometimes show very thinly, which prompts workers on these problems to postulate reasons for their occurrence. Two key events where this does happen are in AD 540 and 1159 BC. Both the usual suspect and most obvious candidate is a volcanic eruption, but while it could also be a plague event, that would be expected to match a building hiatus, when no-one was well enough, or alive enough, to think of erecting wooden houses. The AD 540 line does appear to be linked to famines and plague, while the 1159 BC date caused such concern that in 1991 and earlier, some writers even sought to 'remove' the linked 'dark age' entirely by altering the global time sequence itself, to make everything fit more neatly.

This is not a thing most of us could, or even would think of doing, to adjust history. As Baillie also noted, some dates just do not fit our usual view of history, and some suggested shortening our standard view of that history by several centuries to 'get rid of the problem' (James *et al.* 1987; James 1991).[97] Now that is an extreme action.

A *dark age* chiefly means there were fewer records made at the time that could cast light on what was happening in history. So to eliminate it by shortening world history would take away a large chunk of historical events, and for it to be a dark age, so called, the events must have been extreme socio-political changes, such as wars or either subtler, or more serious threats of some kind. History is one of our greatest sources of learning, whatever it contained. By understanding it better, we can try to avoid making the same mistakes as others have done before.

This is why there is considerable doubt and uncertainty about the actual truth of 'stepwise correlations' in connecting different wood

96 Ibid p109
97 Ibid p129

samples in different countries, at least beyond the tenth century AD in Europe. With great respect to the experts in the field who have worked so hard on doing this, even they admit there is uncertainty in performing this task, and indeed say as much. This, most importantly as we shall see, is exactly why an 'error factor' is assumed to be present.

We have seen how those very systems of dating are also subject to extreme inaccuracy running into many orders of magnitude [1 order= x10], so agreement with those methods may explain why errors occur in all of the methods at once, rather than just one.

Statistics may look impressive to someone who has never studied how they are derived from the figures used to create them. If those figures fed into the machine of the mind are wrong, then no amount of adjustment will ever make them right.

As author Aldous Huxley said in 1927: *'Science has 'explained' nothing: the more we know the more fantastic the world becomes and the profounder the surrounding darkness'*, and very candidly that *'most human beings have an infinite capacity for taking things for granted'*, which is perhaps the supreme pitfall in any quest for reality.

This is the very problem at the heart of all our failures to see the essence of a matter, as we recall evolutionist T. H. Huxley's famous quotes:

'The great tragedy of Science – the slaying of a beautiful hypothesis by an ugly fact' and that: 'Irrationally held truths may be more harmful than reasoned errors', since the truth is often not discovered until decades of progress were lost using it.

The timeline suggested by tree rings is useful, but clearly complicated to analyse beyond 1200 years or so, as many have pointed out.

CHAPTER 10

Carbon Dating in Error:
How major errors have arisen

Science is the knowledge of consequences and the dependence of one fact upon another.
T. HOBBES, 1651

If an elderly but distinguished scientist says that something is possible, he is almost certainly right, but if he says it is impossible, he is very probably wrong.
ARTHUR.C.CLARKE, 1969

These are the days when men...seek the comfortable and the accepted, when the man of controversy is seen as a disturbing influence.
J.K.GALBRAITH, 1958

Essence

Carbon dating has become trusted far beyond its actual capacity. Here are reasons to support this claim, and why we should treat it cautiously. Far from being a source of firm dates, it has provided dates of great inaccuracy that should be revised. The key reason is that the radioactive carbon 'C^{14} atoms' measured are also present in the air and in mobile groundwater. Since the atomic bomb tests of 1945–93, and there were 2,483 of them, the air also contains an artificial amount of these same C^{14} atoms, which can and do ruin many results. These were conducted by America in places like Kwajalein, Eniwetok islands and Bikini atoll in the Pacific, and the Nevada desert, by Britain in Australia, and by Russia in Semipalatinsk and near Novaya Zemlya (ref: SIPRI, *Stockholm International Peace Research Institute*); China and others also carried out tests. Living creatures absorb these atoms in life, but not after they die.

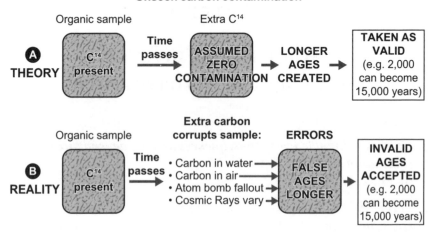

FIGURE 20 *Errors Paths in Carbon Dating method: diagram shows active carbon contamination pathways via air and water, making nearly all dates uncertain and many invalid.*

knowing the rate of decay, rather like the degree of rust on iron tells us it is old. The method relies on the constancy of the $C14:C12$ ratio of carbon atoms created in the atmosphere by cosmic rays from space, but this ratio idea is now 'known to be invalid'.[98] The sums are then matched against old tree rings, such as in bristlecone pines (*Pinus longaeva*), found in America's Rocky Mountains. As we will see, no parts of these tests are 100% reliable.

Many such age tests have been useless, but very misleading, because scientists cannot tell which are correct, and which have been contaminated. Having been used to fix or 'calibrate' other methods, often wrongly, the result is chaos. This can be said with confidence because of some amazing test results: *living shellfish* 'ages' of 3–4000 years old were achieved using this method, yet must be false, since the animal was alive just days before, as noted.

Carbon dating as an age determination method began in 1946–49 with W.Libby, who also worked on the atom bomb in America.

98   Oxford Dictionary of Earth Sciences, 3rd Ed. p474

The question of how to set dates for items is very significant, because it has been used to fix the recent timescale of earth's history of life. Once claimed to function to 30–70,000 years by some, this has not proved right, since it has produced some extraordinary errors. Now it has been reined in to some extent, but even dates of 2–3000 years can be very mistaken. Yet the temptation to test wood, shell, teeth or bones mainly, and receive a range of possible dates, has enchanted scientists since Libby received a Nobel Prize for his work in 1960. It seemed to change dates in archaeology from 'maybes' into firm dates. The excitement knew no bounds, but that apparent certainty was not always factual. Many dates could have been in error.

It is far from the cut and dried matter we presume it must be. The reality is that methods like carbon dating also rely on other assumptions hidden in the background, and they can best be described as 'variables'. The way it works is meant to be simple enough, but several of these factors are so intensely variable that they can invalidate the whole method in some cases, and results can be 'out' by literally *tens of thousands* of years.

Carbon atoms are highly mobile, and so the atoms easily attach themselves to ancient clusters *via any source of water or air*. This is why age results nearly always spread across a graph like trees in a wood, not in one spike. The result can be a string of worthless dates, and it is certain this has happened countless times. English Heritage in England then used an averaging method to 'make' one spike out of the many results, but that doesn't mean this method picked the right peak, which could have been any peak, or none of them more likely; it just looked better. An average is not a sharper result.

As noted, Dr Taylor of the famous radiocarbon laboratory run by Oxford University, raised the alarm about such serious errors 40 years ago in an article, but few paid any attention. The bigger the claimed age number, the more likely it is to be wrong, because of the tiny amounts of carbon being measured…just a few atoms. A wild figure of 35,000 years could in fact be only 3,000 years old, or even half that.

Yet scientists love an excitingly old date for an otherwise dull object.

This high potential error margin ruins the point of the method, if it is ever discovered, so it is worth looking into why carbon dating is far from the reliable method claimed. Some say it never was, and cases like

the Turin shroud have created sensational headlines and deep controversy, so why all the fuss about a few carbon atoms here or there?

The answer lies in the use made of these results, as well as the error.

Some dates might be precise, but it is impossible to tell which ones,
when they may be hidden amongst others that can be incorrect. We
will examine how this comes to be so. Many care little for precision,
while the dates are making their work seem more important. Why let
truth get in the way of a good story?

Oddly enough, human thinking plays a huge part in this and any
other methods used to date materials. Indeed this is the key factor: how
we think time has passed by, and what assumptions we make to base
the method on; if those conditions have always prevailed in the upper
atmosphere, and whether or not those underlying ideas have still held
true since 1957, when Libby set out his baseline, and pioneered this
once exciting technique. 'Once exciting', until the huge errors were
better seen.

The answer, admittedly with the benefit of fifty years further experience, is that we cannot rely on the one vital assumption on which the
method is founded: that the past has always stayed the same in terms of
carbon amounts and capture channels as living cells absorb the atoms
during their life.

As we will see, some huge errors create vastly older dates than are
possible, which shows problems can arise very subtly.

The basic error, usually present in all 20th century dating techniques
of various materials, is this: they start with an incorrect presumption of
constancy in conditions. This mind-set holds that the past has 'always'
been the same as the present, slowly gaining age but always the same
values holding firm each day.

The claim is these carbon atoms are present at the same level every
year. Go back in time as far as you like, so the thinking claims, and
this radiocarbon level was always the same as now. This may actually not be correct, and the errors in dating methods suggest there are
indeed giant mistakes in this deeper level of 'presumptive' thinking.
Conditions can in fact change dramatically, and these are played down
as minor, when in fact they can be so significant that they destroy the
validity of the entire method in some instances.

While we cannot know which ones, there are occasionally other clues that hint at errors so huge we are forced to reassess the whole reliability issue itself. This is not welcomed by many in the world of archaeology, because they are busy with using the data to support a large edifice of timelines, of which this is a key support.

Our view of time is a vital factor, so if that is wrong, the results would be meaningless. The key one is that the level of C^{14} produced by the action of cosmic rays must be constant. Alas there are colossal events like gamma ray bursts (GRB's), coronal mass ejections (CME's) and solar flares that are each able to put so much energy into our upper atmosphere that this delicate balance is totally disrupted, thus creating false readings for scientists centuries later.

Tree rings are often used to check carbon dates, and vice versa. Errors do arise.

Two examples are events that have been found in both Japanese cedar trees by Miyake in 2013, and in oaks in Germany by Ilya Usoskin. This wide location span of odd results of a spike or peak in carbon values points to a source in space, not on earth, and was found in two extreme events in AD 775 and AD 992, noted as greater than the 1859 Carrington Event, which was such an intense solar storm that it caused telegraphy offices to catch fire, or the 1989 event that blacked out light and power in the Quebec area of Canada (New Scientist 10.8.13 pp46–49).

These are serious problems because they remove the underlying foundation that the 'past has been the same' going back in time, and show it clearly has not been the same at all. As we can see, there are also marked differences in values and peaks found in samples taken from different sides of the same tree, let alone in different parts of the same valley, or between other countries. This would upset any correlation attempts, as would the emphasis we place on trusting these methods.

We then find that these errors can account for the very serious mistake of overestimating the amount of time passed.

More serious still, the scientists also use other assumptions in unrelated fields of science to 'date-relate' all the dates their tests produce. This is meant to cross-reference data to get a better result, but it would also perpetuate any mistakes present. This is what appears to have happened.

For example if incorrect carbon dates might be wrongly used to calibrate the tree ring data used, then all the links made to that use of Carbon-14 [C^{14}] ages as a fixed dateline, would of course be wrong too. This can happen very easily, since values of test results are plotted on a graph. Some may be higher and some lower than expected, and so a line is drawn through the middle of these scattered dots to show a trend.

Imagine a white target with pellets all over it, rather like a shotgun fired from 40 yards, with dots all over the place. In science, results can vary a great deal due to all the factors we are about to explore, and so it is impossible to tell which one may be totally accurate, and which are entirely misleading. In a blizzard of dots, it can be either difficult or impossible to know where to draw a line to show a trend that may, or may not exist. Other problems are far more serious, with higher levels of Carbon-14 that completely wreck the results entirely, making them worthless.

Often this trend matches what researchers are looking for, the idea appears to have been proved, and everyone is happy. Again, we are bound to note that scientists have to use their own judgement to decide what is 'likely', and this can vary dramatically from what actually happened. It is an estimate, and if the presumed passage of time has not occurred as it was 'meant to have done', then such an estimate can be out by 300, 500 or even 1000%, or much more.

This can also happen when points on a graph are drawn with a curve at the peak or trough point, rather than a spiky arrangement of straight lines. This creates waves that can look easier to interpret. It also depends on how many tests are made, which are costly to carry out, so often there are fewer than is ideal.

If we then see a few of these points on a graph, we see a visual form of all the test results forming such curves and peaks, we can then try to match those waves of results, known as 'wiggles', to other results from totally separate methods. If they find a match to these peaks, which can also happen by chance, they call this 'wiggle-matching', believe it or not.

The major errors of long age are due to this: wrongly connected dates of widely distributed sites that do not appear to be linked at all. Since no-one had any reason to doubt these methods until now, they exist in all modern reference and textbooks to this day.

This is how such vast errors of 4000% and more have affected carbon dating...

1 Cosmic rays travel through space all the time, and when they come near earth, the magnetic field that travels between our poles forms those curved lines you may have seen at school when you put a magnet under a card with iron filings on top of it, with all those concentric rings.

2 In fact those field lines extend right out into space, so the solar 'wind' of charged 'ions', and cosmic rays, are funnelled along these lines and down into the polar areas, rather than into the equatorial regions. This is why the aurorae/northern lights are seen at Earth's poles, and even on Saturn.

3 These rays are actually particles of high energy, so when they hit nitrogen, oxygen or rare gases in our upper atmosphere, they strike and thus 'knock out' sections of these molecules. The result is that they then instantly become different elements, and this forms radioactive (unstable) materials, or isotopes as they are known, such as Carbon-14 [C14], Beryllium-10, Chlorine-36, Iodine-129 etc. Simply put, if you alter the atomic number of an element by bashing it with another particle, then *it becomes another element* with a smaller atomic number, even when this happens by force of a collision, as in this case. [Atomic number= the number of protons orbiting the nucleus].

4 So we can see this process like this: Cosmic rays N^{14} > C^{14} > CO^2 etc [> = *becomes or turns into*]. So the action of cosmic rays forms the nitrogen (N) and C^{14}

5 Those carbon atoms are readily attached to oxygen, so they rapidly become 'oxidised' as they do this, and are then converted into CO^2, which mixes into the carbon cycle as it is attached to rain falling through it, and then plants absorb it etc.

6 This CO^2 then contains this radioactive carbon, now existing in its newly radioactive state as C^{14}. As animals or plants transpire, this material is absorbed in their tissue, either in bone cells, or in the cellulose of wood.

7 It is then assumed that when the animal or plant dies, this process stops, and that the system is then closed, so that no more C^{14}

should enter those cells. Alas, it is not so. There are actually other ways for C^{14} to enter the system and build up in cells by 'false' means of contamination, which would create a totally false 'age' for that material. [Libby's baseline half-life was ±5730 years, for sample to decay by half.]

This is where the problems with this dating method begin. It is actually not true that no more carbon can 'interfere' with the purity of this 'original sample', as the dead wood or bone, can be called. When scientists try to *'wiggle-match'* their results with tree rings, coral etc, *based on what they 'assume' the age should be*, this can involve using a degree of guesswork. These results can be way out, as we have seen. Alder trees are well known to be capable of having 45% fewer rings than they 'should' have, and in *bristlecone* pines, the amounts of test material are so small, there is also room for sizeable errors.

There is another sequence in Japan of 29,100 strata layers in a lake bed, alternately dark and light, derived from seasonal ice melting, called *varves*. These are assumed to be winter and summer layers, so they count each section as one year. The problem is that you can very easily get several tens of layers in one year, due to ice forming and melting, and since even a high wind for a day or two can cause extra layers to be laid down.

Is there another way for hundreds of layers to be laid down in one year? Yes, there is, and one rarely considered, if ever. Axial oscillations of earth's axis in past events could also do this, and it is still moving now. Evidence shows the axis has altered in the past, altering the day length of our planet, and setting up such wobbles in the axial angle, and the locations of the magnetic poles over the centuries.

The key is this: there is not only one way for these layers to form, but other explanations too, which show they can be much younger. It is reasonable to assume the layers are merely seasonal, but changes in local conditions of rain, snow, temperature, wind and other climatic factors such as these can also create the layering. Add rapid axial tilt changes to these variables, and this would upset the whole method of 'aging' arithmetic.

When we also remember that this particular Japanese set of varves, believed to be perfectly accurate in one pair of layers per year, has been used to calibrate many other systems, we have a problem. It means that if these layers are incorrectly dated, then so are all the others methods that rely on the age decided for them. Actually all the systems of dating materials or layers are interlinked in this way, so if one or two are wrong, they are all wrong. This is the difficulty now faced.

The atomic bomb tests created clouds of atmospheric contamination of radioactive Carbon-14, which floated in everywhere, so that even the flow of humble groundwater has been contaminating samples of charcoal.

These atom bomb tests around the world, 8 in water, and many in the air, ruined the test conditions requiring constant natural C^{14} levels, so scientists keep having to create 'corrections' in the figures to reduce the errors, never knowing if the changes were better. Since they could not 'know' what the answers should be, they were often wrong by a massive margin.

We can tell this is so, when we see some results are obviously incorrect. That is quite a bombshell in dating, but largely ignored to this day.

The Turin shroud, thought to be Christ's burial clothing, is one famous example noted. Their carbon tests were very 'scattered', meaning not coherent, and it was thought to be caused by contamination. The date they got was still AD 1290, so it was likely to be not genuine, but a medieval fake, since it was only seen and 'shown' around 1350 AD. Some said the tests were of a corner only, which may have been a section repaired later, so no one could be sure if the tests were even valid.

These errors also explain why major dating faults have appeared in other actual sample dating cases. Two are often quoted to show how these effects become multiplied by contamination.

One is of the sample of live clams, as noted above, taken from the Murray River in Australia. They were processed and tested for C^{14} and found to be over 4000 years old according to the tests carried out, when they were of course living in the river only a period of weeks before, proving that the samples had collected contaminated material, most likely during their lives in the river itself, being filter feeders in the mud.

A more recent UK case (2008) was of the Jersey care home in which remains of 5 people were found buried in the earth below floor level.

It was vital to determine whether or not these burial finds were of modern, recently living people, whose lives may have ended prematurely, or of much more ancient remains. Carbon dating was used to try and make this determination, but the results were too wide to help. Tests were carried out on several teeth found, but could not pin down a more precise date than between '1660 and 1960', which made a court case impossible.

Why so varied? Contamination must be the answer, by rogue C^{14} atoms.

Sometimes our faith in science is stronger than it should be. Very often we have to be prepared to revise our confidence in a favourite method's reliability.

There remains a mass of reasons why tree rings and carbon dating do not agree with each other. It has always been everyone's wish that these two dating methods, on which so much archaeology relies, could form one trusted body of evidence that assigned dates with assurance. Sadly the error factors have prevented that being so.

Once scientists felt fairly sure that the general chronology they learned at university was the right one, but new information changes that account.

CHAPTER II

Ice Core Dating: is it accurate?

*Superstition sets the whole world in flames; philosophy
quenches them.*
Voltaire, 1764

What a man would like to be true he more readily believes.
Francis Bacon, 1620

Essence

Ice cores come from drill holes bored into polar ice fields, such as in
Greenland, near the North Pole which has no land, and Antarctica. It
has been assumed that the different 'line' created by the tougher hoar
frost of winter is an annual fact. As we will see, this is often not so.
Other factors can also create many more apparent 'years' in this ice
record, that suggest the same axial tilt effects can make the cores seem
very much older. This effect could make a month look like 500 years
or much more.

Over 300 lakes have been found beneath the Antarctic polar ice,
one huge lake being Lake Vostok in the Russian sector. It seems there
were once forests on that vast landmass of 5.4 million square miles,
with coal to prove it. One day it began to snow there, the ice formed on
the lakes, and never stopped, until it reached today's depth of around
12,000 feet. Antarctica is huge, at 1.8 times Australia, with 90% of
earth's ice.

Another strange thing was found in the fascinating snow-free Dry
Valleys near the South Pole...some moss. It was of course dried out
when found, and beside some volcanic ash. When scientists dated the
ash to '10 million years old', it created a problem. That date was impossible, because no moss could lie in the sun for that long. Somehow, the
date calculated must be wrong, and the answer lies in the thinking of

time as a line, and the errors seen in radiogenic dating. The moss would do well to last for 1,000 years.

Ice and snow cover a tenth of the earth's land surface, so it is a big factor in life on earth. It cools the air flowing over it, and even its whiteness is a big deal known as the 'Albedo Effect' which reflects back much of the sun's energy.

Why should this matter? This is a large factor in how warm the earth gets, and how warm it has been historically in the past, depending on how much of the sunlight striking the earth is reflected back into space before it gets a chance to warm the surface. Each material surface on planet earth has a reflection value. The average for cities and rock is about 15% that is reflected, for sand it is about 40%. The angle of incidence makes a big difference too, with calm water receiving solar radiation only reflecting 2%, while 78% of low angle light barely strikes the surface before bouncing out into space. Clouds vary with density, but average around 55%, while flat snow sends back 90%.

Dating the ice is not simple or easy, yet such dates are claimed to be realistic. Some would disagree, because no one has ever factored in the orbital motion of time.

These effects of reflection versus absorption are considerable. If we measure this over the whole earth as 'one huge chunk' hurtling through space, this Albedo Effect is big enough to alter our climate. It is all the more striking to us when we consider only half the earth is facing the sun's powerful rays at any time, so the high reflection values of ice and snow become quite a factor.

Naturally enough, as the season's change when the earth's axis is tilted towards or away from the sun, the amount of snowfall also changes. It is assumed that this process of freeze–melt–freeze has always been constant. One key concern is that repeated layers of snow build up intense pressure on the layers below, slowly turning aerated snow into ice, and these layers have been used as a method for dating the age of the layers. There is a problem, or several in fact. This method has to make a range of presumptions which 'guarantee' that the past has always been the same. If it cannot do this, or have real trust in the past acting uniformly over all of time, the method would fail.

The evidence shows that *time has not been uniform at all*, and

the many examples listed here demonstrate several major irregularities have upset the past centuries to such an extreme degree that all
methods using such past presumptions of order have failed. Top of
this list of oddities is the axial shift of earth's angle towards the sun.
Coral shows the days have not always been 24 hours long as they are
now, and the glacial deposits known as varves have in some places
(e.g. Japan) given dates of '50,000 years' when the real cause could
have been rapid precession as the axis oscillates this number of times
within a few decades. No one can prove it did not happen this way, so
it could have.

The essence of the idea of using ice to assign dates for 'time' is that
the strong sunshine is in the summer, whereas winter allows intense
hoar frosts to form a different type of snow layering to be counted later.
This is fair enough for shorter lengths of time like 100–2000 years, but
several factors come into play after that, such as ice compression and
side slumping of deeper layers: they just won't stay flat as they should
do. This is called visible stratigraphy, where the ice cores are literally
counted by eye, and is used for hundreds of feet of ice cores based on
the same key assumption: that side slumping is *hopefully not a big
issue*, and that such layers are not forming every time the sun shines
in between snow falls with rapid axial wobbles, as in precession for
example. Yet it is possible they may have slumped, and the axis did
oscillate in this way, creating these odd results. It is still moving to this
day, pointing to such events being recent.

Has ice always appeared in such regular hoar frost forming quantities? One may well think so, from the permanent way it looks, but
the truth, as usual, is different. The actual age of ice layers has been
the subject of much speculation over the years, and several expeditions have measured ice cores to try and settle the matter. The idea of
measuring stratified ice layers sounds very simple, with one per year
as assumed, so surely we can just count down the layers in the core
samples, and add them all up. At least you would think so...

Alas it is not as easy or predictable as this, and all this is not quite
as obvious as this ideal picture may seem, so researchers turned to
special types of dust found in some layers of the ice cores collected by
different expeditions. Even the presence of volcanic dust in the layers
was not easily identified as to source country or even area. Many types

of volcano produce dust that comes from similar explosive eruptions, and it often proved impossible to define either the location or the date of eruptions purely from traces of dust caught in the ice.

This is not entirely surprising, since many known eruptive volcanoes over history are to the east and south of the Greenland ice cap. With the prevailing world wind system flowing primarily west to east at that latitude, then all the European, Javanese and other highly active volcano areas of the world would not be expected to deposit dust in Greenland, unless it was fine enough and high enough to be transported right round the world first. This would result in very fine and tiny traces of airborne dust being found, if any dust at all. As markers, such dust layers are often too similar to be reliable.

The largest known volcanic eruption in history is often thought by volcanologists to be the one located in present day Lake Toba, in Sumatra, which is a beautiful and much visited place in Indonesia. Some experts in this field have written that no certain trace of this vast event have been found in the ice layers of Greenland (see below), and thus casting doubt on the dating methods claimed for ice cores using this eruption as a 'known' datum point.

Even using mineral and radioisotope tests, it was still difficult or impossible to define sources with certainty. In such cases, absolute certainty is beyond the scope of the tests, and statistics are used to offer what may be 'probable'.

There were other factors that suggest even the day lengths and seasonal periods did not repeat in nice, neat cycles year on year. Ancient coral beds in the Bahamas for example, have shown 410 layers of growth in a year, it is claimed, and not the 365 expected, as it 'should' if each day did create one layer. As noted, with some ancient corals showing 20 hour days, abnormal axial swings appear to be a fact of past eras within the last 3,200 years, which would change everything. Dates were not changed.

Methane-sulfonate has also been used as a tracer in ice cores, in the hope of suggesting a possible timeline link to algal growth in the ocean, said to be its source, and this within specific layers of ice. Computer models were then invented to generate further statistics of which bumper years of algal growth could be correlated with this chemical, if present in certain ice cores. To achieve this ambitious feat requires knowing the air-snow transfer rate and mechanism of the chemical, which again requires some assumptions, rather than feeding only actual facts into the computer model; not really a certainty.

Results are obtained, of course, but they are only probabilities, and cannot be regarded as solid, undisputed reality. This situation is true of large amounts of data collection in the modern age, now that computers can be asked to work out climatic conditions in the far past, and even the very far past, with claims of hundreds of millions of years being made.

Ancient climates can be deduced by various means, but problems arise when those ages rely on linear time being regular...forever. This branch of science is called paleoclimatology, and while it involves more than informed estimates, the data can be interpreted in several very different ways by using statistical analysis. This leaves large gaps between theory and fact, so while the results may look impressive, they may be totally contradictory, and even clearly incorrect when attempts are made to match them to other detailed research. Certain parts of this science can be very helpful, such as charting past oxygen levels and plant distribution, but ages are a different matter entirely. Attention needs to be drawn to the all-important larger picture, so as to make more sense of all these contradictions, which is the aim: to combine fresh and well-proven evidence and produce an up-to-date chronology. The view of time as 'reliable' ruins this idea, so a secure timeline has not been possible to create. All these methods rely on the classic worldview of Linear Time, so we have to question all these old ages.

The Greenland ice cap is a huge place, but most of us may think the ice just sits there, frozen and still, especially over such a larger area. Even local slumping aside, this is not correct at all. The pull of gravity downwards also has the effect of pushing the ice layers outwards, to the west and east mainly, since the shape of the ice cap is longer (in a north-south line) than it is narrow. Roughly 1600 by 800 miles, and two miles deep at the centre, this lateral pressure is what feeds the glaciers we see flowing into the valleys and 'calving' into icebergs.

This lateral flowing of the ice layers appears to have created so much disruption to the ice layers that the stratigraphy may be a real jumble below the surface. Some layers are so difficult to detect at all, that laser reflection and a host of other attempted methods have been created to try and count them. Since the ice cores show this compression that blurs the layers into solid ice, the number of layers beyond 2,000 or so cannot be relied on to define the annual layering of snow that turned to ice.

The classic linear method ignores such suggestions, so researchers were never looking for such anomalies, yet still found some; although every glaciologist is aware of these problems. It is possible that these older layers are the result of anomalous flow of ice deep below the surface, and also the result of actual rapid climate change in ancient layers that caused unexpected melt episodes...as in the axial shift effects noted above.

However unlikely some researchers may feel this interpretation of the glaciology may seem to be, no-one can rule it out. Other checks that have been made to support the traditional claim that the top 110,000 years of layered of ice cores have remained undisturbed are all based on long linear time. No-one was looking for the axial swing anomalies predicted by this cyclic time model, and so it is hard to see how researchers could have found inconsistencies they were not looking for.

One of the methods used to support the classic view of long linear time in laying down layers of snow that turn to ice, is Carbon-14. We have looked into the errors of this method, and the ice flow and differential cosmic ray rates could equally invalidate this technique as a means of assigning dates to ice cores. This applies equally to tree rings, bones, charcoal and other uses of carbon dating.

These frozen areas may have also been subjected to temperature inversions, which is where conditions in the atmosphere reverse the usual situation of cold air at higher levels. In such cases, cold air is trapped below warm air flowing above the surface layer of air, and the predictable conditions expected become anything but predictable.

Once again we have grounds to doubt the validity of the statistics created by the computer models. Scientists use various 'likely' scenarios to build a picture of past climate, snowfall rates, melt periods etcetera, and though these fit the expected theory used, they may still not be accurate. Even the impurity loadings in the ice and the different snow accumulation rates can cause thin melt layers that can demand more speculative interpretations, when they can be found at all; such factors can alter the resulting statistics, through no fault of the workers in such difficult conditions. [99]

There have been rapid, *almost instant changes* in the ancient climate, even over the ice cap itself and large areas of surrounding land and ocean, that have been compared to the speed of pressing a button, rather as daily weather patterns change in minutes only on a larger scale. Cyclic time predicts this 'flash time' kind of effect because any swing in the earth's axis would be expected to produce oscillation. The result would be exactly the kind of 'over-fast deposition' that we do see.

As Professor Alley wrote in his key book about the Greenland ice core projects:

'Sometimes the climate jumped back and forth a few times...almost as if the person flipping the switch were an impish three-year-old.' [100]

It is certain he is right. Cyclic time theory predicts that they will do this far faster and more suddenly than any current model forecasts, and so we should prepare for that. The chaos of typhoon Haiyan on Nov 8th 2013 shows how such change can occur so quickly, and the need for storing water and food for 2–3 months. The reason for this faster speed could be 'resonant chaos' motion, in which chaos increases at a rate beyond the speed of standard prediction models.

Another question arises about ice. How can we distinguish between daily change and annual change in ice layer features? Some have developed methods to use microwaves that detect polarized light bouncing off hoar frost formations far below satellites in space. This is an idea, but how accurate is it? Even if the data collected is shown to be correct for a period of a decade or two, there is a possible problem. It is still a method requiring long term assumptions before workers are able to extrapolate data backwards in time, let alone for the long periods demanded by the linear time model. Such presumption-based linear methods fail if time is orbital.

Under many millions of tons of compressed and still compressing ice, there is indeed lateral spread as layers are forced sideways into other adjoining layers, often being impossible to detect. Again the

99 The Two Mile Time Machine, RB. Alley, Princeton University Press, 2000, p197
100 The Two Mile Time Machine, RB. Alley, Princeton University Press, 2000, p13

old assumption of long age is used, but the same anomalies remain unexplained.

This must remain the case until complete revision is carried out, suggested by the astronomy pointing to a quantum shift within time. Otherwise no-one is looking for such effects, or wondering if the layers may have formed faster than the expected model predicted, or why it is that the ice age may be dated to 3,000 years, and ice cores in Greenland are said to have 10–30 times this number. Why else would the South Pole show far too few layers if the ice started forming there 15–20 million years ago, as some say? Something must be wrong in some of these old assumptions.

These ice caps are vast, and very strange places that do not behave like any other area of the planet. It can even appear to 'snow' on a clear day, as ice crystals literally fall out of the air and collect on the hard surface below. Known as diamond dust, which is what the crystals look like in the sunshine, this peculiar phenomenon rather sets the cat among the pigeons when it comes to dating ice cores.

There are other reasons to suspect there are some rather inaccurate core dates. These dates can be spectacularly wrong: not just by a few years in a hundred, but by hundreds of thousands of years.

How ice and volcanic ash produce dates

The beginning is deceptively basic. Snow forms when water vapour is cooled into ice crystals, and then becomes a layer not of snow, and not for very long at least, but of ice. Usually three feet of snow is compressed into one foot of ice, but not always. The snow fall is literally crushed flat into a thin band that never quite stops moving over the coming years after its creation.

This ice derives from successive layers of snow, which become compressed into old snow or '*firn*', the German word for this partially condensed form of snow. Further snowfalls compress snow into ice, and then the fun really starts as these layers begin to move like a slow liquid to form glaciers, rather as glass appears solid but some think behaves as a fluid over time.

Therefore, this type of ice becomes glacial, moving invisibly beneath the ice cap, as it becomes a kind of radial glacier, thinning vertically while spreading out in all directions thanks to gravity, as studied by glaciologists. By 2,000 feet down, the pressure has risen to half a ton per square inch, and keeps increasing with depth.

Greenland is a key place for this study, and lies conveniently between Europe and America so that teams from both continents meet on the ice cap's summit to begin drilling downwards. One might expect a small drill hole, but no such small scale project was planned for this.

Instead, the aim was to reach the bedrock beneath, and learn all that could be learned about this massive ice sheet, so the drilling continued downwards for about two miles. The resulting projects were called GRIP and GISP2, lying 20 miles apart, and doing much the same thing as they drilled their ice cores from 1989–93.

Why were there two such similar ice data gathering experiments so close together? The answer is national. GRIP was the mainly European version and stands for '*Greenland Ice-Core Project*', while GISP2 was the mainly American team, with an acronym for the *Greenland Ice Sheet Project* 2. Both wanted the data first.

The aim was to cut cores of the ice, label and stack them in a sub-zero warehouse, and get to work analysing how old they were, chiefly by counting the layers using a bright light behind these cylinders of solid ice. This dating method also relies mainly on a match with other dates of 'known events', so we should have confidence in it being right. At least we would do, if those other 'known events' were indeed known.

Alas this does not appear to be the case at all, and those prominent 'reference points' used to connect all these different methods are not as firmly dated as they should be. The tests could not confirm which volcanic trace was being seen, so if the date of the volcanic eruption chosen as a 'date fixer' is unknown, any 'dates' would be meaningless.

This is how the age dating of nearly all strata works: they are connected to other markers already accepted in science, which usually means fossils. When linear methods are used in this way, then all the systems based on them become false.

Fixing dates by relational methods is one of these, and nearly all dates are calculated like this to some extent. One item is linked to another, a concept is created on how they are linked, and the connection is based on this theoretical 'relationship'. It seems astonishing that the deepest level of thinking could be mistaken, yet it now appears clear this is so.

Sometimes volcanic eruptions like Toba are of an unknown date, being from a time in pre-history before records were kept, which may be any time older than 900 BC. Even then, no reliable historical record exists for all events this far back, and any dates older than 2,800 years before present (BP) have to be treated with the greatest caution, especially in the light of the cyclic evidence.

Claims do exist for much older dates, as in Egyptology or using carbon dating, but they are based on separate calculations, and the above evidence shows they may not be reliable. Statistical methods often give a '95%' accuracy range for a technique that may be entirely reliant on limited data sets. Statisticians know this very well.

An old science favourite is worth remembering here. The often used phrase 'we now know' skilfully adds to this notion of being infallible, and avoids actually admitting any error was ever made. Yet if we 'now know' one thing which conflicts with the old thing we 'used to know', then it must have been totally incorrect. This way, science can avoid ever being wrong, simply by pretending to be in a constant state of knowing.

Volcanoes have become a big part of ice core dating, and can also show that the method is uncertain. As Professor Alley importantly and rightly confirms, dates over 2000 years are never reliably dated by records in history that also left signs in ice layers.

The 'presumed known events' are uncertain, like the date of the last European Ice Age, which no one can be quite sure of, but is usually put around 8–12000 years ago. It is suggested here this date could be wrong by about 5–9000 years. Some recently put it at 600,000 years, which is amazing, and disagrees with others. One scientist gave the date of an ice age event in Europe as 8,000 years BP in 2007, and decided later it should be 465,000 BP, showing that estimates are often not reliable tools to use.

In recent cases, eruptions may be very tightly documented indeed, like the 1783 eruption of the Laki volcano in Iceland. This major eruption was noted by famous, trusted people alive at the time, like Ben Franklin, and made a big impression as it disrupted all of Europe and lands beyond. He was in Paris as poisonous clouds drifted south east.

Paris was especially relevant here, because by chance Benjamin Franklin was there at the time, acting as US ambassador to France from 1776–1785, just after helping draft the American Declaration of

Independence. Best known as a scientist, and for his discovery of the lightning conductor, he noted the severe winter in that year of the Laki volcano; while many observers did not see the link, he cleverly and correctly made the connection between these two events as the cause followed by that effect.

Laki sent out such huge clouds of mixed ash and sulphur dioxide for 8 months, starting in June of 1783. These strange 'dry fogs' were reported all over Europe and into Africa, and surrounded the earth in that latitude to head east far enough to reach Asia, then across the Pacific Ocean to North America and perhaps Greenland too. It was not a fog at all, but gas and ash that choked and overcame much of the life caught in its path.

Usually the prevailing westerly wind in Iceland would have taken the ash roughly north east to Spitsbergen (Svalbard) and northern Russia, but at the time a high pressure cyclonic system is thought to have forced the ash-laden air to the southeast. It caused huge destruction as the sulphur dioxide gas laden ash cloud rolled over large human and animal populations, with heavier powder settling on crops in a downwind plume area.

This level of eruption has been claimed to represent certain levels in the Greenland ice cores collected by these expeditions, since some acid peak layers have been detected. Before dealing with this apparent link with certain specific eruptions used to confirm the ice core dates, it is necessary to appreciate just how massive events like Laki were. This is vital since they will occur again, as the President of Iceland reminded us in 2010.

This was a huge eruption by any reckoning, with about 9 cubic miles of lava emerging as fountains 4,500 feet high in a narrow curtain miles long; tough to imagine.[101] Let's make that clearer with a comparison: as this lava fountain soared into the sky, under pressure of course, it reached a height of over 3.6 times the Empire State Building in New York, once the world's tallest at 1250 feet, or 4.6 times the Eiffel Tower in Paris (985.6ft). This was a large eruption even by world standards, as lava cascaded out of the very same crack in the earth's crust that

101 Volcanoes. Francis & Oppenheimer 2004, 2nd Edition,
   Oxford University Press, p435.

gave rise to all of Iceland itself, and marks the north-south line we call the mid-Atlantic ridge (MAR).

Judging by the wind speeds affecting the fallout plume from the huge El Chichón eruption in southern Mexico in 1982, Laki could have taken as little as 22 days to spread over a huge area, since the Mexican eruption managed to surround the entire earth in that time.[102] Laki is estimated to have produced 120 million tons (Mt) of SO_2, often with hydrogen sulphide, which would combine with water vapour in the air to become 200 Mt of acid aerosol. The simple presence of all this extra sulphur dioxide gas in the air then quite readily mixes with the water vapour to form sulphuric acid...not nice.

The huge 1883 Krakatoa eruption in Indonesia's Sunda Strait, between Java and Sumatra, took only 14 days to do much the same thing, and send ash right round the globe. That was a very explosive 'Plinian' eruption, like Vesuvius, when over 12 cubic miles of ash erupted in three days that rose to 40 kms in height (near the edge of space), and reached South Africa in this time by travelling eastwards around the globe. The blast was so huge at 'ground zero', that it blasted all that debris upwards, leaving three widely separated stump islands where there had been one very much larger conical one; all visible to this day. This kind of global reach dust and gas cloud should be detected in ice cores.

Iceland was also in a special location, then as today, situated near a giant column of rotating air called the *polar atmospheric vortex*, lifting both the gases and dust particles up into the tropopause and even the stratospheric levels of earth's atmosphere.

This huge acid cloud would have been equal to the entire modern world's annual SO_2 pollution levels in one area, so little wonder Ambassador Franklin looked out of his Paris residence and made a note of low light levels and the yellowish-brown haze. He didn't yet know it, but this 'fog' had destroyed crops from Scotland and Norway as a prelude to much of Europe. Iceland must have been a terrifying place at the time, losing 25% of its own people, and 75% of its livestock to these extreme effects.

Volcanoes are still the most intense natural earth mega-event we

102 Ibid p432

know, almost akin to a comet or asteroid strike from space, which has even more kinetic energy.

One noted example is the huge Toba eruption. It has been claimed to have occurred 74,000 years ago by some estimates, yet could have been around 1650 BC. It was huge, that is beyond doubt. Its age is open to new dating parameters. What is also uncertain is the its sulphur output, which causes the acid aerosol 'claimed to be identifiable' in the ice cores, and acidic rain in warmer areas. This shows the facts are not definite, but estimated.

As two senior volcanologists, Francis and Oppenheimer, put it: 'Toba's huge magnitude is not in doubt. But its sulphur content is.'[103]

Studies have shown that the Toba sulphur output may have been barely twice that of Pinatubo[104], yet a great deal more material was erupted from Toba; not the 14 km³ of Laki, but a truly massive 2,300 km³. That is around 164 times as much, yet Laki was no pussycat in volcanic terms, causing great social distress and loss of life. Toba was a titanic mega-eruption by any standard, one of the biggest ever, so any event seen in living memory is as nothing compared to that. These will recur again, so some basic precautions will help, such as roof reinforcing, and digging lava or mud flow pathways in some areas. St.Bernard village in the Philippines is one tragic example of a landslip that was a surprise, killing 1000 people.

It is worth pausing a moment to recognise the scale. Even a single cubic kilometre of hot ash is quite an effort to picture, if we could pick one up and put it in a field somewhere to examine it more closely. At 1000 metres or 3,250 feet in any direction, upwards and to our left and right, this would be an awesomely large lump. Now to imagine 2,300 of these lumps in a line, to get an idea of their magnitude, the line would stretch sideways over half of America.

Luckily there is good news too, the planet is also very good at using rain to wash out all these chemicals and particles, as it always will do thanks to Nature's own ways of regulating these things. Rain actually forms around dust particles when present, so they can act as a natural form of cloud 'seeding' that induces rain.

103 Ibid p438
104 Huge eruptions in 1991 and c1450 AD, Luzon, Philippines.

Toba and similar 'nuclear winter' scale eruptions were really immense, yet here we are today, as if they never happened, and this is why many people find such mega-events hard to imagine at all; though not those who live near active volcanoes. Such places are always very striking to see, but hide a secret past.

North Sumatra's Lake Toba is an idyllic tourist spot visited by numerous travellers via Medan. To go there today we would see a large lake with a giant central hill in its centre. Only from a map or the air can one appreciate that this 'hill' is just the central collapsed cone in the middle of a giant caldera or crater 60kms long (38 miles), so from a single place one can barely see a quarter of its full extent, even by climbing the centre.

The proposal put forward here is that this is not a 'chance occurrence' all that time ago, but part of a global, and indeed universal, change that resulted in two short but intense periods of extreme vulcanicity.

This was when the vast flood basalt flows were active, in the cyclic time version.

Yet this is not the kind of highly explosive volcano that sends dust miles up into the atmosphere, as do the Plinian or Vesuvian types with their *'nuées ardentes'* (*'burning clouds'* in French; now known as pyroclastic flows). Instead, these are fissure type volcanoes that spread highly fluid, low viscosity lava over a huge area, as we see in Hawaii on a much smaller scale today. Volcanoes built the island chain of Hawaii itself, as the crust moved over a 'hotspot' where the crust is thinner than usual. Again, the fact of this mechanism is not in question, since Hawaii undoubtedly does exist by all accounts, but the age of the process is computed in linear time, not witnessed, and thus can be far younger.

Understanding volcanoes is important because they will increase in activity due to the resonance effects that affect all plate margin tectonics. An attentive 11 year old girl saved her family in Thailand by warning her relatives that the sea's drawback was not the amusing feature some thought it was, but the classic sign of a serious tsunami, and to run for higher ground at once. They did, and were saved: basic knowledge for survival.

How does all this affect the ice cores? The answer lies in the ash and the pollution from the poison gas. This low viscosity of the lava and the dissolved gas are connected, with presence of so much dissolved gas reducing the internal cohesion, making the lava 'thinner' and thus more fluid. This happens as the gas goes into solution. Then, as the lava emerges from the high pressure area below the earth's crust, the relaxed low pressure conditions of our surface atmospheric conditions allow the gas to escape into the air as it comes out of solution, very like taking the cap off a carbonated soft drink.

There would also be plenty of gas over such a wide area as the Siberian or American fissure volcanoes. Even so, the SO_2 gas would mix with rain and vapour and drift round the world, and create acid peaks in ice cores…and allow the glaciologists to draw up 'acidity profiles'.

The idea is that these peaks create 'spikes' of higher acidity in the snow.

There should also be the ash deposited in these layers of ice, creating a 'sulphate horizon' or layer. Sadly this is not always the case. The acidity of the Greenland ice cores were studied by the *Desert Research Institute* in Reno, Nevada, who developed an electrical conductivity method (ECM). A pair of electrodes passed a current through the GISP2 ice cores to measure resistance due to acidity differences. These were affected by windblown dust and forest fire smoke if present, which were said to have neutralized the acids, and altered the results. This detection of acid layers can be further complicated by the way CO_2 in the air dissolves in rain or snow to produce carbonic acid. These effects are not simple to analyse or to trust in date terms, making dates far less reliable.

There are also the curious effects of *clathrates*, which is where ice mixes with air inside bubbles to form a gas-hydrate, which reverts to gas if left on the surface for some time, without the pressure of ice layers above. Greyish bands of fine dust particles are also seen in such layers, blown onto the ice from deserts in Asia for example, but again the assumption of long age can affect these interpretations, by already *expecting* the great age stated in the chosen hypothesis.

As volcano experts confirm, there is not full agreement on just how accurate some methods of acidity measurement may have been. This was the opinion of the volcanologists Peter Francis and Clive Oppenheimer in their excellent work on volcanoes.[105]

105 Ibid p425

The Greenland ice sheet is a very wild place indeed. In some areas there are deep sink holes that disappear far below the surface of the ice cap. Melt water forms in beautiful blue pools, then flows down these mysterious cracks in the ice with a roaring sound, rushing along hidden tunnels that lie beneath the surface, rather like arteries.

Attempts to measure these holes have not yet succeeded because they don't always fall vertically, so cameras get snagged after several hundred feet at most. This ice sheet is close to 2 miles deep as we have seen, so this is one monster of a system of water and ice, forming into glaciers that flow slowly to the coast and calve into icebergs. Some are so large they drop debris on the sea floor as they drift and melt, while the local air force mounts a year-long iceberg mapping project, to avoid another Titanic disaster as in April 1912.

Glacial ice is blue, like the sea, which is very beautiful indeed, and blue for the same reason. Being shallow, the sunlight passes through it from above, and makes the walls glow with an eerie blue light, since the slower red light is filtered out. An ice cave at Vatnajokull in Iceland contains such blue ice that it amazes those who see it. Seen intact in 1986, it may not have survived the area's 2011 volcano.

These climate changes are rapid variations, and not slow or gradual, but 'abrupt'. This abruptness is very significant, since it shows that both large scale climate trends, and the local microclimates of ice caps, are highly changeable events that are closely linked, and too erratic to be as fully predictable as the statistics assume they will be. This is a real problem in setting firm dates. Some measurements show the ice age had temperature variations as great as 40°F, which would cause ice formation differences that also complicate analysis and reduce reliability.

Temperature measurements have shown the sun can cause hoar frosting at depth within the ice column vertically, which would further upset any reliance placed on the method above, where it has to be assumed surface layers stay as they first formed.

On a day with a snow storm, there may be a wind factor to consider as well, which blows the snow into drifts in some areas, while blowing it off the surface in others. This process is known as accumulation and 'ablation'. It is also an important factor in mixing up snow depths, and so it can be suggested that each layer may not be a year at all, but a record of the number of periods of warm and cold spells.

Even the lack of bright sunlight in the full winter cannot fully remove this factor of snow movement, and abnormal temperature changes. What they did one to two thousand years ago is by no means certain, and has to be 'assumed'...and there is that word again.

Certain norms have to be 'treated as facts' to make any progress at all in the initial trials of dating, first just to try them out and gain 'possible' statistics, and then it becomes accepted as reality, even when it may just not be real at all.

'Drama is life with the dull bits cut out' as Hitchcock once observed. To the archaeologist or the geologist, fixed dates for their research are as dramatically interesting as the most sensational news story, and often comprise the basis of such stories. Big ages impress us. No one would have been so interested in Tutankhamen if he had died just a few years before the famous find by Howard Carter late in 1922. Alexander the Great would have been locked up as a psychopath for such genocidal behaviour in recent history, but was thought 'great' for such appalling violence a few years before his own death in 323 BC. If an item of research becomes front page news, then its surprise factor is bound to alter.

An oak tree in a swamp is not news, unless it turns out to be 600 years old with a history, then each ring is pored over to gain details. If this date is later halved, the whole impact of the claim ceases to be major news, so the need for dates is imperative.

Science has to assume a perfectly ordered, theoretical world for the purpose of compiling dates, but nature is not always so regular. Weather is famously unpredictable. Huge computers have been given the task of predicting these patterns, and amuse everyone when they are so often wrong.

The El Niño storms of the eastern Pacific have a curious seven year cycle that seems to defy the predictability of Nature herself. Annual and regular they are not, and nor is so much of the past, as we can see in the evidence locked in rock and ice.

The pressure on scientists to come up with dates is a huge one. A great deal of money and effort is invested in the methods invented, and these irregularities show we may still be mistaken.

Computer models are often so complex, that they are too slow to be examined thoroughly. As glaciologist Professor Alley noted, intricate

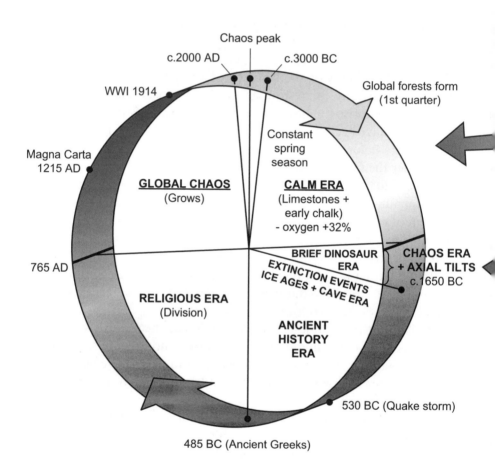

FIGURE 21 *Geological 'Timescale' shown as non-linear in Cycle of Time: diagram showing cyclic sequence of major events causing chaos, after first quarter of order; eras in no actual sequential order of claimed linear time.*

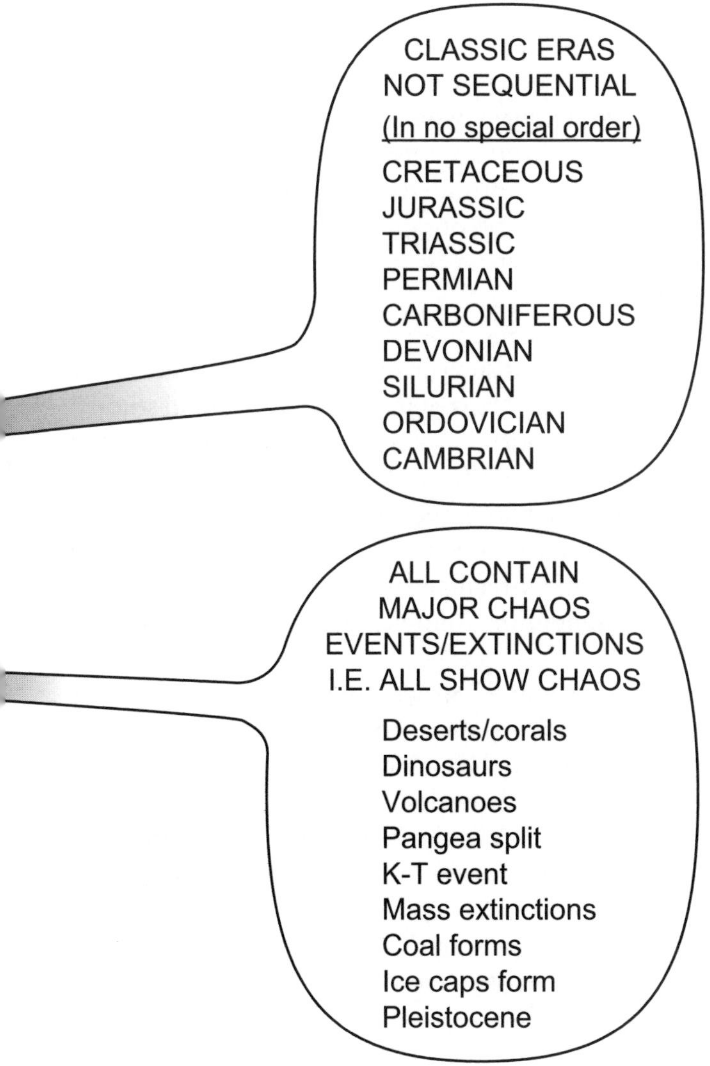

CLASSIC ERAS
NOT SEQUENTIAL
(In no special order)
CRETACEOUS
JURASSIC
TRIASSIC
PERMIAN
CARBONIFEROUS
DEVONIAN
SILURIAN
ORDOVICIAN
CAMBRIAN

ALL CONTAIN
MAJOR CHAOS
EVENTS/EXTINCTIONS
I.E. ALL SHOW CHAOS

Deserts/corals
Dinosaurs
Volcanoes
Pangea split
K-T event
Mass extinctions
Coal forms
Ice caps form
Pleistocene

models need the fastest supercomputers, so they are not often used, due to costs.

Sometimes extreme European freezing happens anyway, as it did in the 1948, 1963 and 2009 European winters, but the lack of this heat transfer from the tropical Caribbean would be something else entirely, causing further collapses in infrastructure and droughts on an epic scale. London and much of Great Britain were impassable during these events, with insufficient distribution of salt and grit, at a national economic cost through losses to business estimated at over £600 million, and all in a matter of days.

We hope it doesn't happen of course, but Professor Alley offers a wise *caveat* that science cannot predict such changes due to our ignorance.

Cycles are recognised in many areas of nature. Gerard Bond studied Atlantic sediment cores and noticed cycles that he judged had lasted 1500 years. He deduced this partly from dust particles and sedimentary shell layers of creatures that favoured cold or warmer waters. This Bond cycle uses the classic linear time model of all these methods of age assignment, matching the Greenland Ice core projects' findings, and refers to an 'iceberg inundation' followed by warming in just a few years or decades.

The German expert Hartmut Heinrich found anomalous layers of iceberg-born debris in north Atlantic sediments he studied east of Hudson Bay, and gave his name to the Heinrich Events of deep cooling. There are also the Milankovitch cycles, which propose long and gradual changes to earth's orbit and axial inclination. Cyclic time also suggests these changes occurred, but very rapidly indeed, in 1000th of the time or less in some instances.

The Dansgaard-Oeschger cycles were cool to warm ice age periods suggested by these Danish and Austrian researchers in the early 1980's, and are often linked to orbital or axial changes to earth's rotation. Their ages were estimated.

Earth's atmosphere today has about 800 billion tons of carbon in it, mostly as carbon dioxide. The movement and alteration of this carbon quantity are unknown, and how it changes over time is still a mystery. Large ice sheets look like permanent features due to their sheer size and mass, yet a larger ice sheet can disappear even faster than a smaller one. [The larger surface of a big ice sheet oddly retains greater warmth than a small one, and allows more heat from the earth to radiate upwards, so it could melt up to 100 times faster than if it was still frozen to the rock beneath.]

Ice melts faster in water than in air.

Modern glaciology recognises two riddles to be solved, which are part of the linear version of time. One riddle is why such small variations in sunlight seem to have caused major climatic change. The other is why the sunlight falling on the northern hemisphere 'cold desert' areas, like Europe, Canada and Siberia, was so much more significant than the sunlight reaching Antarctica and New Zealand. According to Professor Alley once again, not one of these riddles is solved.

Cyclic time appears to solve both, with the huge changes of an axial shift.

The volcanic tracer eruptions have included other Icelandic eruptions such as Hekla, Katla and Eldgja, as well as Italy's Vesuvius in 79 AD, and an earlier eruption of Mt St Helens in America from the year 1479.

Iceland is a most fascinating place to visit for many reasons, and a source of fine waterfalls and intense volcanic activity. As recently as May 2011, the Grimsvötn volcano added to the travel misery of the 2010 erupting Eyjafjallajokull [pronounced *Eye-er-fee-atler-yerkul*] volcanic neighbour, which erupted below the Vatnajokull glacier. Although the 2011 eruption released '10–100' times the earlier quantity of ash, the particles were larger in size, avoiding air travel disruption.

Iceland also has spectacular geysers which can safely be viewed up close.

The Latin motto of the famous Royal Society in London, widely considered the original home of European science, broadly translates as '*believe no-one's word*'. The pioneers thought time to be well known, but this now appears to be a convention we should not have accepted.

CHAPTER 12

A New Geological Timescale

Time moving in very short
cycles: infinite age

New opinions are always suspected, and usually opposed, without
any other reason but because they are not already common.
JOHN LOCKE, 1690

Science cannot solve the ultimate mystery of nature…because we
ourselves are part of nature and therefore part of the mystery we are
trying to solve.
MAX PLANCK, 1932, Nobel Prize Winner

Essence

The Geological Timescale is the foundation of earth history, yet it has
a serious problem that undermines its authority to be that. It accepts
dates relying on speculation. The experts all know this, but have never
revised the whole scheme, and will not do so, until they recognise a
new one that fits better, so the problem persists.

Science does not have a set of dates that are 'absolute', meaning
beyond question.

It is one thing to see fossils as part of the world today, but quite
another to claim they 'prove' how Life came to exist as we see it now.
They lack the quantity to do that.

The basis of geological dating is radiogenic decay theory. We have
seen how that method has a gap between its claim to 'set' ages for
volcanic rocks, and the judgement those dates are real. It now appears
they are not real; this method can create dates that have literally no
bearing on the actual passage of earth's historical events. Those 'dates'
would be entirely false if the decay elements were *already in the rock*
on the day they erupted.

The fossils do not support those dates, because they cannot be dated with any method that is either objective or 'absolute'. It is therefore necessary to conclude that no fixed or 'absolute' dates exist to confirm any of the above claims for a timescale.

In some ways, the perceived age of 'everything' is the key, since few of us ever change our minds about what we accepted in our youth. Sometimes we have to change our minds, if the evidence demands it. Yet what is a fact? Often we take facts to be what we choose to believe. Science is meant to separate the two, but it can also build up its own set of 'facts' that turn out to be myths. It is a fact that some migratory birds, like terns, do fly 60,000 kilometres each year with navigation of GPS quality.

It is an idea that some features of reality are billions of years old. In fact the signs tell us they are far older, and infinitely so, as part of a cycle of time that repeats. No scientist can disprove this point, because of Munchausen's trilemma (see Glossary), which prevents anyone from doing so, since each 'proof' relies on other side issues.

It may sound strange at first, but the whole geology of Earth does appear to be cyclic, so it goes through a set of changes, and then switches back to day one, to begin once again. The materials may be 'infinitely old', but they are subject to change. The fossils would then derive from creatures that live and die as each cycle begins again.

How could experts have missed all this? Very easily, because the clues are hidden.

Science chooses ideas by emphasis. Every philosopher of science knows about this trilemma, and can give learned lectures on how it counters proof of nearly everything we think is obvious. Now it is time we realised the wrong option was chosen, and then used to underpin every key theory in modern thinking. These theories have failed already, but we are looking in the other direction for answers as to why we fail to explain so much. The answer is simple: time is a circle. If the facts are true, the theories have failed.

The timescale of earth's geology is one such casualty. The dates are not as firm as once thought. It is a theoretical concept that relies entirely on time *being linear*. If it is not, the whole timescale would fail. This is not an opinion, but the only logical conclusion allowed by the new evidence for how time 'must have passed'. It shows a continuum of short cycles that repeat.

There seems to be no other option, so 'if not this, then what?'

The evidence seen today, three centuries later, shows time to be cyclic, yet science has not adjusted to accept it. From 1650-1840, the key era when many such concepts were created, none of the modern findings were known, so early pioneers were in the dark.

It is easy to be wise after 300 years of mistaken interpretation, but geological dating has a problem. It never adapted to the modern finds in astronomy, as we can see. Yet neither did cosmology, some observe, for one tiny but vital reason: none of the recent finds in space support the old version of time as a line. The new finds fit a circle, where events repeat, but few saw that coming, and so the majority ignored it.

It all looked too obvious to need attention: days and years passed in a line, they felt, so that was the only answer. Since the different sciences took the linear idea and ran with it, no one thought twice about it being true or not, and few do now. Hubble also misread these signs, and became a champion of time as a long line, as we see later. Nearly everyone agreed that vast eons had passed, with time acting like an arrow that went only one way. That led to the idea of a line being 'set in stone', mentally at least, and all the 'ages' being extended, because a lot of time had to be 'created' to support Evolution.

When a new method arose in 1905, it was seized on as a wonderful solution.

Enter isotopic dating as a method for creating dates. It looked real, but it required us to assume time was always a line. Just two other snags should have been seen as warning flags. The first is one of vision: by ignoring the cyclic time option, the dates all 'look long' and old, just as expected, but they are not scientifically sound. Many may disagree, because nearly every ancient rock date on earth relies on the 'certainty' that time 'began' long ago. Except it didn't begin like that, and fresh evidence shows this.

This is the second snag: the evidence that the universe is oddly young in form and structure has nearly all come to light in the last fifty years... far too recently for science to react across over forty fields, or realise collectively, that the old linear view of time was not just a bit rusty, but needed replacing entirely with a new world view.

Is this a shock? If turning 400 years of research on its head is a shock, then this is a huge one. As shocks go, this one knocks it out of the ballpark. It gets worse for science, because this same error of a line underpins all modern 'knowledge', so any idea using it just became history overnight.

A third obstacle ensured this did not happen at all: the top scientists in each field felt certain both they, and their heroes of the past era, were right in seeing time as an arrow. Expensive TV films were made about it being true, and about the brilliance of modern science to recognise this wonder. Big names were praised for their parts in 'knowing' this, and they get no bigger, with Einstein, Bohr, Dirac, Le Maitre, Kelvin, Hubble, Bell, Feynman, Darwin, Huxley, Lyell, Hutton, Bell Burnell, Witten, Hawking, Planck, Wegener, Hoyle *et al.*, Penrose, Turok, Steinhardt, Smolin and many others; yet only the last five have focused on a continuum of reality in some form.

The linear view is challenged, because the cycle fits much better. Few saw that coming. It is usually the cosmologists who find such errors first. Yet if the physics of 'Cyclic Flash Time' is real, we may have to change our view. For the 'traditional' timescale to be right, there has to be evidence that requires no prior belief. Yet each dating method relies on just such a system. Those existing ages and dates do rely on this circular thinking, and since they counter real facts, appear unsound.

Theory can never counter reality and earn our respect. Facts win every time. Science results that ignore this rule become valueless. This has happened, yet easily escapes attention. Even time is also not an arrow in real terms, since the facts insist we consider a circle of events. In point of fact, as any archer knows well, even an arrow does not fly flat or straight, but in a curve. Follow that curve on any scale, and it becomes a circle. Only this reality fits the few facts we can actually detect, so we must consider it.

Yet Socrates, Plato and Aristotle did realise this pivotal notion of infinity. Blind faith is a hazard in both religion and science. Dr Bronowski's 1973 work *The Ascent of Man* suggested the opposite of a cycle, yet he accepted the need to question ideas to an endless degree, when he said 'The essence of science is to ask an impertinent question, and you are on the way to a pertinent answer'.

As we noted, the radiogenic dating of volcanic rocks is not the definite guarantee of their ages being the millions or billions of years supposed. This serious presumption underpins all those claims, made from 1905–1915 by famous pioneers like E. Rutherford and

A. Holmes. They trusted utterly in time being a long line, while the cosmic anomalies show this central presumption fails, which the early pioneers *could not have known about.*

Now that is a problem, because almost no one in the world agrees... but a few do. To be fair, this is daunting, but not technically a problem at all, since it could be true.

This would mean the entire timescale of earth's geology is incorrect by billions of years, and needs a total rethink, to put it mildly. It would also mean the whole of geological time has been a misunderstanding. Seeing if these changes could form a harmonious alliance between the geology of our whole solar system, and the astrophysics, took time to resolve.

The good news is that they can, and it all fits neatly, if strangely at first. Let's look at a few facts. Chalk and coal are real enough, the earth is a globe, and Copernicus was definitely right to describe a heliocentric solar system. All the time periods of geology would be the same, but the speed of their formation could be far faster if, instead of a sequence, the eras are often contemporary. Then there are no millions of years to find.

It seemed counter-intuitive to begin with, yet why could many eras not happen together...at the same time? Tradition disagreed, but the astronomy, earth's actual populace and a lack of fossils of both people and species, were rather persuasive facts. Earth's sediments cover huge areas, but they don't sit vertically in one neat succession.

Indeed that would be 100 miles high if they did, and we don't see any signs of that. What we do see is areas where some strata types meet others, and plenty of presumption is used to explain how they got there.

The entire timescale suffers from this problem of assuming linear time, and so all of the ten key periods listed can indeed have existed in the two short phases noted.

As the late Prof. Tjeerd H. van Andel once wisely[106] explained, there have been errors in which layers conformably overlie other layers, when in different areas. He noticed two thin coal seams in 'excellent outcrops' in Venezuela which were usually taken as L.Palaeocene and U.Eocene in age, yet '...even the closest inspection failed to turn up the

106 Nature Vol.294, 3 Dec 1981, pp397-8.

precise position of that 15 million year gap.' He implies there may not have been one, showing how uncertain the analysis process can be. That appears wholly correct, since a 'gap' may not exist in one place, yet later turn out to be miscorrelated in another.

His article also emphasised that the '…severe incompleteness of the geological record and its relation to time scale deserve our most serious attention because they affect the history of the earth in many ways.' This truth fits the new cosmology outlined here, and the many discontinuities that exist in many successions, such as four in the Grand Canyon (see page). These are highly significant in our new timescale, because they show the sediments were never laid down continuously, but often in stages *with gigantic upheavals and erosion in between*. This fact shows those areas were in chaos, with frequent periods of vast turbulence, not the calm order lasting eons that is claimed.

No one knows what happened in those gaps, where deposition turned rapidly into erosion, and then back again. This has never been explained, but an axial shift fits it perfectly: fast changes in just this kind of extreme way. That looked promising, but what about fossils? Their serious lack of types and forms supports the above scenario, in that a cycle of short period would create just such sequences. This would be why chalk has those chert layers every 60cms in Dover's white cliff tops, and why mud and sand always tend to overlay coal measures…rapid deposits from the axial shift wobbles. Such 'cyclic' deposits can be seen all over the world, which supports an axial shift that would have tilted back and forth for decades or more, creating just these effects. Examples of such rapid and regular swings exist in the marls of Sicily's south western cliffs, to New Zealand and just about everywhere in between.

Even the dinosaurs fit, with so few seen. The few that lived were laid down on the ocean floor, which then became the Dakotas and Wyoming, China and Europe etc, only to be uplifted in the break-up of Pangea, beside the Rockies in America. It fits. Huge sequences of rock in the pre-Cambrian have no fossils at all, and so are claimed to be of huge age. They may not be. The major overturns caused by the axial shift would see such vast sequences of sediment laid down, often with no fossils, just as we see in the pre-Cambrian.

As the diagrams show, the five or six main Mass Extinction events

Rock strata: part of the Grand Canyon

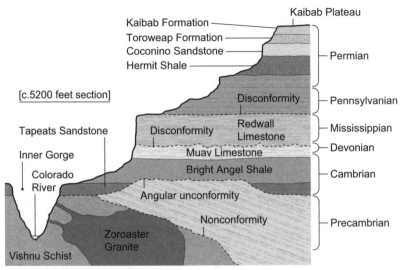

Note unconformities showing irregular deposition.

FIGURE 22 *Grand Canyon: showing rock layers in section. Note unconformities at base of layers showing gap in time between erosion and then rapid deposition phases on ocean floor, followed by uplift and recent incised erosion.*

may have taken place during a rapid axial tilt, and within only a century. This solution would sound impossible to conventional thinkers, yet it matches the geology seen. The traditional dating methods suggesting around 400 million years between them is inferred by relying on several assumptions, such as the fossil record, which does not support the evolution of species required, which worried Darwin. Nor can the estimate of 2mm per year for most sediment deposition rates be relied on, with coal and chalk being classic examples. Prof van Andel's article mentions this, when even applying old, slow rates of deposition, one sequence in Wyoming only needing 100,000 years, not the 6 million years 'firmly' given to it. Adjust that to cyclic time as here, and under 600 years is easily possible.

The standard timescale taught to every geology student has been constructed using such estimates which no longer hold. Even experts disagree, with some saying the chalk bridge that once joined England to France was cut by ice age floods 8,000 years ago, while others claim the same event occurred 600,000 years ago, a difference of 75 times. One or both estimates can be mistaken. The figure of ±3,300 years [107] fits better.

Such events had no witnesses, so researchers have to imagine what clues may help support those ideas. With clues often in contradiction, experts choose the option they prefer, with the huge errors we see. Experts disagree because the facts counter the old view of time as a line, and these problems are only solved by a short cycle and post-Cambrian geology happening within 1400 years.

It looked logical to take time as a line, but nature can look deceptive at times.

Odd features keep appearing, like the asteroid 2015BZ509, which orbits the sun near the path of Jupiter, yet in the *opposite direction* to the giant planet, and that is reckoned to be 'young' to do this. It is also thought this *retrograde orbit* cannot continue forever, since Jupiter pulls it twice on each circuit. This shows the solar system's history is not explained by the standard model. Called 'very peculiar', this odd motion shows the solar system has clear facts that long linear time cannot explain.

Only in a cycle of short duration can these features exist, like Haumea's famous lack of dust on its icy white surface…impossible if it were a billion years old as claimed. The fact is these oddities do exist, and thus prove the rule.

These controversial topics need to be reviewed openly and calmly, because one of these opposing opinions seems to be pure fiction. The question is which one.

So let's review the rocks in a fresh way. The point of geology is an investigation into deep history. Since no one saw most of it happen, we have to deduce the answers. Shocking as it is to say so, it is nonetheless entirely possible that the classic geological eras happened in concert, all within 1650 years and *the violent ones in the same era*. That would be all of them to some extent. We have noted a pivotal fact in geology,

---

107 This ± is the plus-minus symbol, meaning the figure is estimated; should be
     correct here to within 150 years.

which is the recurrent presence of repeating strata or *cyclothems*, which show this was so.

This reveals two things. One is the existence of rapid types of suspended sediment that move in water very fast indeed...in hours. Second is their effect: this is no slow, gentle, quiet laying down of layers as claimed, but proves instead the world's oceans were on the move in a colossal and highly significant way as never before. These were giant events to move so much sediment so far and so rapidly. Coal is proof of this speed.

Whole forests must have been covered in hours to exclude the decaying effects of oxygen, resulting in the astonishing degree of perfect preservation we actually see. This would be why these lenses of shale, mud, sand and coal *are found globally together*, in such identical forms or 'facies'. This *would not happen* if these rocks had formed slowly and locally over the 80 million years claimed. This estimate has been made, the material deposits shoe-horned into it, producing an unworkable claim that 'it all fits neatly, no problem here'. The radiogenic dating method assumed linear time, so cannot be objective.

The effect of this high speed rate of deposition would be difficult to overvalue. It literally means that the whole geological timescale, all of it, really does appear to have been overestimated by well over a billion years. We have seen how mudstone is one such example, and sandstone another, but can we really account for a billion years in 1,650?

The startling answer is a clear yes, because those are not slow sediment types that 'have' to take a year to form 2mm as argued. Layers could build up in hours, and there isn't a reason in the world that proves it wasn't so. These were fast deposits laid down in estuarine or marine environments fed by heavily laden rivers, carrying millions of tons of clay and sand particles in suspension.

We find these millions of tons, so they came from somewhere, and in huge amounts.

Any salt present would just bind or flocculate the particles to form layers even faster. We can do the maths: 2.74mm a day is only a metre in a year, or 1mm in 9 hours. That is both feasible and likely. Some features, like chert or flint, can form seasonal bands. This would explain the regularity of the chert layers in English chalk, and banding in other sediments like the marls of Sicily, the sandstone strata of

Burton Bradstock and West Bay on Dorset's famous Jurassic coast. These cyclothems of repeating strata (eg 123,123) show the order was cyclic, because the same sequence is being laid down again and again in rapid changes of condition that repeat. This fits an axial shift that is still oscillating, not millennia or longer of the same conditions. The sediments are showing periods of change that fit specific sequences in each location globally. That does not signal a 'slow' or constant conditions at all, but an unstable axial spin state. [See Figs 18a-d, Ch.7]

Geological time is said to support Evolution taking 1–2 billion years. These two schools of thought, geology and evolution, have been assembled, perfectly honestly, as the 'double' foundation of one linear theory, where each supports the other. This circularity is a problem, so what about the dates? The dates appear to show the millions of years required by Darwin's idea, but only if we accept the linear model.

With the dates being assumption based, they cannot be relied upon. It is possible we have got all this spectacularly wrong in the light of so much fresh research, and we may indeed have lost about a century of potential progress while some refused to discuss the matter at all. That was when the choice was science or religion, but now we have cyclic time, which does fit the facts exactly.

Sedimentary strata are funny things...they could have been laid down at a time and in such a way that no longer suits the older ideas.

Conditions only have to be different to how we thought they were, and the whole picture of the past changes in seconds...the time it took for us to realise. Science cannot prove, and has never proved, that the bulk of earth's entire surface geology has not been swirled around, in the mixing bowl of very turbulent seas, and then allowed to settle in phases, into the formations we see today. Take away the presumption that the surface geology was all sequential, and those exposures can be largely contemporary, and require only 1650 years, not a billion. The radiogenic dates just received too much emphasis.

An axial tilt is change on another level. Geologists know it happened, and simply never factored in a cyclic universe to explain the cyclicity of layers.

Earth tilting its axis is turbulent sediment sequences 'big time'.

This axial tilt can explain how just twelve hundred years can easily form over 10,000 feet of different marine sediments, then to be uplifted by fast continental drift phases, stained red by classic iron-rich anoxic conditions caused by stagnation or water turbulence phases, intruded here and there by igneous dykes and sills, yet still mostly neat and flat, such as the Grand Canyon. Many other areas match this general profile.

The cyclic nature of alternating banded iron formations are also such examples, in which dissolved iron precipitates into solid iron layers as oxygen arrives. Alternating with anoxic conditions, the bands are formed as above, on huge scales. Some of this iron is mined as iron ore in Sweden, Brazil and Australia, where it can be 82% pure iron content...high enough to weld.

Some layers often have a red stain colour to them. That red staining is not a nine billion ton tomato soup spill, but rust from all that iron oxide. The superb Monument Valley and the Grand Canyon in America show just this effect, with rapid erosion of central sediments leaving the features we see now. So does all central Australia, with huge iron ore mines in the North West at Mt Newman, Robe River etc.

Many John Wayne films were shot around giant columns of red sandstone, with geologists often more absorbed by the spectacular rock formations than anything the Duke was doing. It was part of an ancient sea floor which was then uplifted so quickly that the sea water left in rather a hurry. There was much more to see there. [See Fig 17]

Ever noticed why Monument Valley has such amazing towers that all stop at the exact same height, with the same flat peaks? Those flat peaks marked the old sea floor level, before the entire plains area was uplifted. That ancient sea floor could have taken only 1300 years to form that sediment, in vertical axial conditions, a fraction of that for the continents to move fast to new places (the tilt alone would do that, combined with the earth's spin and centripetal force acting on Pangea). That did not happen slowly, but via water energy and motion of such turbulent power that the current swirled around both sides of each column, as it cut down through the old surface plain at that old height. [eg monadknocks, from Mt Monadknock, New Hampshire, USA.]

These are giant areas of rock formation, but there are bigger still.

Add to this the massive volcanic components such as flood basalts, and the calm sea sediments like chalk and sandstone, a chunk of metamorphism here and there to alter slate, shale, mudstone, sandstone and marble, and we have much of earth's geology in a nutshell. There really were cracks that formed in earth's crust, so deep that lava poured out in vast quantities. There are many such features in the world, which can have formed far, far faster than the traditional radiogenic dates suggested.

They were the largest formations that have ever formed, and they too were rapid.

Some had 10 million cubic kms of lava pouring out, like the central Atlantic magmatic province (CAMP), which was so huge as to raise the global sea level, and there were others all over the world (Ontong Java Plateau, Kergeulen province etc).

On land too, the earth's surface was breaking apart with fissures in every quarter, such as in India's Deccan traps, in Siberia (2mill.cubic kms of basalt), Columbia River in North West USA, and the 5 million cubic kms of the Karoo-Ferrar outflow (now in RSA and Antarctica, but erupted when they were one landmass that later split).

Huge coal reserves lie under the South Pole, untouched by agreement, and formed from forests covered over by rapid deposits noted above.

One day the earth tilted, and all this happened in a period of decades.

Was this quiet and slow? No, it was biggest, most intense global chaos ever seen, dwarfing any event seen today by several million times, and all in the same era. This could have largely happened *within months* of the axial shift, which would have broken Pangea into the plate-sized pieces we see now, and then literally forced each continent to its nearest stable position. Today's plate moves of 25mm/year are nothing compared to those rates of motion, because those same plates are now in stable locations, but not then.

If we ignore the axial tilt, and accept the radioactive dates, some propose this took two billion years or more. The axial tilt did happen, and the dates are disputable, so this short period cyclicity is entirely plausible.

We all agree this took place, including the axial shift. The chief question is when. Standard geology and old linear thinking put those events at 60–200 Myrs ago, and some spread them over a billion years, but there are no unequivocal constraints that persuade us to accept those dates as correct. The 'presumption problem' of radiogenic dating noted can indeed be such a serious error, as the leading experts have so fairly warned us.

If the linear model falls, all those dates fail the same day. It can seem strange to us now, when earth looks calm, to realise that our planet's axis was once vertical, and earth spun round the sun in a circular orbit, not the distorted ellipse we have today. The effects of that vertical axis would have been a period of great calm, with a climate of constant spring and luxuriant plant growth from the warm temperatures. So that is where all those forests came from, ready to become coal a bit later, when the axis tilts.

Tests have shown there was about 32% more oxygen than now, so that would have every living creature hopping about in a very bouncy way. Even the dragonflies were about a metre across, instead of the moth-sized forms they have now.

When the axis tilted and caused the continents to move the same day, that motion began a process of such turmoil that would be hard to imagine. The evidence for those extremes are all locked in the folded and contorted rocks and oxygen isotope records. Today people may ski down their slopes, but imagine their formation scenes.

Such vast changes built all earth's mountain ranges, such as the Rockies, Andes, Himalaya, Tibetan Plateau, Urals, Alps, and the ocean floor mountains that span the globe. This gigantic scale need not require eons of time, as the axial tilt explains. Simple changes in heat and pressure created those 'orogenies' of metamorphic rocks purely by compressing and folding them into alpine mountain ranges.

These conditions also covered over half the world with vast waves, sweeping up sand and mud to create coal, when those vast forests were buried under the rapid flooding from these upheavals, leaving the crushed wood no time to decay slowly. This is why the coal measures are not far thicker than we find them: had there been millions of years of forest growth, we would come across around 153,000 times more biomass than we do find.

Lyell never had this information, nor that it makes linear time impossible.

The same principle applies to coral growth. Other areas became very hot, forming deserts or heating trapped saltwater brines, such as the early Mediterranean area, to produce evaporites like salt, gypsum, anhydrite, limestone and dolomite, and there we have over 95% of our detectable geology.

Our friend the *Blake Outer Ridge* is bizarre proof of this very recent turbulence. What agent could have caused all this? Simple...the axial shift we still have today. It is still wobbling, in spite of the moon's tidal friction effects that should have slowed it down, if time were long and linear. This shows a younger process is at work.

The improbable fact appears to be that we have misunderstood our own geology. This is easily done when something as strange as the above could be the answer, and when no one suggested a cyclic cosmos.

What does all this mean in practise? The classic ten periods of the famous geological timescale may not be a sequence, but huge, brief and contemporary.

All these geological periods, from the Ediacaran and pre-Cambrian, through the Cambrian, Ordovician, Silurian, Devonian, Carboniferous, Permian, Jurassic, Triassic, Cretaceous and Cenozoic, show the same huge upheavals of volcanics, sea level, glaciations and magnetic reversals. With the same chaos in parts of each period, it can be they all occurred within the final 10% of one 1650 year period, leaving a 12–1300 year span of calm for chalk, limestone and coral formation.

Primary problems with evolution are embodied in the claim that 'the world' is proof enough that everything evolved. In fact this is not true, since the gaps are large enough to fit another entire worldview inside them, with room to spare. It is thus conjecture, because the one does not follow from the other. In short, it is not enough to say the linear view 'is true since we see it', which is circular thinking again.

The physical proof is lacking. We see some fossils, but vastly and dramatically nowhere near enough for the millions of years required if they had evolved. Many strata have none, with deep beds of mudstone or sandstone showing no fossils at all, proving they were laid down too rapidly for any life to live in those periods. No one stopped to review their age as younger, which can be seen from the angularity or roundness of the particles, and their size to quantity ratios. Such beds often form huge vertical thicknesses, frequently above and in between coal strata, showing this immense speed of formation, and a complete lack of burrowing signs or 'bioturbation', also required by long time spans. Yet we do have options even here.

By accident alone, it might be the right choice, but on one condition: only if there is firm, unequivocal proof to support the idea. Almost no version of 'proof' makes this grade, and the classic dates claimed certainly do not achieve this gold standard. There is often human subjective thinking used to derive the meaning of each result in the old model. Such aspects are unverifiable, so the method fails. Radioactive dating retains this problem to an extreme extent, since the 'dates' then mean nothing at all without the human element of philosophy brought into play to 'make sense' of the figures.

That maths manipulation forces rejection of the method, which is then seen to create figures without constrained meaning, and therefore fails as proof. This is unavoidably true when using assumptions. If cyclic time relied on such thinking, it could be rejected. The key reason it works is because of all this confirmation from physical reality.

So do those figures of millions of years have an actual hold on the specific historical events to which they have been linked? They cannot do so, alas. While the dates rely on *supposing* those elements derived from the 'presumed decay' of other elements 'thought to exist earlier', the dates cannot be valid. Sadly for the old timescale, those figures cannot have the slightest connection with those past events; so the dates would be entirely unrelated to actual events. They will therefore never have any link to those events, unless science can prove their method is testing true age, not an arbitrary claim about when the decay products formed. It has never shown this, and may not do so.

It is very interesting, and revealing of current thinking, that some have tried to raise the profile of this claim in recent years, by saying these derived dates are indeed 'absolute', so keen are they to show validity. This attempt does not make the grade in logic, since no such high standard has been demonstrated.

In this intriguing case of radioactivity measured, the only firm fact is that the element of argon or thorium has been found. Any inference as to its residence age is supposed.

Sir Karl Popper set a high standard for any proof in science, noting that '...we hate the very idea we may be mistaken, so we cling dogmatically to our conjectures, as long as possible', and that 'science begins with myths'.

The great challenge is when to remove the myths in favour of an advance. The problem is we never quite know for sure, hence the need for objective confirmation.

Any proof has to be made in the complete absence of conjecture, inference, imagination, speculation, supposition or presumption. It has to be proven via inescapable steps that are unquestionably both precisely derived and indisputably correct in their conclusions.

It is astonishing to state this, yet on the above basis it would seem so: both for evolution, and the linear model of time on which it relies, no such proof exists in any form. In 300 years of looking, this has not emerged. If it does, that would be a revelation.

When that has been achieved, we will all happily accept the outcome.

Further detail

Let's see how the idea of using fossils arose in geology, and see if we agree.

William Smith was born in 1769, worked as a canal engineer, and was influenced by the *Uniformitarian Principle* in the earlier work of James Hutton (who mostly ignored strata and fossils), as he set about the task of correlating fossils locally to Britain to establish their similarity in age. Smith published his geological map in 1815.

His map seemed to confirm what was logical and clear: fossils marked out layers. This idea was assumed by all to be right, but it would later be seen to be a giant error.

It all seemed obvious, and since no one had anywhere near enough data to disagree, this concept was then rolled out to cover the world, without any question as to whether time could indeed be drawn 'as a line back in age'. They never doubted linear time, nor needed to, or had any information about a cycle, so the mismatches grew in number and as problems, never to be sorted out until today. Fossils would 'appear' or vanish in strata, so they took it to be preservation anomalies, not a systemic dilemma.

Rather a lot has happened in all science over the last 291 years since Hutton's 1726 birth. To suppose his era's perception of earth science could still be true after so long, may be expecting too much. Even today's quantum physics could not have been imagined by Albert Einstein himself, who helped so deeply to unearth some of its secrets. It was only due to the tragedy of the First World War that he was given enough scope to test such wild ideas at all, and more amazing they were largely true.

Hutton, Lyell, Smith and Darwin knew nothing about modern geophysics, because it hadn't been imagined in their era. To them, the basic idea of a starting date for earth was suitably separate from the Biblical version of Creation, so it would do for now. Any concept of six mass extinctions, axial tilts, asteroids, space weather, volcanic winters, magnetic reversals or coal under the South Pole, let alone 348 lakes found below by ice-penetrating radar showing the climate had changed in days, were unimaginable as facts.

Today they are accepted by everyone, yet have not been accounted for as to meaning.

To the older generation of Hutton's era, geology looked like a piece of cake: just match the creature with the layer, and agree with friends that every such fossil confirms that level as the same age. It looked simple enough, and so 'must be' obviously right, they reasoned. Smith's Laws were even made to entrench these new ideas in stone.

No one disagreed, *without enough data to do so*. They reckoned the various fossil shells found 'must' change over long periods of time, so these changes could be used to date the rocks that entombed them. The snag here is obvious: those changes may have nothing to do with evolving. They can be just different species, which would explain why the differences often do not fit Darwin's idea. Another key problem that would only appear centuries later would be this: a marked lack of the 'right' fossils, showing enough of these predicted changes. A simple idea got them out of that mess, or so they reckoned: the missing forms did not survive! Trace fossils and mineralization discount that claim.

A mass of marine creatures and plants may not a timescale make. There must be deep reasons why the fossil succession does not fit. The early pioneers thought of the strata as simple pages of earth history in a long book, because that is how they appeared, long before the 20th century, and thanks to millions of 'rock hounds' peering at millions of rocks for the next 300 years. Mysteries only grew.

Yet those early pioneers had very little information to use. In that 17–19th century era there were no plate tectonics, axial shifts, magneto-stratigraphy or flood basalts even imagined, so they couldn't consider them. These, and many other giant features, were not factors for them, and awaited discovery far in the future. Now we do have them, it is almost too late to change a whole philosophy. It runs very deeply, and their old way of thinking has already been so firmly rooted in every textbook and in many a mind, that any major change is labelled unthinkable, written off as heresy, and an outrage to 'right thinking'. In 300 years, that thinking is much the same, despite the new facts.

Science has to add in the modern finds. That future they foresaw has arrived, yet still the thinking has not adapted.

The present is not the key to the past as Hutton claimed, because the same rocks and conditions of the earlier eras no longer persist to the present day. As if we need reminding, chalk is not forming anywhere today, and nor are vast flood basalts, which is just as well. We see tiny examples in Hawaii, where lava rolls over houses and along roads. Do we see 2000 foot high (600m) waves these days? They have happened, such as in the Gulf of Mexico in the Cretaceous, but not now. And most telling of all perhaps, where are those trillions (thousands of billions) of bones and shell forms that should have lived in the oceans and on land, if geological time were as old as proposed?

There just isn't evidence for 3,000 million years of those processes as claimed. With such gaps in the traditional story of earth history, we are bound to question that 'ancestral vision' of geology we inherited 300 years ago.

As we do this, we realise none of the earlier large scale claims fit the timescale given for them. This has given experts a real headache as they struggled to match the story with reality. Prof. Tjeerd van Andel's famous missing discontinuity is an example we note here, but the problem is far larger.

It requires a blank sheet approach. Doing this, and what do we find? We find nothing fits. Take the moss claimed to be 10 million years old; did it really lie there in the Dry Valleys for so long, or was the dating of the nearby volcanic ash the victim of the errors noted above? The moss cannot be that old, by any means of physics and biology. The land dinosaurs cannot have lived for 110 million years, leaving only 650 or so for us to find (& 800 bird types). All the world's fossils should number in the trillions, for each species, yet they so don't. The spectacular Monument Valley in America, made famous in John Wayne films, has a flat floor because the water that cut it moved very rapidly, not slowly enough to form incised meanders, as we see further west in the Grand Canyon.

Space is odd too, in old thinking. The claimed Big Bang could not have invented all the matter as claimed, nor formed a string of universes, because it has to come from somewhere...unless it was already here. The galaxies could not possibly be speeding up when everyone predicted they would be slowing down by now...if 13 billion years had gone by. The microwaves in space should not be flat if time is a line, and yet they are.

Few of us mind which answer is true, but we would surely prefer to know, and find a better match to modern facts than the old story ever managed. The line of time cannot solve these issues. This brings us to what can: the solution of a cycle to replace that classic line suggested years ago.

Let's envisage the whole cycle in one image, as in the diagram of Fig 21. There are three key items that are closely connected, the tilt causing the others.

These three major events are:

1 EARTH'S TILTING AXIS from 0° to 23.4° off vertical; asteroidal 'near-miss' as likely cause; set off a train of ultra-explosive events and core/mantle friction plus extra heat
2 PANGEA SUPERCONTINENT BREAK UP, continental plates rush to new locations of precise equilibrium at great speed eg 5 years, must faster than the 2.5cms/year seen today
3 MASSIVE PLATE MARGIN FISSURES FORM, vast igneous lava floods take place; >80% of earth's surface set in upheaval on land and below oceans

All these events happened, but are not yet agreed as occurring at the same time. As the diagram shows, it is possible that all this happened within 5–15 years or less, so we will add 50 years for good measure, making it 65. At 10 years, the Atlantic could have formed in that time, with the continents only moving apart at 1.1mph or 1.7kph. It could have been much quicker, if the upper mantle became much hotter due to the friction caused by the nickel-iron 'NiFe' core rotating at a different speed to the rest of earth. This could occur in this case of a near miss that altered earth's rotation speed and axial tilt. Witness the changes to the diurnal hourly total found in ancient Bahamian corals, which show around 21 hour days. Something was going on to cause such great consequences.

That didn't happen because King Arthur burned some cakes. The forces at play were colossal to crack much of the earth's surface, and a telling reason to think it was all recent is the axis is still moving today. The momentum of the metallic core would have been high, at 2440kms diameter, with nearly twice that including the liquid shell around it, and that would account for the numerous magnetic polar reversals we see in the rocks of every named system. This adds weight to the suggestion that all these events happened in a short period of less than 100 years, as part of a 5,000 year cycle.

Sounds impossible? To most geologists, it must be unthinkable, and here is the only obstacle this cyclic version has: our choice to think of it as possible. Most of those changes would have occurred after the axial tilt, since there was no chaos before. The calm era could indeed have been marked by the early chalk and limestone layers showing calm, warm seas. Earth's earlier vertical axis and circular solar orbit would have produced those climatic conditions.

How could 1.5 billion years of change actually occur within 1,200 years? Very easily, the old date was just an estimate. Without the dates' validation of the conventional timescale, the old ages have no effect on our view of what actually happened. It is equally easy to see how this came about. The early pioneers saw the world, noted the different rock types of Europe, saw fossils in some sediments, and quickly envisaged a linear succession of those same layers, marked out by either rock type or bio-content. No one had any cause to visualize a cyclic universe of far greater complexity, in which the geological eras from the Cambrian to the Cretaceous could be so contemporary.

Few do even now. This mould was set in those early days. Darwin read these ideas in the books by Hutton and Lyell, and noted the long, slow period of change they described as fitting the fossils too, or so it seemed. Without any of the contents of this book, or any facts of astronomy from 200 years later, that theory stuck in the minds of scientists. Evolution was rolled out to cover the world, and explain space, neither of which areas are actually explained at all.

Darwin realised how arbitrary and artificial their answers were, and said so, but the die was cast. Later generations have simply built on those ideas, and the subtle effects of each new discovery never forced the changes in world view that were required.

At least there is no doubt the above events are reality. All this did happen, and that is agreed. The tilt and orbital change would readily have that dual effect on both climate and land areas: if the axis of earth did suffer a sudden alteration that only an asteroid or planetary sized mass could produce in a near miss, then the continental plates would instantly start migrating at very high speed to new locations. We all accept tectonic plate migration took place, since expert agreement around 1969 at least (famously by Vine, Matthews of Cambridge University), so all that remains to be agreed is the speed. Even 1mph is not very fast, and it could be 2–5mph, maybe far more.

Could it have been this much faster? Yes, it could, from the plates' momentum.

Nothing happens by itself, without an agent of change, and oceans are one.

Tsunamis are a huge oceanic effect, yet do not form by themselves, but are the results of tectonic shifts displacing water, or very large landslips indeed, such as in Alaska's Lituya Bay, where a high outcrop of rocks crashed into the bay on 9th July 1958 on a huge scale. One eye witness saw that, and told his son not to look behind him. Luckily they were in a boat and both survived, after the anchor chain snapped as needed.

No one considered the admittedly strange possibility that the continents could once have moved so fast over the earth's mantle that sediments were moved around in huge surges of energy and motion in days, not centuries or longer.

Yet this is what we find, greatly complicated by later deposits of interleaved strata that trick us into thinking those areas are older, but the whole Mid Atlantic Ridge (MAR) cannot be as old as claimed at 60myo, with that lack of sedimentary overburden.

Other finds show unusual results.

Recent permafrost finds are also intriguing, such as the mammoth bones of northern Russia, and the *tropical animals* compacted by rapid processes and deposited in the Alaskan formations, as noted by Rainey and Hibben in the 1940's, who reported lion and mammoth together along with human artefacts found there. All their remains were so broken and thrown together with splintered tree fragments that a very large tsunami has been suggested. The axial tilt would do this too.

The seas are not themselves always the movers of material. *Evaporites* form when brackish or other water bodies contain dissolved minerals, such as salt or gypsum, which then become sediments as the water evaporates, hence the term; so in this sense, the presence of the minerals is the key factor, and the water enables the process to take place. The entire Mediterranean Sea has been a large lake at times, known as Lago Mare from the Latin, because it had been cut off from the Atlantic by the cyclic changes to its shores, such as when the Strait of Gibraltar would open and close, causing the water to become concentrated due to evaporation. It remains saltier than the Atlantic to this day, and oddly free of planktonic life.

This is called the Zanclean flooding of this sea, and has an estimated age of 5.3 million years, but a more recent date of only 3,200 years is not only entirely possible, but most likely. If so, that is over 165,000% degree of error.

Could we really have been this wrong? It appears so. Now we can argue about this as much as we like, but it isn't going to do any good. The area below the sea floor is full of salt from evaporation, so it was hotter in those days in that zone. The axial tilt of the earth could have caused this rapid climate change and fast evaporation, with intense and rapid hot and dry spells.

Our key question of 'can geology be cyclic' has been asked: many already agree it can. Indeed it was suggested by Tuzo Wilson and others that the igneous surface geology is constantly recycling at the continental margins, where ocean floor material is 'subducted' under continental plates, meaning that it dives under them to be re-melted in the mantle, and returned to the surface later on. The standard theory is that this process has gone on countless times over billions of years, but that is an assumption.

Some residual chaos is still very apparent. We see major earthquakes and waves occurring quite frequently, such as off the east coast of Japan, the North West coast of Sumatra in Indonesia, and Turkey in the northern Mediterranean. This will then stop when the chaos peaks, and the next cycle begins with flat calm and order.

Summary of 28 key events

We can set out a new geology that does not rely on linear time. Here is a condensed list of main events, showing the rapid changes which may take only five millennia.

A proposed Cyclic Earth History within 4,950 years

1 Cyclic clock re-set by quantum pulse…Cyclic 'start', known as the *Flash Time Moment*. Population small but always present
2 Continents grouped together as Pangaea 'supercontintent', India by Africa
3 Planetoid incursion passes by earth, altering elliptical orbit to circular
4 Axis tilts back to vertical at this time, with calm climate and stability
5 Earth's core is also stable, with no quakes or tsunamis, poles aligned N-S
6 Warm climate is ideal for forests and plant growth, later to become coal
7 Oceans also calm, bulk chalk and limestone, sandstones laid down, massive beds show calm and regular conditions prevailed; corals of Jurassic and Cretaceous eras, + no ice caps; Sahara wet with rivers, lakes and sub-tropical climate, found below current sand layers by radar + tribes and petroglyphs [images on stone]
8 Antarctica, vast yet not ice-covered, but heavily forested and with lakes: warm era, landmass still part of Great Australian Bight
9 Mediterranean Sea in its Lago Mare era, cut off from Atlantic, very saline
10 MIDWAY CYCLIC CHANGE, due to chief AXIAL TILT from 0° to ±23° as present; planetary orbit now elliptical causing global climate + seasonal extremes
11 Sediments show over 50 cycles (*cyclothems*) in current USA coast to coast as alternate marine influx and regression events, from Recent back to Cambrian, always with unconformities, which can be rapid; Carboniferous and Permian *sediments on most*

continents globally also show cycles of sea level rise and fall: can be due to same axial oscillations, and rapid switches possible in months, hence common sequences far apart.

12 Core of earth changes magnetic polarity *chrons* (same polarity time interval) rapidly as inner core spins, creating polarity reversals and dipole degradation

13 Polar ice caps form, sea level changes globally as axial tilt + poles oscillate

14 Rapid break up of Pangaea into current continents due to axial shift, as heavy landmasses move at high speed to locations of equatorial balance, credibly between 1–300 years *[NB next 10 points almost contemporary]*

15 Dinosaur era short and rapid hence fewer finds than expected, ended by instant K-T event with 12km Chicxulub meteor impact & 195km crater

16 Ocean floor spreading at equally high speed, hence uniform depth below current sea level of 4400m; Mid Atlantic Ridge forms and extends around planet through southern Indian Ocean, becoming fracture zones in the south and east Pacific Ocean. Recent + thus still highly active, e.g. Juan de Fuca

17 Igneous re-set times confused by decay daughter remnants in all rock; no distinction between 'young and old' crustal material in 'cyclic earth model'

18 Cambrian Explosion of life apparent, yet not actual, hence why complex life appears without origin; unconformities common,

19 Carboniferous era deposits form by being overlain by other deposits in huge tsunamis caused by equally vast tectonic uplifts worldwide, global areas show same 'mud, sand, coal' bundles of interleaved cycles or rhythms, which show same conditions on a global scale over short time period.

20 Human cultures in low areas covered by floodwaters, e.g. *Rann of Kutch* coastal area below Indus Valley and others. Nile delta cuts below sea level

21 Continental Flood Basalt (CFB) eg events in Columbia River USA, African Karoo, Deccan in India, Siberia, cover 70% of land, not to forget the giant sub-ocean events eg Ontong-Java Plateau 57 mill.cu.km^3 in W. Pacific.

22 Axial tilt and core rotation create unstable crustal areas with
   constant switches in polarity, quakes, tectonic uplift zones with
   massive tsunamis, large abnormal deposits such as Atlantic's
   700km Blake Outer Ridge, and upheaval of all major sediments
   laid down & cemented in earlier calm era

23 Sedimentary strata globally uplifted or overlain, [hence anoxic/
   redox events & banded iron ore deposition] metamorphosed
   into current mountain chains and alpine orogenies; Himalaya
   and Tibetan Plateau formed by India shift, monsoon rains begin,
   climate pattern unstable, winters & seasonal heat more extreme;
   Grand Canyon and Colorado Plateau large scale deposits

24 Extinction Events, e.g. Permian, Ordovician, Cretaceous caused
   by extreme wet/dry changes and tsunamis, wide desertification,
   + uplift altering climate, e.g. Andes, Gobi Desert, Sahara; aeolian
   deposits, Loess etc.

25 Messina Salinity Crisis (MSC) occurs with Mediterranean Sea
   repeatedly wet and dry but cut off from Atlantic, *evaporites*
   formed; Zanclean flood as Atlantic flows in, about 1200BC, not
   5.33my, taking only weeks to fill sea

26 Axial oscillations cause rapid fine and coarse grain <1mm layers
   [i.e. varves] to appear seasonal yet can occur within weeks, e.g.
   Jurassic *'high to low carbonate cycles'* found in France and sea
   floor cores in Atlantic; coral day-length anomalies of Bahamas;
   cyclic strata bundles common globally

27 Present day: geology showing no clear origins to Cambrian 'start'
   of life claim, and anomalous biostratigraphy that presumes linear
   time as factual.

28 Above events and sea level changes can occur very quickly, yet
   current chronology based on radiogenic dates that have been
   calibrated by linear systems, not absolute dates; decay quantities
   would be upset by cosmos scale quantum spin re-set of matter
   as set out earlier; evidence in *Flatness Problem* of cosmic
   microwaves [CMB].

As we shall see next, there are a few more surprises in the cyclic time
model that explain the mystery of why we missed the clear evidence
we can now see.

PART 3

Evidence for Time Rotation

CHAPTER 13

Astronomy and Cyclic Time: how time repeats

When people are fanatically dedicated to faiths or any other kind of dogmas or goals, it is always because these dogmas or goals are in doubt.
ROBERT M. PIRSIG, 1974, Zen & the Art of Motorcycle Maintenance

Have the courage to know: that is the motto of enlightenment.
IMMANUEL KANT, 1783, philosopher/ scientist

Essence

How to separate fact from theory, when the two have been well mixed up? The chaos in the world is increasing so rapidly that there must be crunch point very soon, so the mechanism would be vital to know.

As one leading scholar in the UK's upper House of Lords recently said, how many '1 in 100 year' events do we need in the last five years before someone realises they happen very often? That is a good question: old theories have been overtaken by events. The universe has all the signs of a continuum that lasts forever. This means it will not die out as claimed, but the entire system is regenerated at this time of extremes, and calm is restored.

As we will see next, the clues that the human consciousness acts like a spark of energy, a dot of energy affecting the whole system, mean that we will never die out either. Most people already think that can be so, but now there is physical evidence to show how it works. The fact we are still here, alive and fairly well, is proof that it could be what happens. The accelerating galaxies are another clue, since they 'should be' slowing down so long after the claimed 'big bang', yet they are speeding up. This suggests a recent force or 'big push', otherwise they would be slowing down, not accelerating.

Our old friend the F Ring of Saturn is another powerful clue that mystifies experts: if this vast collection of ice pieces, some the size of houses, had truly been clanking around against each other for 4.5 billion years as claimed, since they theoretically 'came into being', they would have been reduced to powder long ago. Yet they have not, showing their formation is young and recent, not ancient. This is a crucial point.

A cycle of time would also account for the huge difference between the rocky and gaseous planets we have as neighbours, since if they all formed from one disc of material they 'should' be very similar. Our own solar system therefore appears to be part of a continuum, not a simple Big Bang, which these signs show did not occur as claimed. [See astrophysics papers: arxiv.org] This cycle is a new world view to us, yet every culture in history treated it as normal...only modern thinking disagrees, preferring theory over what nature does all day long: moving all the matter around in circles.

The vast realm of space is literally crammed with evidence for cyclic time. Why did we never find it before? Simple...we never looked for it.

For anyone who enjoys astronomy, here we will try to separate theory from reality. While a bit more demanding than some chapters, the basics are really very simple indeed, and the glossary will help explain unfamiliar words or concepts, so the whole process of untangling this 'code' becomes amusing and exciting.

Why does this matter at all? This is the story of all our lives. Whatever culture or belief system we hold, this is our story, so we have to get it right if our lives are to hold the full meaning they actually possess. It is therefore very important in every way. These details flatly contradict nearly all our major 'accepted facts', and Einstein's endorsement of time being linear. There is no point in clinging on to old ideas that are about as useful as a toad in a tornado.

Let's look at the 'Dark Matter/Energy' issue. The universe appears to have a shortage of gravity. It 'does' things it should have no power to do, if time was a long line. So let us switch this idea to our new version, and see time for a while as a cycle that always exists. In this case, the galaxies are always there, and are not formed afresh as each new cycle begins. This is 'step one' in a sense (the full picture comes later).

It has long fascinated observers in astrophysics and other sciences that fully 96% of the 'mass' or matter in the universe is unaccounted for. They recently changed this figure to 85%, but the point is still the same: scientists do not know what is going on. Entire galaxies, billions of square miles in area and extent, are apparently rotating in space, filled with stars which are vast even on their own. Our own sun is a good example of a huge star, at 1.3 million times the volume of earth. At any rate, the galaxies should no longer be accelerating because they 'would have' slowed down long ago. They haven't slowed down at all, therefore the 'age' of the universe may have been misunderstood entirely. After all, in a cyclic universe there would be no start or end dates. Even the theory of inflation does not work without forcing the mathematics to suit the idea.

Every cosmologist knows about this serious problem.

Since they cannot explain these movements, it has been imagined that some hidden force of gravity must exist and is secretly and invisibly the cause of this bizarre motion. Science firmly and confidently predicted that the universe must be cold and dead if it is extremely

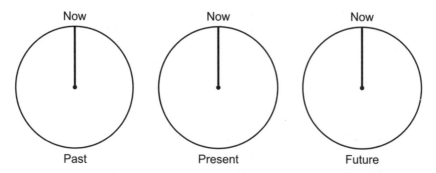

Time cycle relative to 'now'

Now   Now   Now

Past   Present   Future

(Courtesy of Paul Mortensen) © BGI

FIGURE 23 *Time relative to Now: 3 cycles connecting past, present and future, showing repeating time of 'now' that explains déjà vu as experienced by so many.*

ancient in the linear sense of old. They were wrong, and instead of being dead and motionless in places, the universe turns out to be highly active and in rapid motion.

Experts tend to ignore these signs, because they directly contradict the whole idea of time being long and linear. So instead of questioning time itself, and their concept of how it unfolds, they invent a long list of clever reasons how it got this way, while never reaching the heart of the problem...time may be a cycle instead.

To account for this odd state of the cosmos, invisible materials like Dark Matter, and the force known as Dark Energy have been invented and put forward as 'likely to exist'. Their existence is inferred, but not proven. The answer here is more radical: both are an artifice that is not even needed, if time always exists as a continuum.

Cyclic time shows there is no need to invent all this gravity.

Fairly recently, some time lapse images were captured that almost certainly do show the existence of a black hole in our own galaxy. A small red cross was super-imposed on the centre of the activity seen, and nearby stars were seen to be speeding up as they came under its influence, only to 'slingshot' outwards as they increased their velocity, and were then thrown out again into areas where they regained their original speed. All this could be seen happening when the images were speeded up in a short film clip of a few seconds, yet in the region marked by the red cross, there was nothing whatever visible to us at all.

This is most intriguing, because we can fairly draw inferences from this discovery. It is certain that some kind of extreme physical force, perhaps as mass of some kind, was exerting a strong gravitational power over any object that strayed into its sphere of influence; so we can be sure *something* was in that area.

Our view of matter also needs updating. We are so used to thinking of mass and power and energy as material, composed of lumps of things we can usually see and easily detect, that invisible forces like sub-atomic particles that can pass through even a whole planet like earth without disturbing a single atom, require a shift in our understanding. Another interesting and less dramatic example is the way a slab of rock salt is a solid piece of crystalline matter we can hold up, and yet it allows heat to pass right through it as though it were not there at all. Any object using it for shelter from the heat source will be burnt as though nothing were there. Even glass cannot do that, while we can see through it so perfectly clearly. Light can pass, heat much less. In sub-atomic physics there are even stranger happenings that can shed light on this strange world of counter-intuitive facts.

Perhaps the most fascinating are the Cooper Pairs. Discovered in 1972 by Bardeen, Cooper and Schrieffer, it became part of BCS *Theory* in which weakly bound electrons do not act separately, but as a dynamic pair, even though they may be *many miles apart*. Therefore, if you have two particles spinning in the same direction, when you alter the motion of one, the other *instantly* alters to match and mimic that new motion, even at a distance from each other. Scientists measured no time difference in the change: it was instant.

No-one knows how it happens, yet it does happen, and it is still the subject of wide research, the reason being that it offers a clear window on the workings of a world we do not yet fully understand. One answer is the existence of a 'grid', so matter is linked even before anything happens. We'll come back to this.

Superconductors are special materials that show a unique effect. This is important in our study here, because these effects show that matter behaves very weirdly compared to what we expected. It can 'do' things (i.e. make energy transfers) once thought pure fantasy, and the 'switch' of matter from a state of chaos to order in a nanosecond or less becomes possible.

Very briefly, here is how. Often found in metals when 'super-cooled' to near absolute zero, they begin to lose their electrical resistance to current flow entirely. They also show other interesting effects, once thought impossible, and Cambridge wizard Professor Brian Josephson won a Nobel Prize for showing these in 1973 (with Esaki and Giaever). Named the Josephson Effects, currents of electricity can also pass from one superconductor to another without applying a potential, and other zero-resistance and alternating current effects occur that are used in high-speed logic circuits, all entirely unknown before these discoveries. It is thought that in a toroidal or circular form, a DC supercurrent could move round unimpeded without loss of energy, which is also quite a thing, since our old friends the Cooper Pairs may then moving freely through the lattice, which is a 'quantum mechanical effect' thought earlier to be quite impossible.

Therefore, we clearly do have a complex and 'intricately connected' universe that is highly dynamic in ways we barely recognise, and do not yet understand, and it definitely does all this at a far deeper level than in merely the narrow spectral band of light we can see with our eyes.

As a result, it is now possible to infer a hidden or 'additional state' for spacetime based on these findings in new research, so we can say this:

'A quantum spin state, Super Grid or 'flux', sub-atomic in nature, exists between and throughout the atomic world we can see and detect, and which Grid is the primary dimension of interaction between both visible and invisible spheres of influence; pulses of energy move through this grid are instant, thus move at faster than light speed.'

Otherwise, how could pairs of apparently unconnected electrons miles apart suddenly alter spin and, crucially, do so without any detectable link or even gap in time? They could not, so the inference appears correct in reality, and we can add to it and build up a new picture over time.

We are used to measuring the 'energy density' in situations, such in the ocean or air, so there may also be such an 'energy state' operating at a primary quantum spin level, which is of supreme authority in its effects. This can be a kind of 'Super Grid' that is present continuously, and with which we interact as we move though this 'soup' of energy particles, which relates to the word Max Planck first used: Quantum. That just means a 'parcel' or quantity in essence, yet the cosmos may be composed of energy that is so finely balanced, that just a tiny influence would have universe wide effects instantly.

This simple motion of cause and effect then sets off sequences of events, only part of which we can see. When those events switch states in an instant, time can repeat again, with the same ideal results each time. it may look chaotic as we see it, and often unpleasant compared to our sub-conscious 'memory' of what it should be like, but that is only due to the chaotic 'spin state' of all matter. When it flips back very shortly, then the whole state of disorder becomes ordered instantly.

Triple Cyclic Time

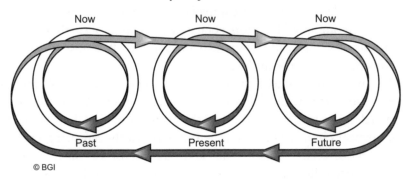

FIGURE 24 *Triple Cyclic Time: 3 cycles or time phases 'entangled' with each other, since all events in spacetime are a continuum that always ends and begins again with Order: the perfect sequence, hence why the disc was copied by all ancient cultures who revered the natural order of the universe as a known cycle of time. No other outcome is then possible or happens, since this ideal cyclic sequence must be completed, as day always follows night. Our existence now can be evidence of this ideal cyclic time sequence.*

This is the concept of a 'Perfect Cycle of Time', and no one has ever disproved it.

Such a state of matter where it begins to act as one unit is what is proposed here, and current research has found such states as clues to what else may be possible. The suggestion is that Matter may not only be a closed system, but can also act as one sub-atomic unit in its entirety. The classic example is that of the CM defined previously, which shows signs of recent realignment.

Closer to home, we can see more. There is a similar concept used in physics called the Bose-Einstein Condensate, as noted earlier, in which atoms cooled to a few nanokelvins above Absolute Zero (-273.16°C) would merge to form a 'syncytium' or pool that acts as a single coherent entity; rather like a bag full of atoms subtly joined. The idea proposed here is very similar, in that all matter in the universe could be acting as one single unit that is constantly interconnected, in this case, twice in our 'cycle of events', the entire system switches between order and chaos, and then back again, on a continual basis to become a truly 'cyclic continuum'. It is suggested this situation may be happening as normal on a larger scale in the universe, and that by altering quantum spin even in one small location, such as a small area of earth, the entire cosmos *as one unit* could 'snap into a new state'. It is possible that we humans play a key role in this.

This 'ultimate moment' that defines the end of one cycle and the start of the next is what defines the Flash Time event. If you like using the word 'KAPOW!', now would be the perfect time for that. Since this fundamental change would happen in a perfectly repeating cycle in this model of reality, this is what gives us a sense of 'machinery', in which events follow an ideal sequence that never ends, thus solving the enigma of a start that does not exist; 'change' is a better concept, and could literally happen in a 'flash moment' in time's sequence. Once again, it is the CMB flatness aspect showing it happened recently.

This would be the Flash Time moment in which the universe's entire 'energy flux' reverts to being an obviously coherent system which can function as a true Cycle of Time. At other times, the system would appear random even while not being so at all, without this view of the energy flux as a whole entirety acting as one single unit.

Our personal view of all this would always be so severely limited by the astonishingly small physical scale of our perceptive powers, that we could not possibly appreciate this without the help of science. Even today, it is only thanks to science that we can detect any of the effects that have accumulated over the years which give any form at all to the evidence predicted to be present.

It therefore appears that time really can be cyclic, and that events may indeed repeat identically in this 'perfect cycle', the mechanism for which can indeed require the close interaction of Matter with human beings, but on a deeper level than science has so far been able to analyse.

In this way the universe may alternate between periods of several thousand years in one higher state we may term Order, and then gradually lose power and integrity over that time-span during a classic descent into chaos, the final segment of which we are seeing now, only to return to the higher state of Order as the system is *re-ordered* by the next major event strong enough to cause such a change.

Matter is not the solid, predictable collection of simple particles that we understand. Science clearly cannot yet explain how or why even matter or pure energy work, nor the mind, nor memory, nor where life came from, or where it is going, nor the gaps in the fossil and other records, nor the other hundreds of contradictions raised in this book and elsewhere, so a new vision is needed. The more we learn of sub-atomic energy and its ability to function and move 'through' matter as we see it, such as in the little understood or detected behaviour of neutrinos, the more likely could be this cyclic version of how the Grid may function.

At least it seems able to explain a little more of what we actually see, and supports the premise of a true or 'perfect' cycle of spacetime, which may move in a perfect and continuous action of 'Rotation', yet to such a degree of perfection and accuracy, and on such a truly vast scale that is cosmos-wide, that we can still only wonder at the precision shown.

Diagram of 6-Dimensional Reality

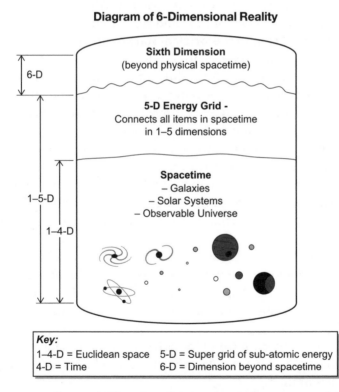

FIGURE 25 *Space & Time in 6 Dimensions: diagram combining 5 dimensions of spacetime and one beyond these.*

Yet while we remain unable to identify most of these subtle levels of sub-atomic quantum power, we can definitely detect a wide range of effects, and thus confidently infer their presence. This is possible to say since we can see a significant part of what they do, which at least proves the existence of otherwise unexplainable findings, and thus infers the existence of this hidden power flux or Grid, referred to earlier as a 'Flash Time Energy Flux'.

What is suggested is that spacetime runs for a period of years, and then comes the moment of Flash Time which re-sets it all to 'zero', and the same sequence begins once again. This zero point does not mean that nothing remains, but something quite different: the re-arrangement of all matter in its ideal 'ground state' of order. This version of reality never needs the invention of Matter or Time to appear out of nowhere, because it suggests they are always in existence. All that happens every few millennia is this switch of time and space that 'flashes' the whole unit as an entity, back into this original state of order.

Once again, as time passes, chaos gradually increases.

The linear framework has some difficulties which have been put on the shelf labelled *'Not sure...we'll figure it out later'*. That later period never arrived, so science had to continue bolting on new pieces to the linear model, in an attempt to make it work. It never quite did, but at least valuable data continued to pour in. Nearly every science paper has come across puzzles that do not fit linear time, so on the shelf they also go. Now that shelf is groaning under the weight of thousands of such uncertainties, with more being piled on every day. Without a working model that functions, there is simply nowhere else to put them.

As noted by Prof. Lee Smolin, this may have been why Einstein's generation were allowed to work on those ground-breaking theories during the First World War years, since 'there simply weren't many senior scientists around to tell them they were crazy', and stop them in their tracks.

Even great scientists have made errors. Einstein made small but significant errors in his formulae, the effect of which was to support linear models of time.

Nils Bohr in 1905 became fascinated by the finding of Professor Ernest Rutherford at Manchester University that radioactivity particles could pass straight through a very thin film of gold leaf only a few atoms thick, while as few as 1 in 8,000 might bounce back as if hitting a solid object. They learned later that these 'emission' particles were hitting the nucleus head on while the other particles went through what was essentially empty space. Bohr was intrigued to find that *there was so much space* between the nucleus in the centre of an atom, and the electrons spinning round it at an incredible distance away from the nuclear centre.

To put this amazing fact into context and a comparison of size that is easier to grasp, it has been calculated that if the nucleus was the size of a football, then the outer particles are spinning in their 'shells' about a kilometre away from the centre. Indeed there is so little actual solid matter involved in atoms, that if you put all those nuclear particles in one place, a human body of average size would be reduced to a grain of salt in size, and even all the 6 billion people of earth would barely fill an apple in volume. Even all the oceans of the world, with their billions of tons of weight and crushing pressures at depth on the abyssal plains of the sea floor, could similarly fit into the volume of just one glass of water (BBC 2 documentary 'Atom', 21st Jan 2008).

This is an astonishing thought, and one of the few scientific findings we can have some faith in, as many do not match experimental data. The age of the earth is always talked about in terms of years, reasonably enough. Yet this question itself could be a misunderstanding.

We would be assuming it had a 'start point' of formation of that age, which has not been proved. To ask 'is it old or not?' ignores the orbital option so often found in Nature, in which matter rotates in a sequence of states, and not the artificial 'Start-End' one-time thing we tend to seize on; perhaps we have been rather narrowly restricting Nature to our own preconception of what we think 'must be so'.

This old linear thinking could be the whole problem: too narrow by far. So when we ask 'is it old' or not, we forget if *the question itself* may contain a misconception. If time is a circle, then there would be no beginning as such.

This usually receives one reaction: we conclude it can't be true, and ignore the oddly short dates as 'errors'. To a traditional scientist, any oddly young age for an item could never be correct. This is how many still think, yet the problem is well known, in which radioactive decay products are 'assumed' to be due to long decay times, whereas the evidence suggests they are already present in the rock at the time of formation and eruption. Since this method underpins the whole of evolution, it is a problem.

We can now gain clarity on one or two other crucial matters: one is that nothing could have happened by chance, since no random events can occur in a true Cycle of Time. Things may look random, yet they are clearly connected, since nothing is happening in isolation, but has to occur causally from other pre-existing events.

Secondly, the worry about global warming is only partly correct, because it is just one part of the global state of decay at this point in the world cycle, moments before the universe 'snaps back' into the state of order. There will be chaos of course, but it is happening for these deeper reasons: the effects of chaos are entropic and endemic, and cannot stop until balanced. The good news is that the state of order predicted would happen inevitably, and so the currently chaotic state will instantly revert to the level of calm; and just as well.

Events may be perfectly and profoundly cyclic. We do see such effects in every part of life. New always becomes old, and then Nature reverses the situation.

A new state of equilibrium is being found by both ourselves, and Matter, as atoms flash across to their positions of balance. It may even be possible, as suggested here, that humanity plays a key role in both halves of this play, first in assisting order to degrade into chaos, and then the inevitable climb out of the dive as we reverse descent into ascent.

If thoughts do indeed affect our Super Grid, this would happen as above.

In this model there would be no final end to this process of cause and effect, but a rapid snap back into Order again, right across the cosmos in the same moment.

Whatever we may think of this suggestion, there appears to be no other option that can explain so much of what we observe that was once so puzzling. This could indeed be the missing solution to the mystery of how reality works.

CHAPTER 14

Atoms and Humans

…science is too important to leave to the scientists.
ASHLEY MONTAGU (New York Times, 26 April 1964)

All method is imperfect. Error is all around it, and at the least opportunity invades it.
DR C.NICOLLE, 1928, Nobel Prize winner

Essence

Now to see if we can harmonise two main opinions. Is one wrong, or both right? We have a very interesting situation.

One group of people, and it is a big one, feels certain that there is a kind of magical cause to Earth's situation that is not explainable by science, or not correctly so anyway. Then we have Group 2, which is based on the traditional reliance on science as the answer to all things, period. With deference to the older system, we can call the first party Group 1, since the modern view of 20th and 21st century science is the new kid on this block by a couple of millennia, so there it is.

Is there a riddle, then? Well, the scientists in Group 2 don't all think so, yet some do, while the scientists and others comprising Group 1 feel certain there is. Barely anyone has a workable idea of what it may be, but here is the strange thing: the more we find out about earth and space, the less this new bank of data fits into the little we do know.

This study seeks to resolve it. In fulfilling this task, it became increasingly clear over the decades it took to write it, that there are indeed major unsolved problems with both sides that do need to be sorted out, if they can be.

The central issue seems to be the nature of Time itself, and also what has happened during that time span…especially on earth. This takes us into tricky territory, which includes the origins of life itself. The scientific explanation has some large pieces of presumption built into the huge thinking brickwork of ideas it has so enthusiastically created over the last 200 years or so. This search for truth has not been very orderly or peaceful at times, but often very forceful with strong opinions expressed.

The central issue is an odd one: us. Do we have a greater effect on the order of matter than we realised. If the Super Grid exists, the answer is yes. It would mean that our very thoughts are so precisely linked to the atoms around us, that they alter our situation second by second.

Science has missed this. Yet the evidence is there. We even think about altering it when we have thoughts like 'let that not happen' or 'let this happen'. We have seen how thoughts affect our bodily health, so the real sphere of influence could be far greater…why not the universe, and at faster-than-light speed? Why not indeed. The order or chaos of our thinking does alter our health, so why should the energy wave stop there, when the sub-atomic 'grid' sees no difference between our own atoms and the external cosmic atoms? This is not just a wild idea, but a solution derived from all we can see, and it explains rather a lot. It explains the déjà vu experiences that are so common, and the phone callers we recognise by name even before the phone rings…because the thought arrived well before that physical step of dialling the number.

This is the Super Grid in action. It clearly exists. Contrary to what Einstein thought, there is an influence of energies that can indeed move faster than light, and thought is definitely one such example. We may have missed the full effect it has.

What we do on earth could have a strong effect of sufficient power on the right level to alter the very fabric of space and time itself. The existence of Josephson effects and the unity of the Bose-Einstein condensate are evidence that matter can be entangled on a larger scale than just two particles as in Cooper pairs (as in BCS theory). Many atoms could join together and act as a 'super-atom', with a correspondingly larger influence. Since there are no wires or lines of force detectable to explain such effects, it implies there is a kind of fabric to Matter in general enabling it to act at times as one unit, and if the force is powerful enough, to alter all of spacetime in an instant. This would only be possible if matter were in a state of 'continuous connection', reacting to the energy vibration state from moment to moment.

For these above effects to happen at all, even on a small scale, there must be such a precisely poised and balanced 'energy flux' that forms the basis of this spacetime fabric. For this to happen, as it does, there would need to be a structure of some kind that forms this invisible network along which energy can flow, and signals can be both sent and received. It is even being used by communications researchers to create systems of quantum messaging, in which signals can literally be sent between quantum states held within a similar apparatus in two different locations, only being decoded by the receiver, and then falling out of existence the instant that has been done, as the connection is broken, leaving no pathway or trace of the message itself. The military quickly realised the value of that effect, and it is at the forefront of modern research into quantum physics.

The secret effect of people on events is becoming a pivotal concept.

It is possible that our influences on Matter could indeed dislocate the natural equilibrium of the world, and the cosmos too, which once existed naturally in complete harmony. It is logical that this could be so, and if it is, that the influence reaches right across space to touch every particle's spin in every corner of the cosmos. This may also be true no matter how small the place or part of the system that is disrupted, if the vibrational energy is of the right attenuation. This happens when a frequency is reached that can break a sheet of glass with no great effort. The famous Tacoma Narrows Bridge disaster is an example of resonance and of frequency: just a 45mph wind speed of the right wavelength is reached and even giant steel structures of great rigidity crumble and fall apart.

Their rigidity is of course part of their weakness, and ours too. This may be how the influence of just one small planet, and one relatively small population, in space terms, could affect an entire cosmos. We have here an explanation of why the Drake Equation may be a misconception, and why alien life could never be found in a cyclic cosmos, simply because there has never been enough time for life to evolve as claimed. We have never found any such traces, despite looking so intensively, so this explanation is supported by the lack of such life forms.

We are all about quality. We want to do things perfectly, so far as we can, and that includes our number one task...to explain where we came from, and when. Somehow this final step of placing a firm 'when' date on humanity, and the earth's surface of course, is not actually a separate step at all, but part and parcel of our first enigma of 'where' we came from. These are the biggest questions we can ever ask, since they dictate how we live, and what decisions we make about the future. We have to get them right, since either side of ideal will count as a miss.

Now is the moment when we can at last put the few facts all together and take a close look at what we have. What we have is alarming….a universe that clearly exists, but one which *could not conceivably have come into being in the way we were told it has.*

Some of these gaps between what theory predicts compared to what we see can be colossal. One constant used to measure energy densities, called the 'cosmological constant' because it is so important, is not just a bit separate from reality, but so much so that this difference between theory and the physical is a ten followed by 120 zeroes! Even when 'supersymmetry' is used, another theory invented to patch the gap, it only brings the figure down to ten with 60 zeroes after it. Is that a match of any kind? Not remotely, and this is meant to be some of the best maths in today's world. This shows the usual model is worthless.

That proves two things: Big Bang and friends are not just wrong, but spectacularly so, and whatever the answer may turn out to be, 'linear time' cannot be it.

In a true cycle, the end always re-joins the beginning. This re-joining of the ends to make a single continuous span of time does appear to solve all these difficulties in one. The short or young apparent age of all these features could be accounted for by the existence of a looping back mechanism that allows continuity, yet without requiring a Big Bang, which requires the sudden appearance of matter, heat and energy from nowhere…an impossible feat of magic.

This is one of modern science biggest problems solved, since any number of universes have to get their energy from somewhere, so many more of them is just another version of the ancient and mythical elephant and turtle suggestion…with turtles 'all the way down' being the given answer to what the turtle stands on.

It is possible the speed of galaxies rushing across the heavens can have been due to a major change in the fabric of space, and also of Time as well…which may not have 'created' the cosmos out of nothing as scientists suggest, but only 're-created' it.

So if the sudden appearance of Matter and Time is not supported by evidence or experiment, this would be a serious problem, both in science and the exacting definitions of philosophy. It would mean such a theory is no longer realistic, or 'allowable'. This would make the current Big Bang theory well beyond improbable, which Roget defines as:

'...out of the question, illogical, imaginary, unviable, unscientific, unnatural, fly in the face of reason, exceed possibility, unbelievable, irrational and to have no chance whatever'.

Quite a list, and not quite the ringing endorsement most of us expected, yet the conventional version has been the most globally accepted theory still used to explain our whole existence, and that of the cosmos. It seems we have a problem, Houston.

Our own sun, a star in its own right, has a fascinating eleven year pattern of repeating calm and chaos energy flows. Its magnetic field 'winds up' over time, creating sun spots and a rise in hugely violent explosions known as coronal mass ejections (CME's). A peak is reached, and then it all calms down again. The Maunder Minimum is an example of a quiet period in solar history, and occurred from 1645–1715, with a mini ice age.

So now we come to examine how the Western world, whose maths and philosophy is largely founded on the thinking of the famous Greek ancestors, managed to become the only civilisation in history to depart from the idea of a cycle.

When early explorers found marine fossil exposures in rocks at the high altitudes of the Himalayas, they were amazed. With no obvious mechanism for such a finding, they naturally assumed a long period of time must have elapsed to account for such movement and distortion of the strata they were looking at. To find the very same sediments which had clearly once settled quietly on the sea floor, being lifted bodily and vertically the considerable distance of almost 8 miles towards the stratosphere, was quite a surprise, to put it mildly. Actually they were stunned, like finding a Roman era Swiss watch.

Only later would it be realised that India had also moved nearly 4,000 miles horizontally from a location beside the current South Pole, which in those days was not even cold at all, but thickly and tropically forested. So much so, indeed, that in modern times coal would be found there, derived from those very forests, compressed below rock and ice. This finding of marine shells high in the Himalayas was not just strange, it was a bombshell of a finding.

It was entirely reasonable to assume all this Himalayan motion was based on similar sediments being formed now, and so will have crept along exactly as it does today, and so therefore must have taken many eons of time to reach its present location. It now clearly appears to have been an incorrect assumption based on slow events today.

The original Antarctic rock surface is now be under 11,000 feet of ice, but very significantly there are over 368 lakes found recently to exist there even to this day, trapped 2 miles beneath the frozen layers. It was warm, and trees covered the land there, only to be covered over in a matter of days by huge waves carrying mud and sand when the axis of earth tilted. The trees had no chance to rot, so it must have been instant. The lakes froze too, and the snow built up. These lakes can only be the remnants of that earlier warm climate age, since water does not move vertically through the ice in Antarctica, as it does with such noise in the dark labyrinth of sub-surface tunnels beneath the Greenland icecap.

It can be predicted that future findings of the current project to investigate the largest of these lakes below the South Polar Region, will prove to be such a remnant. This large lake, about 100 miles long and partly separated by a ridge, has been named Lake Vostok, since it lies below the Russian Antarctic sector, and further evidence to be found shortly by the planned entry probe is bound to show that the lake formed much more recently than thought, if time is cyclic.

The essence of time may therefore be this: Time did not just 'begin' one afternoon, some time after tea. There is the plain observable fact that we are here, even though many even doubt that these days thanks to String Theory mixed with a hint of Buddhism. After all, what are we standing on whilst considering all this? So planet earth exists in real time. That clears up 'space' as being real, whatever Schrödinger felt about the cat in the box. Time and space do not exist separately, but exist together, so that Time exists along with space, and hence why some speak of 'spacetime' in one word, as explained in 'The Road to Reality'(2004) by cosmologist Professor Sir Roger Penrose (Emeritus Rouse Ball Professor of Mathematics at Oxford).

Often in science, what we want is not what nature does.

Now we have the fresh potential of a new idea: well, new to us anyway. It seems the ancients expressed the concept of a perfectly repeating cycle very clearly when Bishop Emesius wrote that *'every blade of grass, every town and every village, will be restored again, just as it was'*, as we noted.

This is quite something, and rather astonishing, when we consider these words were written over 2,000 years ago. It shows what may indeed have happened, as Nature is restored to its original zero date of Order, ready to being a fresh cycle of events.

Ancient history also holds clues to these effects.

We can only guess at the greater detail that may have been destroyed with the loss of Egypt's famous *Library of Alexandria* around 48 BC, which scholars have described as the greatest storehouse of knowledge in the ancient world. Even the Roman world was highly advanced, and even built one aqueduct system at Nîmes in France which dropped only 17m over its length of 24 kms: a superb vertical accuracy of 1.4 mm per metre. Yet deeply impressive as this accuracy is, the far more ancient Indus valley had superb stone-lined sub-surface drainage systems 1,500 years earlier. As we have seen, the Neolithic houses at Skara Brae in the Orkneys also had under floor drainage, which is an anomaly only cyclic time seems able to explain. They did that in the Stone Age.

The ancient cultures were no fools, and we still revere the Greek philosophers to this day. They were not the first, and there were many Hindu, Islamic and Chinese scholars from 12–1400 BC who were the real pioneers on whose shoulders the Greeks rose to shine so brightly. Yet the Greeks, Persians and other major cultures were not peaceful peoples, but warlike too. Many were drawn to India by prevalent legends of great wealth that were apparently true to reality, and the Cycle was known there well before the Greeks, known as the *swadarshanchakra*. The signs of this cycle are global.

Alexander the Great crossed the Indus River in 327 BC and would have conquered all of India had his troops not had enough of war, and forced their leader to return to Greece. This left India's vast wealth of jewels open to the Mogul invaders 1,000 years later, including Mohamed Guznavi who 19 times looted the Somnath Temple in

Gujarat by taking a reputed 10,000 camel loads of gold and jewels, including doors made of gold, and possibly part of the Koh-i-nur diamond. The current stone was only 108 carats before recutting, and is reliably reputed to have been part of a huge diamond the size of a coconut, which sat inside an earlier Hindu temple built on the same site.

[Extra detail: To this day, the famous 'old-mine' emeralds, rubies, sapphires and diamonds of India remain the finest ever seen or mined, and the sublimely perfect white Golconda diamonds make modern versions of top colour white 'D' colour gems look off-colour by comparison. The GIA in America have even toyed with the idea of making a 'C' category above 'D' to accommodate their matchless high grade of 'white' transparency.]

Intriguingly, there are signs of a 'cycle of Time' in every age of history, and in every rock and tree and fossil found. From the Ordovician, Devonian and Permian mass extinctions to the vast volcanic flood basalt events seen globally, we can equate this new cyclic thinking to the simple template of a cycle, and it all fits in neatly. Why else are there these periodic bouts of major destructive force, preceded and followed by total calm? A feasible suggestion has not as yet solved this enigma, and we will return to it later on.

When we combine this finding with the awareness that great intellects such as Plato, Socrates his teacher, and Aristotle his pupil, used to discuss the cycle of time with friends and peers, based partly on what Hesiod wrote nearly 450 years earlier about a pure Golden Age followed by a degraded Age of Iron. All over the globe, the most common symbol in almost every single culture is the *quincunx*, or 5 dot round sign, which appears to represent the 4 main quarters of the cycle, with a central dot as the pivotal axis, and this discus or 'o' symbol in various forms. The Book of Kells and the Lindisfarne Gospel have superbly illuminated manuscripts that show the triple circular 'flowing curved droplet' motif which is also thought to show the cycle of Past, Present and Future flowing in a circle.

Using this cyclic time template, it is now possible to re-interpret all the data we have, and arrive at our own decision as to whether or not the linear or the cyclic version of Time is correct, and also, most interestingly of all perhaps, how long it took to turn full circle. In this way, we may be able to gain an unprecedented clarity of how the future may unfold, since in a cyclic universe, the past is the key to the future, and even human history may yield many more clues about our reality that our present culture has yet discovered. This closely fits reality and explains why time 'travellers' have not appeared.

The theory of evolution is both clever and very imaginative. It seems perfectly logical that we arrived at life today via life yesterday. Why did no-one think of it before? It all seems so obvious, and therefore many do feel strongly that the older ancestral cultures, lacking the new science and maths discoveries, just didn't see it.

The truth is a little different from this praise of modern science. The ancient Hindu, Chinese and Muslim scholars were the real pioneers in calculation, and at least some evidence remains to show these earlier origins. Even the respected Greek thinkers were much later, and had well documented links to the Asian and Eastern intellectuals.

Our maths comes from their maths, and they were brilliant thinkers all. There isn't today a modern version of an Aristotle or Socrates, a Euclid or Pythagoras, who commands a universal respect as did those early ancestors. Yet, like the personalities of those intellectual giants, evolution as a theory contains this fundamental flaw: it does not fit modern biology or geology, or astrophysics, oceanography, metallurgy, quantum physics or maths. That is not one problem, but several dozen.

Each of us must decide upon reality for ourselves.

Further detail

Only a few decades ago, such a cyclic time concept was indeed considered very strange. In the 21st century, Cambridge scientist Professor Neil Turok *et al.* had a theory involving a cycle, but it did not repeat exactly, and relied on the 'Membranes' of string theory, which still remain theoretical. Indeed, since Einstein's work in 1929, a concept of a 'constant' universe became established as Steady-State Theory, but while it removed the necessity to invent a 'Big Bang', it too had flaws that needed revision. James Jeans also researched the theory in 1929, and Pascual Jordan a decade later, that matter could be created spontaneously.

As noted, in 1948 came Bondi and Gold, followed by Sir Fred Hoyle's revisions and 'nucleosynthesis', but there were still major logical and mathematical problems to resolve, not least of which is that nothing on earth or in space appears to appear out of nowhere, *ex nihil*; to say the whole universe has done just this, is proving impossible to justify, and for good reasons. These difficulties now appear to find a solution in a new version of a cycle that goes back much farther still in our historical thinking process, to the cultures that pre-dated the Greeks or even the ancient Egyptians; so it is not actually new at all. What is new is finding out if Time is cyclic in the light of the latest research and data.

Oddly, the answer is affirmative, and unusually precisely so.

Science & Maths detail

Much of linear cosmology relies on the constant known as *h-bar* [ ] as invented by English physicist Paul Dirac in 1928. The latest research shows that there is an apparent error in the famous *Dirac equation*, which of course uses *Dirac's constant*, derived in turn by dividing the Planck constant *h* by 2ϖ. The fascinating new finding is that this basic equation is used to tie relativity to quantum mechanics, and uses only the ½ spin of electrons, or 180° instead of a complete rotation of 360°. By re-writing this equation and altering the constant used, it is possible to show that *spacetime* can indeed be a completely and exactly rotational system that repeats precisely over a set period of time. It is now clear even Einstein's 3rd and 4th Transformational Equations may also be incorrect as well, using different values for the speed of light.

These developments profoundly alter everything. Gone is the need for matter to create or invent *itself* at any stage in Time, which solves the problem of how the whole universe could arise literally 'out of nothing', since that theory still requires a missing force or causal event to bring the cosmos into being. If spacetime already exists, but periodically requires the restoration of the original levels of power, then the facts we see begin to make sense in a way not open to the linear or 'straight line' version of Time.

CHAPTER 15

Statistics In Time

There are many who reach their conclusion about life like schoolboys...by copying the answer out of a book without having worked out the sum for themselves.
SOREN KIERKEGAARD, 1837, philosopher

It must be possible for an empirical system to be refuted by experience.
SIR KARL POPPER, 1934

Mathematics may be defined as the subject in which we never know what we are talking about, nor whether what we are saying is true.
SIR BERTRAND RUSSELL, 1918

Essence

It is often said that statistics can prove anything, because so much analysis is pre-selected. It is not intentional to skew the results one way, but we will have to devise a method for reaching a conclusion, and that is always bound to be full of human influence.

Here is a little about how it works, and how alarmingly easy it is to be totally wrong about anything, and yet still have solid and impressive statistics to prove the exact opposite, allowing us to appear right. Usually no one does this on purpose, although it has happened many times. We must spot the factual ones, such as 1m is 100cms, from the theoretical ideas dressed up with impressive figures that may mean nothing, literally.

Knowing is vital. As Francis Bacon said in 1597: *'Knowledge itself is power'*.

Any theory starts with an idea called grandly 'the hypothesis'. This explanation shows how that initial idea can be mistaken, and yet allows us to decide it is true. Using statistics, experts may still devise a way of testing it, and find it is proved, even when it may later turn out to be mistaken. It all depends on what we assume to be true.

This may look like the strongest part of modern science, yet it is actually the weakest, for one simple reason. It may use dozens or even hundreds of 'unknowns' to derive its striking final conclusion, and that too has been interpreted by a person with one mind-set.

We don't usually see a piece of research where the scientist in charge has said: *'this could be how it works, but here are nine other ways to view the same data, and honestly I have no idea which, if any, is true'*. Scientists are not encouraged to do this, because the aim is to be decisive, positive, coherent and certain. Sounding vague is not an option, so an idea is hatched out, and put to the test. Some giant errors are never found.

Step forward the world of statistics.

In making any statistic about the age of anything, certain gaps at once become rather obvious. No one saw it happen, so we have to make educated guesses about what may have happened.

It contains guesswork, and if any trace of error exists in any of that guesswork (sorry, 'estimation'), then the results may mean nothing. We cannot rule out the chance that we happened on the right solution by accident, so any method cannot be called useless, however full of holes it may be, because of this reason.

In statistics, the aim is to show how some variables are usual, and some are unusual. From all this data the researcher can derive a 'normal' distribution, and then draw some useful conclusions. Even then, it is possible to measure one or more groups of samples to calculate mean values that can appear normal, while not being. The samples have to be random, and not selected, but it is also possible to choose a place to gather samples and unwittingly select the unusual items which skew the results. Of course researchers go to great lengths to avoid such pitfalls, and statistical errors called Type 1 or Type 2 errors which give either a false positive or a false negative.

So how do statistics have room for errors anyway? Numbers are impressive. They look specific, ordered, calculated, neat, numerical, computed, decoded and therefore factual. It rarely occurs to us that even such precise things as numbers rely on such airy fairy things as beliefs, yet they do. Try as we might, we cannot entirely get away from the human content of all statistics.

Statisticians go to great lengths to try and remove abnormalities and errors from their final presented results, but there would be no way to avoid larger errors of meaning which would be present if any of the above presumptions were seen to fail. One part of one method used is the Central Limit Theorem, which provides helpful constraints within the method itself, and there are also non-parametric tests which have been developed to try and reduce the variation abnormalities from the figures. These methods show how variation can easily be found and wrongly interpreted to have a desired meaning, known as the 'expected outcome', which may mean something quite different in practice.

Once again, the researcher may never learn the truth of the matter being investigated, for the simple reason that an expected outcome in several related test areas can appear so convincing that firm conclusions may be drawn that are in fact misleading.

Any statistic from a small sample is open to this type of error, and almost no sample size could be large enough to be safe. This is how we have created and retained errors so large that they can appear 'normal and expected', in spite of being derived from research using an invalid hypothesis. This becomes a pathway for serious misunderstandings to arise in any field where probabilities are a factor, as they often are, and Bayes' Theorem may be used, developed by Thomas Bayes (1702–1761) but published from his notes after his death in 1763. This commonly used technique works by taking a definition of probability as a measurement of belief from which statistics are inferred to have a particular meaning as derived from evaluating empirical observations.

This sounds like quite a mouthful, but its meaning is simple enough: a range of samples are measured in some particular way, and a meaning is inferred from that research. The basic danger of using statistics to support a theory is the misleading appearance that could be derived by inferring the wrong meaning on a perfectly good set of figures. These risks never quite vanish because every theory on Earth usually contains some variables which affect or dictate the outcome.

If that outcome is the one expected, we may then have a very serious problem indeed, because we may place too much trust in the answer apparently given by that result. A large number of people may then accept that obvious outcome, and treat it as factual, when it may in fact remain 100% incorrect. Others may fairly point to these risks and reject the outcome, yet may not be part of mainstream science and hence might not be believed. Therefore it is usually the majority opinion that often holds sway, even though it may be incorrectly inferred in one or all of the above ways.

This has happened in the case of Evolution, which is why both sides appear so certain of their ground, and yet so implacably contradictory. It is impossible, clearly, that both can be right, therefore one side must be using incorrect parameters.

One particular problem can arise with global statistics. Some types of measurement may have been tested so many times, and worldwide, that the results can give a high [yet often false] degree of confidence in the values obtained, and also in their implications. An example of large sample quantity analysis is that of the isotopic composition of ocean water, known as VSMOW (Vienna Standard Mean Ocean Water), or the speed of earthquake waves through certain rock types. Yet even here it is possible to draw conclusions that may one day contradict the way reality actually works. No researcher on Earth could conceivably be expected to foresee such colossal changes in thinking, yet it must be checked all the same.

As in every case, it is our worldview that dictates the results, not vice versa.

This mental approach factor cannot be overestimated in its importance. Our worldview is absolutely pivotal in deriving any meaning at all, so that even a superbly accurate and well measured set of data turning in a 95 or 99% level of confidence could be rendered meaningless if the time factor used was not correct. In the example of dating igneous rocks, it would ruin all statistics showing their apparent age, if based on the wrong linear parameters. This could happen purely because the dates derived could no longer be set firmly within a long and guaranteed period of deep time.

If the thinking is misjudged, the results mean nothing. Even statistics can create a false picture. When we extrapolate and speculate, it can all go very wrong.

CHAPTER 16

The Velikovsky Debate

Convictions are more dangerous enemies of truth than lies.
F.NIETZSCHE, 1878

The scientific mind does not so much provide the right answers as ask the right questions
C.LEVI-STRAUSS, 1964

Essence

The name of Velikovsky is unknown to many people today, but must be well remembered by others who noted the upheaval in science created by two books of the many he wrote, namely *Worlds In Collision* in 1950 that caused the main rumpus, and then *Earth In Upheaval* in 1955. In short, he was a catastrophist, and he disagreed with the inherited old idea of geological strata forming very slowly at 2mm per year as a loosely agreed standard rate (which it still is), and instead proposed that certain features must have formed very rapidly. He also found clear evidence to back this claim.

As an original debunker of the million year myth, his work created a storm, and even more so since he was not a geologist by training. He even commented on astronomy, particularly the expected temperature of the surface of our neighbouring planet Venus, which outraged the astronomers at the time, and even more so when he turned out to be right, proving the old ideas all wrong. Some experts were shocked.

The books he wrote caused an atomic explosion of contention in post-war America and Britain, with some scientists turning to deeply unscientific methods in their attempts to derail it, as we will see. Firmly made up minds are hard to change, and this is a danger to progress, when a fresh reading of old facts can seem outrageous and plain wrong. The scientist who took up Darwin's cause was T.H.Huxley, which he did from his fine house in north London, and he raised a good point in 1860 about being too certain of things:

'Sit down before fact as a little child, be prepared to give up every preconceived notion...follow humbly...or you shall learn nothing'.

Even today, an older scientist may take a sharp intake of breath at the name, but this reaction is very out of date. Much of what he wrote is now widely accepted. What really upset them was that he had revealed some major flaws in the old principle of a slow, uniform history of earth, known as *Uniformitarianism*, which is a mouthful. Certain influential American academics didn't like that at all, and even tried to stop his book being published, chiefly by threatening his publishers they would withdraw huge contracts of trade if they did not submit to their wish.

Today, those two books would not have caused such a stir, not by a long way, but in those days, they certainly did. His main thesis was that a body in space (he chose Venus) had collided with earth, and produced huge changes in geology and geography. This sounded close to insane just five years after the 2nd World War, but today is not that strange an idea.

Now science has much weirder ideas, like inventing other dimensions from which all matter is said to have popped into being in our cosmos, which is magic by any yardstick, but no one minds. This was different.

What really upset the science community in America were not just his ideas of revolution, but that he was a medical doctor, and so not their kind of scientist at all. They reckoned he had no right to question matters in 'their field'. Even this distinction means nothing, since the maverick thinker and biologist Dr Rupert Sheldrake has some unusual ideas, such as *morphic resonance* and telepathy experiments, but also a doctorate in biology, so in his case, scientists can only resort to outrage, as he certainly does have relevant qualifications.

Frankly, it should not matter even if he didn't, since any bright 10 year old has the right to question any matter in science, or indeed any field, and expect a serious answer. If the mighty study of science can't manage the question of a child, or to answer an adult, either with a doctorate or no formal training whatever, then people may well think the less of it as an authority. This has become so.

Once science had criticised religion, now the tables were turned. So the public saw all this and took another view: Science needs to quit complaining, and start explaining, and it had better be pretty good at it. It wasn't. Thus far, it is not always the case, and here are some examples of the legendary poor PR that upset the case of science, and made Velikovsky a global success.

Velikovsky was born in 1895 in Russia. He was a thinker, and later became a close friend of the famous Albert Einstein. They lived in the same American town of Princeton, of university fame, and liked to meet and discuss these issues. Einstein read both of the above books by Velikovsky, and offered many comments by writing them in the margin, slowly altering his own views over the years, so the gaps in their opinions became smaller. From 1921–24, they edited the *Scripta Universitatis* together, and until Einstein's passing in 1955, spent a lot of time in discussions.

In those days, the huge meteor craters we know today had not been discovered or identified as having a space origin, such as Meteor Crater in Arizona. The meteoric theory of the dinosaurs' demise was yet to be discovered with a link to the *iridium* layer at the Cretaceous or K-T boundary seen in America and at Gubbio in Italy; which contained tiny spherules of unknown origin that would later become evidence of intense heat, from a space impact. No one had ever imagined that could happen in that way.

Also yet to be found was the perfect crescent arc of 'cenotes', or fresh water caves, that mark the outer edge of the huge 112 mile wide asteroid crater in the southern area of the Gulf of Mexico. These caves are connected and situated on the north coast of the Yucatán peninsula. Filled with fresh water, they link up to the sea. This fresh water kept the Maya alive for centuries, until their mysterious demise, possibly due to climate change and the consequent drought in their tribal areas.

It is a strange turn of fate that their culture, which was deeply focused on astronomical predictions and events, and which predicted a 5,100 year cycle in their Mayan writings, should be located in the very area of this massive strike by an asteroid.

We do have traditions of an apocalypse, and any large event would have seemed much the same to anything living in the same hemisphere, they were so vast. The wave from that strike (as we consider elsewhere) has been estimated at 500–1,000 metres high which would be hard to miss, and equally hard to survive.

The strike formed a crater, but it was mostly hidden under the Gulf of Mexico.

This 185 km wide structure was named after the nearby town of Chicxulub, and located by petrochemical scientists. They were searching for oil-bearing geological structures using seismic and radar surveys of the sea floor in that area, when they came across the central mountainous area within the blast halo of what can only have been a strike from space on a huge scale. Velikovsky would have enjoyed that.

His main concern was the old principle of Hutton's 'uniform' long past, based on current calm conditions of sediment deposits which are seen today. This idea is now even lodged in dictionaries on earth science as largely discredited, but not then, and even still not by everyone in geology today. We have a love of simple narratives. We like regularity, and the idea of huge, largely unimaginable events that upset our ordered view of reality is not something many of us like to deal with. Not everyone thinks like that of course.

Some scientists, like Prof. Bill McGuire of University College London, make a profession out of estimating risks of past events repeating, and they always point out that such huge events will return in time; the only question is when, since chaos and entropy tend to increase.

These experts were not surprised by the Mt St Helens eruption or any other, as they had studied the past events. Their time estimates now take care to include the phrase 'which could happen tomorrow', in case it does, since it easily can. If our cyclic process is correctly assessed, we have some internal and external preparations to make.

This future certainty of further and greater disruption to life was also pointed out by the Icelandic Prime Minister in 2010, when the volcanic ash cloud grounded all European flights for weeks. He was not referring to that volcanic source, bulky as it was, but the future return of the mighty volcanic eruption of Laki, which caused far greater chaos across all Europe in 1783.

Velikovsky, and many writers since, realised that the apparent calm of today is not at all an accurate way to assess the past, and it is simply incorrect to assume there were no huge changes to the environment in past days. Modern finds of large craters and huge ash accumulations from major eruptions have shown him to be spot-on. He brought up many examples in geology, none of which were refuted, and have been expanded so much since his writings. Nearly his entire thesis has proved to be right, while other areas cannot easily be proved wrong, despite claims to the contrary.

Gone are the days when they felt certain such mega-events were low likelihood matters, that they may happen only as 'once in 10,000 or 100,000 year' occurrences. It is something we have to get used to well ahead of time, each of us, so we are not surprised when they do take place, as they must according to the laws of both Time and ordinary resonance effects. It doesn't matter what we believe, since Nature will do what it does anyway. The ideal is to be ready beforehand.

Velikovsky saw evidence for all this. He is also right in cyclic time terms. The future will undoubtedly cross over this chaotic phase and reach a state of calm in the geological upheavals we are seeing. This is why they are happening: simply the balancing of extreme energies imbalances that have to move from one place to another, despite what may stand in the way. Such scenes are part of the near future, before the following future stage arrives. It is very likely these extremes of chaos and calm should be very near indeed. Such a time would be very testing for all of us. Whatever science may say, we have to get ready in our own way, because arrive it must.

Nature is already showing us that energy movements are part of the picture on earth at the moment. Velikovsky also caused a huge fuss by predicting Venus' 450°C hot surface in the post war era, which was odd when astronomers had decided it was a balmy 17°C. He was right.

The global public realised these may well be some interesting new ideas to assess for themselves, and his books sold out as hardback editions all over the English speaking world. By 1964, one book had sold 15 hardback printings in America, 14 in Great Britain, with 6 more print-runs between 1972 and 1980. The debate between catastrophists and others still rages now and then, but only as a ripple instead of a tsunami, now that so many meteor and asteroid strikes prove that space does impact the earth, and has created some mega-events that no one can deny took place.

When Hutton published in 1795, he had paid little attention to organics or stratigraphy, so no-one knew much about how anything worked. Hutton was not really a writer, but a pioneering naturalist, and his book was considered such heavy going that in 1802 the mathematician and fellow Scot John Playfair re-wrote his work to make it more readable. The Uniformitarian view was up and running, and it was 200 years before most people realised it was '*a considerable oversimplification*', as the modern Oxford Dictionary of Earth Sciences rightly put it.[108]

Once a group of influential experts settled on an explanation of how Nature worked in the far past, it was then used as a building block on which to construct the next generation of discoveries. No-one saw any need to change it, so it stuck as a basic theory.

At some point, they felt it necessary to stop checking those basic assumptions, and elevate them to the status of 'fact', but perhaps a little too quickly, and well before sufficient results were in. Having done this, it is then very difficult to turn the clock back and allow our thinking to be flexible about such basic concepts.

If you still have any tiny doubts about this, just read the preface (to the 1972 Abacus edition) which the catastrophist Dr. I. Velikovsky wrote for his hugely controversial book '*Worlds in Collision*', which appeared in 1950 to the total horror of the scientific establishment. It woke many up to the facts of giant changes in geology that were not calm and slow by any stretch of the imagination, but so violent and large scale that any living creature within 1,000 miles or more in some cases, would have died instantly; perhaps like the dinosaurs. Their finale was a total mystery for years until such disasters were contemplated. Even this notion is in contention, since they lived around the globe. Flash Time suggests a different scenario entirely.

The effect of Velikovsky's initial book was an academic explosion of a similarly powerful kind. A group of academics called it 'a heresy', and even boycotted it, successfully halting the book's initial print-run with Macmillan Books '*...who had to give it up, though a No:1 national bestseller*' [*Worlds In Collision*, p8, preface to paperback edition]. For those interested in volcanoes, glaciers or more radical views of

108 OUP, 3rd edition, p602.

earth's complex history entombed in rock, his book *Earth in Upheaval* is also a very interesting piece of history. It is easy today to blame the scientists for acting so negatively, but they were only trying to maintain a convention they felt strongly was the truth, little realising that it may not be as true as they thought.

Science was showing another aspect of itself, which shocked many. In the process of all this upheaval caused by this challenge to their orthodoxy, science itself had become a religion in a sense, with high priests ready to defend it if necessary.

Even technically, Velikovsky had at times proven correct, which just maddened them even more. Human nature is a curious thing, and even though science is meant to be focused on finding new truths, we cannot always avoid the territorial disputes.

As we have seen, he successfully predicted various facts. His volume was later re-issued to a very interested world. Scientists continued attacking him and his work, from even before the first book appeared in print. This became known as the Velikovsky Affair, and books have been written about it over the years, such was the impact of both the book itself, and the astonishing treatment the author received.

A telling comment is a quote from Princeton University's student newspaper, the *Daily Princetonian*, which wrote in an editorial in February 1964: 'What the Velikovsky affair made crystal clear...is that the theories of science may be held not only for the truth they embody, but because of the vested interests they represent for those who hold them'.

Sometimes we like or favour an idea so much, and so intensely, that even criticism is not just discouraged, but actively shouted down and every effort made to remove it from the discussion table. That is not science; a true idea will always survive by itself.

The late and famous author Isaac Asimov wrote in his contribution to how science could 'deal with' the threat to their thinking posed by Velikovsky, after the huge furore created by the publication of his sensational 1950 book 'Worlds in Collision'. Writing in the foreword to set the book's tone, the clue was in the 1977 title 'Scientists Confront Velikovsky'. Asimov wasted no time in summing up the astonishingly dark mood of the day, for 1977 at least, when he began: *'What does one do with a heretic? We know the answer if the "one" referred to is a*

powerful religious orthodoxy: the heretic can be burned at the stake.' [109]
Asimov also pointed out there is no simple way of separating '...*the
stroke of intuitional genius from the stroke of folly...*'. [110] How true
that is, and a constant problem in science.

Yet the specifics that agree with Velikovsky are not intuition but solid
and drift geology. The real difficulty presented to us on seeing them is
how to process the reality that 300 years of careful research could all
be falsely interpreted. We must therefore never tire of having an open
door policy for new generations of thinkers who want to question our
'facts'. Any theory can be mistaken. Progress is realising they can.

109   Scientists Confront Velikovsky, Norton 1977, page 8
110   Ibid page 9

CHAPTER 17

Heaven: myth or reality?

All the things one has forgotten scream for help in dreams.
ELIAS CANETTI, 1973

Everyone insists on their innocence...even if it means accusing the rest of the human race and heaven.
ALBERT CAMUS, 1956

Dare to know! Have the courage to use your own reason.
IMMANUEL KANT, 1784

Essence

Now to explore a suggestion. Are the global legends of a Heaven or Atlantis based on real events that actually happened? If there was an era, before recorded history, when life was far more civilised that it is today, that may well explain why it is remembered in every culture on the planet, even up to the present day. A myth? The evidence says not. When we recall that every ancient culture, and so many great thinkers from deep history took this to be true, we may at least consider the clues. It would be rude not to. When we check, we find that all that lies between heaven as reality and modern thinking is a set of assumptions that no longer hold water. Now that is amazing to find, and no one can prove it isn't so (or if they can, write it out and claim a prize).

It is possible that earth was once calm and ordered, and that period of real life on earth could explain the millions of references we have to an 'original garden'...heaven.

If time is truly cyclic, then just how ordered and calm might be that first quarter of 'order'? Hesiod wrote in 800BC that this era, known in many cultures as the Golden Age, was 'wonderful beyond description'. This account was passed down to each generation in detail, and every person on earth has heard of Heaven, and uses the word often. That is a major presence in human awareness globally, so is it all just myth as some claim?

Logically, and in science, it can be real. Every system begins with order and then degrades. Nature renews many such systems so they are clearly cycles of such processes, and earth itself may be a part of this motion. Is it possible there was an original society of such purity that its status of power and calm would remain legendary forever?

The answer is yes, because no one can disprove it, at least not without using artificial assumptions which we have seen do not stack up. The stories all describe the same situation, of a place with no sorrow at all, nor even a word for it, let alone crime, old age, hospitals or doctors, nor the division of religions, but simple wall to wall happiness and hummingbirds. Whose heart does not soar to see a butterfly? There may be a deeper reason for that, if we had once lived in a heavenly era. One thing we all agree on is the thought of Benjamin Franklin, when he said in 1750: 'The Golden Age never was the present age'. Society has hit new lows, and some of us are noticing.

Sophocles observed sagely around 430 BC that: 'The happiest life is lived while one understands nothing, before one learns delight or pain'. Computers are not the solution either, because they only do what they are told. As Cobol inventor G. M. Hopper once wrote: 'We have tended to forget that…no computer will ever ask a new question'.

How does this relate to Earth?

We have seen how geology had some calm periods. So many songs tell us 'Heaven was a place on earth'. Could it truly be a reality? The astonishing answer is that it can. The legend is common around the world in every age, as is the notion people have to be good to go there, but it can be true as well, if geology and time have been misunderstood. This may seem fanciful to some readers, yet the apparent errors noted about the whole geological timescale do allow reality to be cyclic. There are no absolute reasons why this could not be so.

After all, if we behaved well, would the world not change before teatime? Confucius is famous for being very clever, and he recognised the value of a thing or two in 500 BC, when he asked what one word would sum up '…life's key aim? The word altruism'.

Religion has been much misused over the years, and even the Koran notes that we should '…aggress not. God does not love the aggressors'

(Sura 2). George Bernard Shaw noted this in 1898 when he wrote that 'There is only one religion, though there are 100 versions of it', perhaps meaning the peace we all require and recall.

Put simply, it is human activity and thinking that causes the chaos, so if it were to end for some reason, we would move over to 'heaven' a moment later. This, believe it or not, is what Plato and other great thinkers in history, like Hesiod, reckon actually happened, and there is now evidence we have all seen in the CMB to support it.

The way we have assumed time to be a line is all that removed this future from our minds, or some minds at least. So is the age of things so well worked out?

There are some interesting problems with the timescale we find of earth's history. Take the recent finds of a sunken city off India's Rann of Kutch area, near the Indus. When did that exist, and how did the sea level change so much? The axial tilt is of course one answer, and the reality of a city shows it was in recent times. Could the whole of deep history be misconceived? The 1938 find of the 'extinct' Coelacanth fish, and so many other unaltered 'Lazarus' species, are strong evidence of a major error in traditional timescales.

Science has a mass of inventive schemes, yet nothing factual to counter this unusual idea. Saturn's famously young F ring joins Active Galactic Nuclei and the CMB to show curious signs of mystery or youth not possible in long linear time models. This suggests a young cycle, with humans perhaps always present in some part of earth. The circular jigsaw pieces now fit neatly.

It is possible that the period of calm we see in geological sediments, with proof of warm seas and 32% more oxygen, could have seen human beings living in a culture before recorded history. There are many legends of this being true, but of course we cannot rely on that as factual. What we can say is this: it is possible our planet's history is cyclic, which means that events repeat, and that just as surely as this chaos is real now, so too there could have been a period of order in the past that was later remembered as 'heaven' on earth.

Could that have been the source of stories like Atlantis? It could be, yet not as described by Plato, since that showed chaos in his account.

The fact that Hesiod also mentioned this era, as did Bishop Emesius, who both noted the idea that Time itself may be repeating exactly, along with the Mayans, Hindus and many others globally, is a point of vast significance, since these cultures are separated by such an expanse of impassable geography they could not have bridged.

The ancient Greeks were well known for their innovation, which shows ancient cultures were very clever the further back we go in history.

Hero and his steam engine, or Archimedes and his 'death ray' which focused sunlight onto ships and set them ablaze, shown to be possible in recent televised tests, or his grappling hook which overturned Roman ships sailing too near the harbour wall, show a high degree of invention using simple tools. Few were cleverer.

Some say Archimedes' workshop could have been the source of the mastermind required to make the Antikythera mechanism that worked like a computer perhaps as far back as 220 BC, but we will never know for certain. Perhaps the lost Great Library of Alexandria had some information about it, and we will never know that either.

It remains possible that there was a high culture that did live before history began, yet one that was destroyed in such a way that no trace was found. The stories of a golden age could also be true, with tell of palaces of gold being made and lost. The South African gold mines are full of derived gold in sedimentary rocks, and Australia and N. America as well, and it is not impossible for those gold deposits to be secondary deposits of gold from an earlier civilization.

The ancient Greeks thought so, and gained much of their thinking from India during their early history, as documented, along with Hesiod's famous cyclic time view. This concept is so deeply woven into the cultures of every society in our history, globally, that there may be credence in it. The only obstacle is current science, which loses the key objection it may raise with the failure of linear dating methods to be 'absolute'.

We may therefore consider that the cyclic view of time could include these events in those first 1,250 years of the cycle. If this is true, and there is a cycle, then Heaven would soon be back, just as surely as day follows night. Even an ancient map is noted showing its location as near India, which is the Mappa Mundi or 'world map' in Hereford Cathedral, Hereford, England. Many modern books on rock dating revel in claiming this idea as absurd, but they all omit to consider a cycle in their timescale, which makes this claim into a valid one. It is amusing to think heaven could be real, but this study shows how it can be so in practice, if science has made an error about time being linear.

As Thomas Ellwood once remarked to Milton in 1665: 'You spoke much here of Paradise Lost, but what have you to say of Paradise found?' There is much to say.

We can now bring the threads of our studies together in one coherent unit. What was this period of 'calm' in the cycle's first quarter? Could the world have been 'new', with earth's people as one unified culture, a single language, no purpose for religion, and no trace of crime or chaos of any kind? Is this not just pure make-believe? It appears not.

This story has lasted for millennia, but has been dismissed by many, thanks to Plato calling it Atlantis. This led researchers to look in the Atlantic, where there is no trace of it. There are actually powerful reasons to suppose there is more to this legend than the fantasy some have claimed. The continents could also hold a clue, as we shall see, in symbols.

If so, then there should be some legacy of such a period, both in anthropology, and in geology. Do we see any such signs? Oddly enough, we do, and plenty of them. Indeed every culture on earth has a rich heritage of such thinking, in every quarter of the globe, even when they had not met to share details of such stories; even then, their accounts are remarkably alike.

How can that be true, as it is, when pre-Columbian cultures had no ships? Only a cycle of time seems able to explain this strange fact; a truly Jungian 'collective idea'. How else did Easter Island become populated by people with links to both Peru and India, with the Brahman topknot and long ears of that caste, now far away in the eastern Pacific?

Only this solution seems to answer a key question: how come every ancient culture on earth shares the same discus symbol of rotating time when they never met, unless they had met in the last cycle? No one ever considered that answer, and it remains a mystery without time being cyclic.

We have also seen how the super-continent of Pangea split into the shapes we see now, and how all earth's Neolithic tribes share the same symbols showing the 'wheel of time' as a disc with four parts.

This fact clearly shows they existed before as tribes, and were marooned where we now find them, in a 'post-apocalyptic' era after the 'Garden of Eden' or heaven era fell apart. That would also explain why they retained no infrastructure to help them, and thus lived as primitive peoples in each land, keeping their symbols in mind of what had gone before, handed down by word of mouth only, not in writing.

The Celts, also originating in India before being located in Europe, retain many links with India showing their origin, language and white skin colour, never wrote down any of their heritage...just the symbols. As we have seen, they also retained their clever minds, and burial rituals, with a royal system of society that created order, along with jewellery, brain surgery and medicine. Even Neanderthals had much of that form of society, which shows the whole of the old linear time notion is no longer viable.

Seeing that those cultures clearly had such links before that event, only this answer explains how they came to live so separately while retaining the same symbols in mind to draw as art and stone circles *under the Amazon rainforest*. Add the pyramids all over north and south America, the value placed on gold, and skill in metallurgy, the roads and town hubs now being found, and we have the evidence of a short period cycle in which earth's people play a different set of rôles, from the rôles old science gave them in a supposed linear world view. The new details show the old view was incorrect.

All of this is now known as factual, so it should change our world view.

We have noted how heaven, shown as 'Paradise', appears to be marked on the *mappa mundi* in Hereford Cathedral, posters of which exist as the much clearer interpreted copies redrawn. There it is, large as life, just beside India. This may be no coincidence, since India's Vedas are the oldest system of thinking ever written down. That could be the location of the world's original civilisation, remembered as Paradise, since that is the country which first held the cultural paradigm of cyclic time as actual history.

Now here is the thing. The island this ancient map shows near India could mean India itself, often cited as the oldest culture on earth according to scholars. All over the world there are statues of 'deities' shown in metal or stone. Are these the icons of beings that lived 'special lives' in that first era? Each culture seemed to think so. There are deities revered globally, and in the Far East, and India in particular, shown as idols, and the worship of whom is a major part of earth's oldest religion, that of the Hindus, meaning the people of the Indus Valley, (hence the name *Hindusthan,* which means 'land of the Hindus' in Hindi).

Why are there 330 million of these deities claimed? It appears to represent the entire land and culture some time ago, when there were this number of those 'pure beings' living on that continent. India may have once been so ordered.

There is even a link to England's oldest monument, Stonehenge, which is that famous circular set of standing stones representing what exactly? Some claim it was of more deities, with astronomical alignments thrown in to connect the whole edifice to the sun and moon at the solstices. Why is it circular, along with thousands of other standing stones set in the Neolithic and other eras? It appears to be cyclic time again, because no other explanation fits so precisely. The triple spiral at Newgrange in Ireland (Meath, Eire), near Dublin, is a perfect example of all this combined in one mound: a circle, the triple spiral of Time's past, present and future, and a holy place to commemorate the ancestral deities....not just the recent ones, *but the same set of deities worshipped all over the world.* One Madagascan antiquarian, flown over to England by Prof. Mike Parker-Pearson, at once identified the stones as representing 'ancestors', claiming 'anyone tuned into the ancient ways of thought' could see it.

Easter Island is another classic case, as we have seen, of 'deities as statues'.

All this talk of ancestors over eons has been confusing, because anthropologists tended to think of them as no more than local grandparents, and of no great significance in terms of world population internationally. The reverse appears true.

As a result, it is possible an era of 'heaven' on earth is not a strange idea, but a period of early history that may have actually existed in real life. All the ancient cultures had signs of such thinking, so it may have been the most significant concept in their culture, and apparently all cultures, with those 'pure beings' worshipped for being present in it; so that their statues were carved in every culture for millennia after they disappeared. There are indeed such images of 'special beings' in nearly every part of the world, who were worshipped as deities. Often shown with halos, they were depicted as superhuman, and this has been confused with aliens. A halo is the likely answer, since aliens have never been found, and could not exist in a cyclic universe. Like evolution, they are part of linear time and populist thinking, and this may be the reason the evidence is lacking.

Was there really an ancient culture so pure and perfect we still remember as Paradise?

It may sound rather quaint and even absurd to take such an idea seriously, yet we say 'heaven knows' nearly every day, and fully 85% of the world's people really feel that Heaven is where departed spirits will go if they have been good here on earth. Even so, there can be a basis for ancient legends.

Why else would the concept of Paradise have pervaded our cultures all around the world unless there was some reason for the idea? It is too easy to write all that anthropology off as mere fancy, when what we may actually be witnessing is the memory of a recent era, not long past, that was the wonder of the world. Science is full of wonderful finds that changed in a day from folly to modern discovery.

It is perfectly reasonable to suppose that the old supercontinent of Pangea could represent the only period of rotational stability ever found in the earth's crust. If so, then this could have been an era when an earlier population existed in a very different type of lifestyle to the one we know today. It is possible this really happened, and in a cyclic world that matches reality when other views do not, only this answer offers an explanation for the evidence we do see. How else would the world's cultures all begin with the same symbols, yet never having met, unless they began on the same land mass? It is equally possible that culture left no trace of having lived there, except in folklore.

Atlantis could be part of that memory of an original culture, yet not in the Atlantic.

This would also explain why no one has ever found the submerged continent of Atlantis, because it never existed in the Atlantic or Mediterranean areas as assumed by many from its name, and since it could merely be the present land mass of India, much of which lies under the Deccan Traps of volcanic ash and basalt. Lemuria[111] appears

---

111 Lemures: 'spirits' in Latin, ie Land of Souls possibly.

to be another name for the same concept as Atlantis, simple meaning an ancient pure culture which has since vanished.

There is an intrinsic understanding that good actions of kindness and justice are vital in every society. The chaos that ensues when this is ignored is obvious to us all. One needs no belief in religion to realise that the very geology we walk over each day could hold the clues to solving this puzzle quite easily.

The curious thing is that every person on earth may still hold a subconscious, personal blueprint of such a place, and strives each day to recreate it, in our homes, our gardens, our buildings, our societies, and in dreams. How else could so many millions hold such thoughts of reality unless for some specific reason? The fact many do is highly significant.

It is far too easy to dismiss this as mere human fantasy, and invent a Big Bang instead, but there are numerous reasons why Big Bang was the invention. An error could have been made, and science could have misunderstood time as a line, and ignored the common experience of déjà vu, which could add to the cultural implication that we really were here in a past cycle of time. Was there really a calmer form of this same earth, really quite recently? There is actually no fact beyond question that disagrees.

In many ways this is very good news indeed, since it cannot be disproved, and this means that cyclic time can indeed return to calm order once again. The future predicted by science, of an end to all life, would then be the mythical one, with no evidence.

The rushing galaxies support this short cycle. They show such motion is recent, otherwise the earlier prediction they 'must have' stopped by now, or be slowing down instead of speeding up, would have turned out to be true. It has not, so the Big Bang thinking may indeed have been profoundly mistaken.

Ever since Plato wrote about a past civilisation of perfect peace and harmony, no one has been quite sure how to react. Did he make it up, or was there a much better and more ordered society before his own? In his era, it was the talk of the world, as was the recent upheaval period in which it was all destroyed or submerged. Only the statues remain.

What does this mean? It shows that the Hindu culture, named as noted after the land of the Indus that now flows through present day Pakistan, had an influence far beyond its own borders, and one that deeply impressed the ancient Greeks and others in pre-historical days. Even the name Pakistan is a clue, meaning Pure Land, and the Indus Valley could have been part of the 'original place' and culture from which the world population sprang, since we already find that global DNA originated in India, not in Greece as many believe, and that many European languages are *'Indo-European'* for this reason. This may be the reason that India contains traces of every global culture, with the north east showing Far Eastern and Malaysian genotypes, the north west showing European genes, the south west showing African genotypes.

India has this ancient and close connection to Greece, and thus Europe. Along with Persia, the cultures are closely linked in maths and philosophy. The notion that Africa's Rift Valley is the source of all world cultures is no longer thought valid by many scholars, as the DNA suggests. The real source could be India. There is also the suggestion that, if Pangea was the original 'supercontinent' *with a population*, then there could be shared DNA strands in both East Africa and India, since they were adjacent at that time.

It is already known that these two ancient cultures, of Greece and India, actually had a great deal of contact in terms of both trade and intellectual exchanges. So much so, indeed, that the Greece of Hesiod and Plato appears to have adopted the Hindu explanation of cyclic time, as we noted in Hindi as the *swadarshanchakra*[112], which is the central theme of Hinduism. When we translate and parse this curiously profound word, it means literally a 'vision of the self in the cycle', or as it is often translated: 'the cycle of self-realisation'. This may have a simple explanation: to see the self as a star or 'soul' within cyclic events, with life being seen as a theatre or drama, for which India and Greece are equally famous; to understand the role of the soul, as a deeper aspect of life.

Many Greeks thought and wrote about the existence of a 'soul' being of supreme importance in understanding time, our origins, and especially our purpose here on earth. Could this be the clue that cements it

112 Meaning: Swa- self, darshan- look, chakra- cycle.

Human population growth by religion/culture

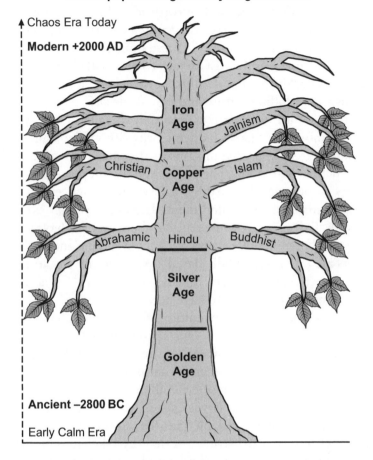

FIGURE 26 *Human World Tree: Human population growth by religion and culture in the classic 'tree' form, showing original Calm era followed by increasing chaos as variation of cultural ideas sees rapid growth.*

all together, with the soul being a cultural word for the quantum self we have considered as a point of light? It is a logical explanation.

This Indian view would have impressed the Greeks as familiar, and as older and therefore more senior. Indian scholars did travel to Greece in ancient times. The ancient Vedas and Upanishads are part of those ancient writings, and set out the moral and legal code that was later followed by the Celtic tribes of Europe, including the Druids, all of whom were actually the direct descendants of those ancient Indus Valley and Himalayan cultures, as these links show. To those oldest peoples, cyclic time was not just an idea to play with, but the only real and relevant worldview that dominated their lives. It lasts to this day in every aspect of Indian culture and even trade.

It is possible they were correct, and that there is such a cycle that runs the cosmos rather like a hidden clockwork mechanism. There is far-reaching agreement from our observations in the world, and the quantum field of sub-atomic particles is equally supportive.

For this to be true, the earth's rocks would show certain eras of calm and chaos, and we do find them. The five key mass extinctions show it was all destroyed completely, but there may not have been millions of years between these events as claimed by conventional dating. Sediments are often relationally dated as seen, so there is no cast iron proof whatever that the accepted geological timescale is accurate. A gigantic mistake does appear to have been made.

It all points to a separation of cultures that used to inhabit one land mass, which then broke apart. Our current population needs only 4,900 years to form, so the linear version fails. The lack of human remains is surely powerful evidence that millions of years of human history have not elapsed. Those 600 billion missing cavemen cannot just vanish. It is certain they never existed, so the old timescale has a problem. It is no longer plausible that they existed in large numbers over long periods, only to leave fewer than 250 skeletons globally.

This is a huge problem for linear time. There should be about 18 million of tons of their bones and skulls, perhaps a mile deep in places, yet there is no such thing. We even assumed they were brutish and primitive in all ways, yet the latest evidence is of a sensitive and thoughtful people with similar poetic burial rites as we use today, such as Taung Child so charmingly laid to rest under a large bird's outstretched wing. They built houses and used religion and medicine, which are all measures within archaeology of an advanced society, not a primitive one. Were they the refugees of the earlier culture that was destroyed in floods? It seems likely, since all the evidence points to this answer.

Easter Island statue

FIGURE 27 *Easter Island statue or moai: Head is capped by stone 'topknot' linked to India's Brahman priests, showing links to Hindus and deified 'Golden Age' ancestors, and all later cultures via 'time disc' symbols.*

All this new research confirms the creative, artistic, medically skilled and sensitive cultures of prehistory, allowing their lives to be ruled by belief and rituals, which is all very different to the brutal primitives the old antiquaries of the 17th and 18th century took them to be; an idea we inherited, and hastily accepted because it made modern Europe look better and more sophisticated.

If there was an earlier race, where might it have been, and are there any clues as to why we might choose one place over another?

We can sum up a few ideas about this:

1 Which is the earth's oldest culture? India may have all 'global cultures' in one land.
2 Is there any evidence of 'better' being linked to 'older'? Oddly, yes there is. One example is the lack of defence items found in Pakistan's three oldest sites, and its famous drainage system at

least 3,000 years before London's in the 1860's. The Antikythera as noted is another, being an early computer that could calculate planetary movement, made in a workshop in about 200 BC and likely earlier still.

3 Is the world worse than before? It is as bad as ever history can show, yet the scale is so much larger with 6 billion extra people than 200 years ago. Today's conflicts are larger than those in earlier eras in some ways. This is a key factor.

4 The continent of Pangea could be more recent than ever imagined. If so, then the split up of that continent, and its population, would have been distributed globally.

5 Was Atlantis real? The lost areas of Atlantis or Lemuria appear to be legendary, but they can be based on India's movements, which might be supported by its central focus on cyclic time, having the oldest scriptures and populations, as well as the DNA diversity.

6 Was Atlantis real continent then? Yes, but not west of Gibraltar as claimed, and thus not one based in the Atlantic, in view of such good ocean floor mapping in recent times. No such continent has sunk there, but the legends do fit the tectonic split of Pangea as above. In that case, India would have been part of that continent.

As ever, the reader decides, but it is curious to find our oldest story of 'Paradise on earth' could be the first quarter of our cycle, and cannot actually be disproved.

CHAPTER 18

Can Mind Energy Alter Time?

We measure shadows, and we search among ghostly errors of measurement for landmarks that are scarcely more substantial.
EDWIN P.HUBBLE, 1930

We must be the change we wish to see in the world.
MAHATMA GANDHI, 1930

I must have a prodigious quantity of mind; it takes me as much as a week to make it up.
MARK TWAIN, 1869

Essence

Quite literally, our thoughts create the world. We never realised how profoundly. This key section explains how Matter may be more deeply affected by the human mind than most of us ever thought possible. The idea is this. That the universe is so finely and delicately balanced that even the mind can affect it. Most of us tend to think of the mind as a minor or zero factor in the way the world works. It is so subtle and invisible that we often forget the mind's actual power. World history is altered by thought alone, because action follows. Gandhi had a single thought of India's independence, and led the group that made it happen.

This proposal goes much deeper, because there is evidence that human thought energy is directly connected to the network of atoms we see around us. The old saying 'the mind creates the world' may be literally true at a much deeper level than we realised. Science has all but ignored this effect, but since the quantum age arrived, it is clear that we do influence matter at both atomic and sub-atomic levels. This changes everything. It shows there is also a cumulative effect of our entire race on all matter.

The mind is profound, and yet we treat it as an object by linking it with the brain in a physical way that is insufficient. Empiricism, or physical testing, can be inadequate, as linguistics expert Noam Chomsky may be suggesting here: *'The empiricist view is so deep-seated in our way of looking at the human mind, that it almost has the character of a superstition'. 1958.*

And that: *'As soon as questions of will or decision or reason or choice of action arise, human science is at a loss'.* [Prof Noam Chomsky, 1978; Nobel Prize winner.]

The human mind generates energy, and lots of it. We sense that as feelings and atmosphere. After we think a strong thought, where does it go? Does it fade away to nothing, or does it add to what already exists? Energy accumulates, so there is the answer. This is crucially significant, because if there is such a connection, each thought would alter the universe. If so, then all our thoughts would combine each day to create a really colossal effect. There is ample evidence of this. It is logical, and fits what we see.

The nature of the self is the key, because until we can be logical about the essence, the seed of the tree of thoughts, the leaves and branches have no meaning: they become obstacles like Alexander Pope's 'loads of learned lumber in his head' (1711).

Cicero and others said in 50 BC: 'The spirit is the self'. Science can now agree, simply by equating the 'self' as a massless point of conscious energy. This is the key, because it shows how the mind could persist after the body stops, and this unlocks the meaning of time and events. As Sir Roger Penrose once wrote: 'Consciousness...is the phenomenon whereby the universe's very existence is made known'.[113]

We recall the quote (in the heading of Chapter 6) in which C. G. Jung noted a powerful experience of déjà vu. In the same book of his life, he felt certain this was a deeply significant impression or window on reality, and wrote that he 'knew even more' that 'man is indispensable' within the running of life itself: 'Human consciousness created objective existence and meaning...in the great process of being'.[114] We can go further and suggest mind and matter are exactly connected.

---

113 The Emperor's New Mind, Oxford University Press 1989.
114 Memories, Dreams, Reflections, CG Jung , p285, Fontana Press 1995.

Such experiences, which many of us share, can indeed be powerful signposts to how the whole universe ticks like a cosmic clock. A smile of the ethereal Cheshire Cat in our minds may be no less a fact of real life as a tornado, if we were to realise it. Jung trusted careful insight, and he was perhaps the most perceptive psychoanalyst in history (apologies to the Freudians). We get so used to regarding reality as composed only of noisy material clashes like lightning flashes, that subtle realisations are too often dismissed as having less meaning. Every science paper relies on such insights, and while some have been spectacularly mistaken, they still have to be weighed carefully.

What is possible is a link that can exist between each mind and the Super Grid mentioned earlier. All our minds can then be the key driving force that runs the universe, moment by moment. All that energy can be spread across the universe the instant it is generated via the grid that exists. It is logical that we are not only altering our own health by how we think, but are even affecting our climate, and our society of course. Bearing in mind all the evidence, it seems certain this is the case, so we can also spread an energy that calms it all again.

In cyclic time terms, this is how the cycle would switch from chaos into order: by building the thoughts that have that effect. Since human influence can alter tests (Bell 1964), it is inevitable that the effect can be wider. There is no mechanism or obstacle that would prevent this wave altering the cosmos itself, and do so instantly. Without a viable mechanism for such a switch, there could not be a cyclic pattern of events. With one, there is no other pattern of events that can exist but a continuum. There we have it.

The new answer is that the human mind holds the key to that energy switch. There is no discernible way that nature shifts herself from chaos to order without our being a part of it. Such a shift would take energy, and Humanity is arguably the only source. In essence, the reality may be as simple as this: the mind can be a point source of energy, matter is full of points of energy, and these two types of energy could be interacting in a permanently linked way. This implies our thoughts are *continuously altering* the cosmos.

Since we have seen matter can be 'entangled' as with Cooper Pairs, it is logical that our minds may also be constantly entangled with *all of Matter*. Think gently, and events move in a cool way. We all know what happens with chaotic thoughts...chaos follows soon afterwards. Would that work on a giant scale? It seems it would. Logic and reason agree. Our bodies also react to these patterns, as we are all aware.

Now we can put all this together. Matter is in rotation, so all matter could be revolving in the same kind of way. We see the universe as one complete system, as science must do for its mathematics to work, so *all energy can be connected* in this way.

The final step was to see if quantum physics had a role in all this. Of course it does, but the question is how. The mind can be linked to matter via our Super Grid, so that 'all matter is entangled all the time to some extent, and we are part of that link'. Therefore whatever we do affects everything and everyone else. We sense this each day.

How could the mind have enough energy to do any such thing? It could if it was not just a few electrical impulses in the brain, but a 'separate yet connected' kind of quantum energy in its own right. If so, it would explain many things. For this to be possible, another question had to be solved: is the mind separate from the body, and able to act upon it in the way Jung discussed, with the world 'impinging on the senses'? If that is true, as it appears, then the human mind can influence all matter, not only the body.

This would all be logical and possible if the mind itself is a 'massless point of energy' like a star, if we could see it, living in the brain, yet separate from it. This would explain how the mind is capable of far more than mere electrical impulses in the brain ever could be. It would also explain how the memory persists even when all our cells change over the course of every seven year period. If we were only physical, that could not happen.

Now we can look at the universe. Could our cumulative minds acting together control spacetime itself? They could, so each mind then creates the world. We never quite realised how deeply that may be true. This can answer all our questions. Try it and see.

This solution fits what we observe. Once again the CMB shows an energy re-alignment process has taken place, and has done so very recently indeed. The heart of the answer seems to lie in the quantum world of entanglement, as we have seen. The observer can indeed influence the experiment, and so the way is open for the state of human minds on earth to alter the spin state of all matter...on a rolling basis,

Spirit within the Sub-atomic Grid

Diagram of the mind in the cosmos:
linked life of mind and matter

The subtle human self   The physical universe

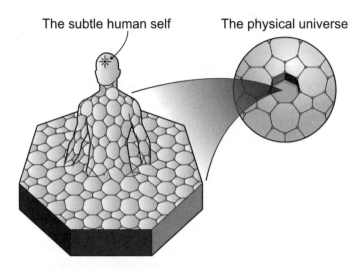

FIGURE 28 *Mind within Matter: diagram showing human/anthropic effect of the 'spirit' or 'human self' within the cosmos, and how such energies are exactly linked to the continuous motion of cyclic spacetime, whether consciously or not [causing the idea of thoughts altering events].*

24 hours a day. This amounts to a kind of *'human chaos and order law'* that governs what takes place. We see this rule at work in our own lives very clearly, and in our homes, with our relatives, friends, pets, and so much more.

Each tiny change in mind feelings influences our environment. The mind can alter matter, and does so constantly, affecting the atmosphere, and our health mainly. This is easy to see and feel.

All it takes to generate change on a huge scale is a large enough group of people thinking the same way with enough purely focused and directed energy involved. If there is any trace of chaos or violence in the thinking, then the net effect will be even more chaotic than before. The Super Grid holds the key as to how this happens, offering a channel by which the atoms are all linked: *alter a few, and all of them switch at once.*

Human nature is a powerful force as we can all see.

The Arab Spring uprisings are an example. Before they happened, many were thinking change was needed. Some were peaceful. Violence is never valid, as Gandhi wisely knew. This has been observed over history on many occasions. The important part is the influence this smaller chaos has on the gigantic scale of spacetime itself. The proposal is that the mind, like Jung's 'collective unconscious', can reach a *critical mass of power that switches the entire cosmos* from chaos back to order again, in less than a second. Not only is this logically and now physically possible, but the fact we are here shows a cycle can do this.

What could constitute such a power? It may be as simple as pure goodwill but on a very profound level, but now we are moving into other areas of human thinking, so here is the essence of how this could arise.

It may sound like a leap to suggest this, but nothing in science clearly excludes this potential for us to effect total change in our world, and space. It then becomes a viable option to propose a fully cyclic mechanism that 're-sets' periodically in a perfect way, returning to the same sequence of events on each occasion. Only this solution can explain the common experience of time repeating identically, which we see as déjà vu, and only this answer can explain why the CMB is so flat, why Dark Matter has never been identified, why every ancient culture already knew about this cyclic repetition, why galaxies are still accelerating. Experts think they should have slowed down.

Weird as it might sound, this answer may be a universal explanation, or 'Theory of Everything'. Ignore the cycle, and nothing fits. Add it to what we know, be ready to reject old theories that use assumption, and it all fits.

Since the human mind is composed of conscious energy, as we see, then it is logical this energy may alter in strength and effect. The human mind may have a constant 'rolling' connection between its own energy state, and thus the precise behaviour we exhibit as people from day to day, and moment to moment. This state of energy might also pass through transitions of chaos and order, rather as Time seems to. It may also be true that these two, Mind and Matter, could be connected at a much deeper level, so that the state of one influences the other constantly via an 'energy network': the Super Grid.

We already know from our own lives that our own mind very much affects our body, with just a thought being able to induce every kind of experience from minor gasps to clinical shock so strong we can no longer move or function, so it is conceivable that Matter in general may be affected. Such matters are a little outside the usual range of science, but we can at least suggest a further connection that is both logical and potentially true: it appears possible this 'human energy value' may even influence spacetime itself, since the two are linked, not totally detached units.

Energy affects energy, so thoughts would have an influence as well.

Where does all that energy go? It alters the matter that forms the Super Grid, and waits there. Energy cannot vanish, it just spreads out, yet 'we' can also focus it.

We have seen how the mind powers our own health and lives, so there may well be a larger and even cumulative effect on how the energy of one kind builds up over time to form an unstoppable force that, in this new combined form, reaches a point where it overturns the 'balance of total energy' existing. There is even evidence that this crisis or 'peak situation' may not only have existed in the past, but does so to this day, and will continue to act in the same cyclic pattern of precise predictability.

However we may feel, there is nonetheless evidence that such a switchover can, has, and will happen. The evidence is strong.

This may seem a bizarre idea, but it is based entirely on the natural principles of earth and space that we see played out every day. As Dickens wrote, take nothing on its looks, but take everything on the evidence. Nature is about balancing energies, and it does so in what we call storms and disasters. Yet our theories of reality contradict this natural process. The fact so much remains contradictory is proof that our thinking could be off-centre, and must be so. Now we can go a step further.

For this to be possible, and for matter to be affected by people to a greater extent than would seem likely on the face of it, the human mind would need a form of energy that is 'point specific'. As we have seen, this could be possible if the mind has the form of a point or dot of energy. If this is correct, then there may then be a subtle and yet profound connection between the self, each one of us, and matter, at both an atomic and sub-atomic levels. The brain would merely be the interface between the mind and orders to the body, which show up in tests as electrical impulses, and often mistaken for thoughts.

In this case, the people we are would not merely ramble through life in a broadly aimless way, remaining largely uncertain about our origins or goals, or those of Nature, but may instead be the conscious part of a larger 'energy coherence', similar to the 'syncytium' referred to in the physics of one unit...the super atom. This is where atoms do begin to behave as one unit, as in rubidium as mentioned, rather than just a jumble of random energies going about their own business individually.

This is highly significant. The evidence all agrees, and it makes the universe a coherent system, not the random or chance place some suggest.

This presents an intriguing possibility, that all matter may be connected to all of us as people, so that any action anywhere would inevitably have an effect on the whole as if it were one single unit; if this is the case, then although acting as separate beings within the world of Matter, we would actually be part of such *a unit that acted and reacted as one entity.* This does not imply that matter is conscious, but it can be seen as a coherent whole on which we ourselves, as conscious beings, have both a daily and cumulative effect on Matter. We do not see plates hiding behind cereal packets in the cupboard, or forks running away across the prairie to be free. Matter is not conscious as we are, but we can affect it. That energy forms part of the system.

The idea is really very simple. We have all seen how just the effects of being happy and peaceful have a great effect on a person's health and even lifespan, yet every person has a different degree of influence on all these factors.

Now we can consider if this 'people-matter-energy' unit is true. The key implication of this suggestion is that we would see signs of people accumulating the effect of actions. The millennia old presumption by some in the Vedic and later traditions of ancient Bharat (India) has been that the self or 'soul' may be immune to actions. The daily effect of our lifestyle and habits on our health shows this cannot be correct, yet at a deeper level of the self as a point of intense energy, there would have to be a highly accurate, precise record of each action, right down to the level of thoughts.

Do we see any evidence of such energy exchanges? It seems we do. The way the human mind can quickly degenerate into frustration, as a factor of anger, is similar to bursts of energy being emitted from the sun, rather as in a small coronal mass ejection in the same sort of way the sun gives out at times. Bursts of anger are very intense, and we can feel them as clearly as if they were bolts of electricity.

No instrument can detect such things, but there would be a reaction in brain waves. From what we know of the human mind, there are such strong waves of energy, be it anger or love or kindness, we as people can feel them, and react to that energy in a similar way to Newton's Third Law of action and reaction. Science cannot pick up such effects directly, but we can observe them, and we have all experienced such influences in our lives.

Our laws are all based on being kind, calm and balanced, yet our human reactions to negative scenes may be anything but cool and calm. This may be such a sign of the constant changes going on within the human psyche. The delicate balance of the mind is easily upset, hence why we try to create our home decoration just so, aiming at maintaining an ideal balance of mind and surroundings.

As the saying goes, the light that burns twice as bright shines half as long. Slowly the candle dims over time, and the person becomes almost ready to move into the next phase. Science could have missed a major insight here into how the mind works, but innovators like Dr Sam Parnia are showing how subtle information remains in the mind, and that NDE's could be important experiences of what really happens. Logically, such 'near death experiences' should exist. It takes energy to run our lives, and we can nearly all relate to the notion that our own power as people could outlive the basic material energy of the body.

Just because some scientists (yet not all) maintain that there is no such thing as a self that is separate from the body, does not mean no such entity exists. Much of the information described here shows that there is good reason to think this is another major mistake in science, because if time really is cyclic in nature, then there would have to be a 'self' largely as set out here, for time to be able to function in this way.

Gödel, the mathematician and Einstein's close friend, agreed this cycle is also logical in the reincarnation of human beings. It may be normal to presume the brain is the material seat of the conscious mind, but the evidence shows the opposite.

This strong-minded determination to refuse to adapt its thinking has left science having to make some big and embarrassing claims: that it will one day decode how dreams or human memory work, even though it never has. Until that day, we may be permitted to think that déjà vu might be explainable in another way than the time-gap theory that is so unconvincing. It is truly a tall order for thousands of such vivid NDE and reincarnation cases to report such similar experiences by chance, or for us to suspect each person of being either deluded or 'in' on some giant global scale hoax.

Logic shows they would be telling the truth, and most of us can see the reasoning for accepting they are. The ancient Greeks called the existence of the soul the surest aspect of understanding they knew, which had far-reaching implications. Plato had a very spiritual view of this when he wrote around 380 BC: '...we shall believe the soul is immortal...and pursue right consciousness with wisdom always and ever...we ought to fly away from earth to heaven as quickly as we can...to fly away is to become like God, as far as possible, and to become like him is to become holy, just and wise'.

Their view was one of making sense of reality using logic and experience, which today are not always valued quite as highly as they were then. Petrarch agreed in 1352 when he wrote that mundane events are fleeting: 'Whatever the world finds pleasing is but a brief dream'.

The ancients were intent on finding meaning and value in patterns. Quality was the great aim, as George Chapman wryly noted later in 1654: 'They are only truly great who are truly good'. A chaotic and vengeful mind was seen as a serious negative, as Euripides wrote in 430 BC: 'Wrath brings mortal men their gravest hurt'. Empire building was noted as a great increaser of chaos and pain, as Erasmus wrote in 1517: 'Let a king recall it is better to improve his kingdom than to increase his territory'. Few did.

Dreams are a fascinating insight into ideas placed in the subconscious by daily events, usually, but occasionally there are deeper experiences that are even harder to account for, and may relate to much earlier memories than we can explain from one life. Having had such experiences, many are bound to look for explanations to account for them, and this rich heritage of subtle thinking accumulated over nearly four millennia is something that needs explaining, not just dismissing.

It is too easy for modern science to write off much of human history in such matters, but the modern physics points to a cyclic pattern within time itself, at which point all those hidden and very ancient accounts for human thinking can be put back on the table for consideration. For this to be so, there must be a separate energy from Matter, yet acting upon it. The mind seems to be the apparent source.

A further situation we see is the extraordinary bond that exists between us all. We do feel connected to people globally, with cultural differences being no obstacle to this most positive experience. Their state concerns us all. As the poets have said, it is as though the events that take place within cyclic time are part of a drama or play. We feel linked to all people, and share their feelings, so our lives unfold in a continual series of interactions that conform to a Newtonian set of rules. This is why charity is so deeply important.

It does appear to be possible that these complex human interactions may be equally as exact and precise as those within the atomic world; indeed they can be intricately connected to the atomic and subatomic worlds as we have seen. This is the energy Grid. If this is correct, then the idea this world is just a set of random or chance events would be an illusion, rather as it is an illusion to accept what our eyes tell us when we look at the sun crossing the sky, and succumb to the temptation to think that the sun orbits the Earth.

The earth may look flat, but the evidence convincingly shows it is a sphere, as are the other planets, moons, satellites and stars. Sailors see this hourly as ships appear over the horizon gradually while actually being close. It may seem easier to believe the world has conspired to deceive us all in saying the earth is round, but the evidence is clear: not everyone is out to deceive. Even the word 'planet' has been confused as 'evidence' of a flat earth, claiming the word derives from the word 'plane' meaning flat. This is untrue, since the Latin for plane is *plana*, quite different from the Latin *planeta*, which derives from the Greek *planetes*, meaning wanderer, and not a plane at all.

For those lucky enough to circumnavigate earth, there is the experience of moving forwards in the same direction, either the west or east, and arriving back at the same place from which we departed a while before. Our sensory human perception gave us an entirely false reading that we were moving over flat ground. Human perception is therefore often at odds with the real world. Airline pilots fly round the globe every day, and are deeply trusted people, not hoaxers or deceivers.

Being human is a complex experience, and it is entirely to be expected that our theories can be every bit as mistaken as our senses. The *scotoma* is a possible example of this, which can be a 'blind spot' in the mind. Much more likely is the choice to suspect everyone is being devious, which is not remotely likely, so we can decide.

The human mind could hold the balance of energy for the whole system, when we act in concert. The Super Grid could be so finely balanced that mere thought energy is enough to tip the scales one way, and cause a sub-atomic cascade effect that acts instantly. In this case, the effect would be super-luminal, or faster than light. This does contradict some of Einstein's theories in General Relativity, but it may also be true.

The unifying factor in all these suggestions is 'reality', combining what we see occurring in real life. The central reasoning is that there must be an equalisation of energy on a continuing basis. The final scenes of each cycle would then be simply this equalisation process reaching a more extreme level than before, as the constraints of time require an ever stronger rate of change towards full equilibrium.

If this process of cyclic time is actually short, then it follows logically that all forms of energy would also pass through an identical phase of increasing speed of change, including ourselves as people in close connection with the world of Nature that we currently inhabit. This would mean that both ourselves and the natural world follow the same process of order followed by gradually increasing chaos, which then culminates in a complete 'energy reconciliation', and Order once again.

This interpretation of reality may function using only three key processes enshrined as laws in physics and chemistry. One is Newton's third law as we have seen, and the other two are the twin laws of the conservation of matter and energy. In this way the total content of the universe as a closed system can remain constant, without the need for inventing new universes.

One can then propose a fresh 'Time Law', which can act as a principle that: *'Time repeats in a triple set of identical cycles as an infinite continuum'.*

The present is 'recorded' as it unfolds, as it did in the past, and will in the future.

Nature may therefore run very precisely in terms of cause and effect, rather as a train runs along a set of tracks, rather than wandering over the prairies looking for butterflies and collecting flowers. There are clearly causal energies that produce specific resulting effects, so that randomness may appear to be widespread while not actually existing in the way usually suggested. In this way, the world can appear to be random in smaller locations while at the same time being precise and perfect at the largest scales.

Nature has to balance the books. Even chaotic winds are merely the rapid balancing of unequal forces. A hurricane may look wild and untamed, yet it follows the precise guidelines of strength and direction laid down for it by variations in pressure and temperature as it passes over the warm ocean that create its power. Yet even amid the chaos of hurricanes' circular rotation of great force, lies an ultra-low pressure centre, known as the eye, like the empty centre of a doughnut, where there is still air and a clear sky. A tornado may also look random and yet it too follows precise guidelines that dictate its power and direction.

All such natural effects have to balance the books in the same way, exactly, and cannot stop until this task has been completed. There is no 'intention' involved in such extremes, because clearly nature has no mind, but blindly carries out this same task of energy equalisation. Sadly such events often have tragic effects on anyone caught in their path, but it helps to know why such events have to take place. This way we can mitigate the resulting chaos and do what we can to get out of their way ahead of time.

Everything that happens in Nature is like a train of events that has been set in motion, so this process cannot stop midway through its course any more than the giant planet Jupiter could wander off and spend an afternoon having tea with Saturn, its sister gas giant in our solar system.

We are therefore part of this gigantic natural process in which these often colossal forces move from A to B. The moon cannot stop creating tides because it is precisely located to do so, and the seas are bound to respond; except for smaller bodies of water like the Caspian Sea or the Mediterranean which are too small to have the same tidal extremes as elsewhere. It is extraordinary to find that such a small disc as the moon, which we can cover with the tip of a finger, can pull billions of tons of water into a dome far beneath its spectacular trajectory, and do so twice a day.

We can therefore see that Nature is full of various complex types of energy, and we human beings live in one small part of it. Now that science has found that experiments may be affected by the presence of an observer, we have some grounds for agreement that our human minds may be affecting matter on a much larger scale. Our own bodies are a curious example of how we affect matter, and the old case that the brain does all this by itself is no longer a credible answer; as *hydro-cephalus* graphically shows, the mind is the real controller.

It is therefore likely that the mind is able to record events very precisely in terms of action and reaction, and that we may never escape the results of those actions, be they kind or less so. It may well be true that even people are subject to such universal laws as that of cause and effect at a much deeper level than science has yet to realise. Since the self is clearly not material itself but more of a subtle entity, this would explain why no one has been able to find a 'soul' or put one in a jam-jar for study, despite trying. There is logic and some objective evidence in how our minds work to support the notion of the mind or self as a massless point of energy that does interact closely with matter, so that when it moves away, the body ceases to function as before, and we declare the body to have died, if the self is pulled towards a new location to take on a new role.

The near death experiences (called NDE's) support this version of reality very thoroughly, and so we should perhaps recognise this possibility as a more accurate way to explain what we witness in practice. If physical evidence did not so exactly mirror this version, then it would not be tenable, but since it does, we have to accept it could be true.

Dr Rupert Sheldrake's work on telepathy has been mentioned before, and since it is well above chance gains of 33%, it becomes a viable option, not least because we also feel this on a daily basis as a normal effect, in phone calls particularly.

It is interesting to note that this is where religion and science are merging into a single view of how the real world may work, where a 'massless self' could act in a similar way to a sub-atomic particle, and be held in place in the body by its own *karma*, simply meaning the power 'quantum' of our own personal energy, and thus remains there only as long as this force holds sway. The second this power or dynamism ceases to be dominant, the self may be able to leave, or might be pulled to leave that body, at which point we say the body has stopped working. This allows for both a rational explanation of the self as conscious and reactive to exist alongside the spiritual or religious description of the same self as being a spirit; then we simply have two versions of an identical answer which are complimentary. Both are then correct.

We seem to know these things already. We get so used to seeing relatives and friends as people based on how they look and act, we tend to forget that there is this evidence for a deeper level of being that also conforms to how the universe itself works, and confirms our experiences as beings of light, rather than as the bodies of matter we appear to be.

It is time we adjusted our world view to bring ourselves up to date with what has been achieved and learned over the last two centuries. Indeed it is stranger still that we have not managed to do this, but quite understandable, since science does not have a ready system for agreeing very unusual items that re-write much of modern human thinking, in the West at least. Minor changes are absorbed into the old linear world view, but major rethinks that alter everything cannot be....they are seen as disruptive and in need of so much reassessment that they have to be shelved for later work over coming decades. Those decades are now complete, and it is time we revised all our knowledge to ensure it is still valid.

We also see a close fit with the work of C. G. Jung, who coined the phrase 'collective unconscious' for the combined thought of the world's human population, as well as the connection we feel as people, no matter where we come from, or what language or culture we are part of.

Key to this understanding is *the self as separate from the body*, and residing inside the brain, rather than being the brain. It could be this crucial separation of the mind and body that solves the riddle of who we are, and why Jung and Freud created such a debate over who was nearer the truth in their accounts of the human psyche. In this way we can be both part of the world, and experience it as real, and yet be able to influence it in our own way, while being separate in form as an entity.

This can also explain how we can be conscious of the three aspects of time as past, present and future, which would be impossible if the brain were the only and ultimate form of the self, firmly set in the present as a material object broadly like any other.

Parts of the brain play a key role in this. The exact way the *thalamus* and *hypothalamus* are able to interact with the conscious mind has also evaded full understanding, and it may be this artificial concept we have created, where some still regard the brain as the seat of consciousness, rather than with a subtle, non-physical entity as 'the self', which has confused the issue. A separate self may instead be the superior controller in this complex picture, which would account for the time-slips that are inherent in human memory and so much more.

Electricity and synapses are not enough to explain the complexity of the human mind, especially this unconscious ability to travel back and forth in time via our memories and future perceptions. No pulse of electricity has ever achieved that miracle, and there is no reason to suppose they do now, nor that one has ever done so.

To suppose that the entire wonder of life on earth happened by chance and a process of evolving runs counter to what we see everywhere; there is connected complexity, not random events that do not quite match or fit. It all matches and fits very well indeed, amazingly so in fact.

The majority of humanity show great concern for acting with kindness in every way in every day, while a violent few ignore such concerns in their passion to enforce their views on others. This aggression breaks the cardinal rule of being non-violent as people in any society, since we must never, ever hurt others. To do so harms both ourselves and our own society, and deep inside we all know that. Kindness is thus the key essential.

This law of being kind and peaceful overrules any other cultural or religious overlays, as we all agree, and our laws are there to protect us from those ferocious few. The only global aim is to remove any vicious behaviour in our own selves, and this age-old truism refers to all of us.

If this is accurate, then this would explain how Nature enforces these basic rules, and the world becomes a better place, at which time that cycle is complete, and a new one begins, without the need for religions at that point. A key fact shows this appears to be true: each religion has a beginning in time, *since they did not always exist*, and then there comes a time when there is no religion, which has become so deeply divisive, since our real 'religion' is perhaps being open and peaceful beings. The current conflict between ideals is totally destructive, and so any calm alternative is better for everyone.

The whole stability of the world is affected by such concerns, as the situation descends into serious chaos. What we do is vital, both as individuals and a race. We seem to have lost power, and if so it needs to be restored, as well as that of the world in general. Is it possible this is true, and both people and matter suffer from entropy over time, creating more of the chaos we see around us? If so, we may be able to fix this loss, whereas if the materialistic model of people as machines is indeed incorrect as suggested, then science will never solve these issues using that old vision of reality.

Some say that the materialistic view of life has been responsible for spreading depression and despondency, since it suggests that no positive outcome is possible.

Some have even said that this old interpretation of people as little more than plants, bacteria, ants or any part of nature, could be to blame for the present inhumane treatment of some people, since it implies a low value to each person, rather than a high one. If we remove the vicious nature that presently upsets our lives to some extent, then we would have a different world. This is something we can do, so that power to decide to help is something that sets us apart. Violence has no place in civilised society, and neither should we send it overseas in the mistaken belief it will make life more peaceful.

Now that we see there is no way around the astrophysics, even the most dyed-in-the-wool linear time supporter must stop to think if their view is still supportable.

All these questions, and their answers, boil down to two things: the time span available for life on earth, and the nature of the self. Could we have got both so wrong in our centuries of thinking? There has always been this debate about both these pivotal aspects of our thinking, and it shows the position has changed since the 1850's.

At least some live in a society where we can offer our opinions and try to advance our understanding.

CHAPTER 19

Spirit and Science

Science must begin with myths, and the criticism of myths.
SIR KARL POPPER

Philosophy is a battle against the bewitchment of our intelligence through language.
L. WITTGENSTEIN, 1953

The man who listens to Reason is lost: Reason enslaves all whose minds are not strong enough to master her and *All great truths begin as blasphemies.*
GEORGE BERNARD SHAW, 1898

Essence

Now we hit a wall in our voyage of discovery, or at least physics has. There is no clear way to explain these odd 'facts' we see, so science is full of theories, with few answers. There are effects without clear causes, so what can the answer be to that? We need a source of energy. In astronomy they invented one, but cannot detect it, and called it 'dark' for that reason. Can mountains be that energy, or elements in some form? It seems not. What we missed may be right in front of us... ourselves.

Pure science cannot explain what we see in reality. It relies on materials being the centre and hub of reality. Small scale physics shows this is incorrect. The appearance of solid objects looks simple, yet is not. They appear to be obvious, solid lumps we can move around as we please, but this is too narrow a view to use on a deeper level. The evidence all points to an energy source barely considered as worthy of mention...we the 'people'. We are used to the electromagnetic spectrum, a fraction of which we can see, but not the human element that may hold the balance of everything, even sub-atomic energy. This may be the vital key.

Obviously Matter does not have consciousness, but it is affected by it, as the body and quantum effects have shown. This is the central part of opening a new gateway into the future: understanding how we affect the world around us at a far deeper level than we ever guessed was true. Here is the cutting edge of progress in fresh thinking. One of the greatest errors in human understanding may be just this simple: the old claim that events are random, and so it matters not what we do in our lives. Cyclic time predicts the opposite to be true, that the human mind is part of a much larger grid or 'fabric of spacetime' that interacts with our own human energy level precisely. In this case, every single tiny action and thought would be recorded, a kind of 'akashic record' stored within Matter, while simultaneously accumulating either calm or chaos in different places.

Gradually these two forces of mind and matter reach a peak, at which time the whole system reverts to calm again. The imbalance being corrected in this natural process is largely hidden, because it works on a quantum level, which is why we cannot usually see or detect it, even though it is not only real and powerful, but forms the whole underlying energy and function of the universe. This would be where the 3,000 year old idea that every human action and thought do actually matter. If this prediction is correct, then all the ancient cultures, with their symbols, rituals and deep concerns about the 'state of the cosmos', would at heart be right. Prayers can of course be ritualistic and superficial, yet may simply conceal genuine efforts to use the mind to 'wish for' wrongs to be righted, and order to return.

The ancient Egyptians, for example, used to include priest castes who would pray all night for the safe orbit of the sun in the cyclic process of life that restored light and energy to the world at dawn each day. They waited below the pyramid, it is said, for the sun's first rays to catch the gold-covered capstone high above the ground (when it was still dark below), to blaze an intense spark of light in the semi-dark sky. Quite a scene to picture, and a remarkable sign of how the early Egyptian culture saw the sun as giver of life, with Ra shown with the ankh symbols. The Mayan culture had similar beliefs and their own style of pyramids, and shares the identical aim to restore 'cosmic order'.

How could they all think the same way never having met, unless time were indeed cyclic, and they were merely 'remembering' what had worked before, the last time the world descended into chaos and became in need of freshly powerful thinking?

It is easy to write off all that ritual as mere fantasy, but it appears they were apparently closer to explaining reality than we are, because we have lost the ability to interpret what Nature helps to happen naturally: to restore order.

The elements cannot be relied on to embody our world view, because they are subject to change. The universe is not just material. Matter is not solid, but mostly space, and capable of changing into other forms in an instant. Atomic energy shows that, but the violence of that fission can be replaced with the better ideal of fusion, as the sun uses so effectively.

Natural forces are at work, and they will complete their task. We see tiny 'windows' of these effects in what, to us, are giant events, such as tectonic movements, and solar coronal mass ejections or asteroid impacts. In cosmic terms, they are at the atomic scale. The reality of the universe is carried out at the sub-atomic level, not just the lumpy 'rain and rock' level we see. Our ability to perceive events is largely governed by the narrow band of visible light our eyes can see, but science has enabled us to 'see' gamma and X-rays and so much more, even while not being sure what they all mean.

The start and end concept may be just this: a human invention a few of us like because it is simple, and absolves us of any apparent responsibility for our actions. Only in such a mind-set could our leaders feel it was justified to terrify the entire world with nuclear warfare, the very human and insane concept of 'mutual assured destruction' (MAD, a real term used in politics). Science was called on to support this idea, having given form and birth to it in 1859 with the evolutionary work by Wallace and Darwin, and so arose the modern world view of materialism.

It is not a coincidence that modern science cannot explain gravity, time, space, galactic speed, history, conscious thought, or memory, nor even give a definition of 'life' itself. Biology is, of course, part of all this rotation and cyclicity. The frozen frog in the boreal regions of Canada, during winter, freezes solid and should be 'dead' according to normal limits we consider life to work in, and stay dead. It does neither, and all these things point to one inescapable conclusion. The old 20th century world view has a serious problem with reality, and thus cannot solve these questions. This is modern science...brilliant in fields like astrophysics and others, yet unable to describe our origins or the cosmos.

In Sanskrit the self is known by the word *Atman*, from which Hindi gets the word *atma* meaning self or soul, the conscious being that each of us is. What type of energy is this that can think, create, paint, sing, dance, judge, discern and feel? We pick up ideas from each other, and feel the power of an atmosphere as 'electric', while it has nothing to do with electricity. We feel the power of the gathering we are in, whether it is 3 or 4, or a million more than that. It is an immense power, not a small one.

Should we combine science and spirit?

To remove chaos outside, we must logically remove it inside. This could be why the oldest writings in India suggest this, and why the gentle would one day run the world.

The self does have such power, and when we act in calm harmony the effect is huge.

We can see a close parallel in the way particles+people work. When together, under special conditions, strange effects occur. When atoms approach super-cool temperatures, they begin to act as one super-atom as noted. Therefore the self and others may combine to form a kind of *Human Bose-Einstein Condensate* (a super-atom acting as one unit) where a cumulative effect could create an effect far beyond what any of us quite thought possible. The self can affect the body, and perceive feelings that no machine can quantify, and does so every waking second of each day.

What does it mean? It means that the delicate balance of the universe, not just earth, could be affected in such ways to govern even spacetime. Looked at in the broadest scale of both earth and space, along with the astrophysics data, we can see a solution here that joins all these threads into one line of logic and evidence. If each person is like a sub-atomic point of light, much like a pocket star on a smaller scale, yet equally powerful, then all the effects we see within reality can be explained with this fresh world view.

We may have a new principle here. This combined human effect could alter the balance or order of all energy in the cosmos. It may be so, since what else could?

This becomes possible with just two ingredients. First, the mind having in reality a form like a point of energy with no mass or size, yet immense energy of exactly the right type to influence all other particles. In this sense the physical and the spiritual become the same... just pure energy. Second, the universe would need to be balanced on a fine fulcrum of power as we have seen, and if so, the tiniest addition of force would tilt the scale from one side to the other in an instant.

Is there any evidence for this view of energy transfers that have increased in chaos *over recent time*? It is difficult to find any part of the universe in which these signs are not clearly present. The young rings of Saturn, the white ice of Haumea barely touched by the assumed billion years of gathering dark space dust, and well over a thousand other examples, are there to be judged by each of us.

Is it pure coincidence that every culture on earth contains such a spoken story of a Time Continuum that never runs out of time? Passed down through the generations from parent to child for all of human history, sung about in a million songs of chaos and order, 'heaven and hell', this same classic story of time now fits perfectly into the astronomy of spacetime and quantum physics to form a concept of everything, from time to eternity.

The 'human' force of 'atmosphere' is a major part of life. The human mind is part of an energy flow which we can sense and respond to. Many feel this atmosphere very acutely, and most house purchases are made on this basis rather than cost or location alone. Even pets can often sense our moods, and we theirs. Dogs are good at this, and 'seeing eye dogs' help many blind people to navigate the streets, or warn deaf people of sounds to improve their lives at home. One English sheepdog not only famously woke up a whole family at night to warn them of a fire, and led them all out of the house, but then even decided more aid was needed, and went for help to a nearby home; a clever success.

All these examples, and there are tens of thousands known about, demonstrate that mind energy is special, subtle, powerful, important, and shapes human history and survival in a unique way. Added to the other factors here, and we have a new way of seeing reality: that both mind and physical energies appear to combine to form a field that governs what happens right across the scale from micro to macro levels of energy transfer and interaction. The intangible force of the mind can clearly be felt in sports matches and each conversation we ever have, yet science cannot measure it directly, and for this reason has denied there is such an energy at all.

Human experience is an even more powerful argument than such measuring limitations, and at the frontiers of science we are compelled to remember that an inability to detect a force that all of us can pick up, does not mean it is not real.

The near death experiences (NDE's) are also a powerful witness to a situation that scientists in the medical professions are just now reacting to. When we join up all these dots we get a glimpse of what may be the next frontier of human advancement in understanding our 'human condition', meaning that science may not know the whole story of life; human mental processes are beyond maths and simple analysis. This suggestion may be a step too far for some in science, but let's look at the evidence in essence only, to save another 100 years or more of research time. Not a scientist on earth can prove the mind does not have this capacity to influence spacetime.

Does this fit in with geology and history?

We can also see a very interesting pattern of changes, with large effects still in progress. Even a famously stable island area like Great Britain (UK) can have periodic earthquakes, such as a large one in the North Sea area off the east coast a century ago, or a really large event in 1607 which created a strong tsunami in the Bristol Channel, and flooded both coasts of north Somerset and south Wales. That 1607 event was thought to have been the result of a sub-sea landslip on the continental shelf further out to sea.

The whole earth seems to go from one state into another, usually at a slow pace over time as energy dissipates from high order into lower states. The geology is the clue here, with the calm sediments proving that there were ages in which calmness was the order of the day, and a global era in which stability reigned for a while. The chalk and limestone measures have been noted to show this. Neither has it ever been seriously considered that there could have been people living on earth at the same time. Yet it is perfectly possible such a past civilisation could have existed in that era, while leaving no surface trace of their ever having done so.

The ancient Greeks like Hesiod and Plato wrote of such a society, and if they were right, those periods of geological calm could have occurred together, at the same time, and left few signs beyond traces we find on the sea bed from time to time. The Rann of Kutch is one such area where offshore 'city' traces have been found, and in the Indus Valley delta region which many think is perhaps earth's oldest.

This is no easy task for a conventional geologist to accept, because it would require the telescoping of all the classic 15 geological ages into a new world view where all the ages happen in quick succession, the majority being completed in 1,800 years while laying down different sediments at the same time, and all in about 4,900 years. This has been more fully explained in earlier sections, but it is possible if we recognise the problems in dating all rocks are substantive problems, not matters of opinion. The model of time as a line is the matter of opinion that is at issue here, so with that placed firmly in the realm of theory, we are then allowed to propose alternatives that could fit the facts better.

Now we can explore the next step, which is simplicity itself in terms of logic, but rather a leap in its contrast to conventional thinking. Anyone who has studied religion knows there are some interesting parallels to science, and between these two varied solutions to earth's history lies an answer, but neither fully explain where life came from.

Here is the point where science and the spiritual are not as separate as they appear, because both relate to the search for order in life. Both see quantum dots of power as the basic building blocks of the cosmos, and a full explanation requires both, because science alone cannot explain these facts.

The events that occur in our world mirror the events that occur in space. There are quiet areas, and empty ones, and there are flashes of extreme energy that explode into action when they have to happen. We have choice, they do not. This makes us a set of key players in the universe, not just on earth. We therefore cannot ignore the effect discussed here of the combined power of nearly 8 billion *'quantum selves'* on the matter around us, and on ourselves as well.

Others rightly judge us by how much positive benefit we bring to the world, and yet even violent people think they are acting correctly. We recognize that causing others sorrow is wrong. There would be an effect of such actions or 'karma', and this is what drives the enmities in the world today. Our beneficial effects are the wonder of humanity, and put a smile on every face that sees them.

Diamonds are an analogy. If each of us is different, we can also grade ourselves like diamonds, according to clarity and 'mental' kindness or 'colour'. The highest value of diamonds is based on these two key factors because of their rarity. A rock full of flaws is a common thing, with every house, desert, cliff and beach full of them. Even rarer still are coloured diamonds, which can be every colour of the rainbow's seven spectral colours, as well as black or fancy white, and they are the most valuable objects on earth.

Some, the rare chameleon diamonds, can even change colour from yellow to green according to the energy they collect in their vicinity, in a curious parallel that is rather like ourselves. When left in darkness, the diamond's atomic structure slowly returns to its ground state of usually yellow. If we see ourselves purely on the basis of how 'diamond-like' we may be, then that purity of goodwill can be identified as one factor that distinguishes each person, and forms the key bond that unifies humanity.

What would someone we all judge to be the 'best person' actually be like? We meet many such people in our lives, if we are lucky, and we value kind people very highly because it is vital to be kind to others, no matter what their background. We sense this need because it is a vital part of how nature also works...kind actions benefit everyone.

This is where the so-called survival instinct breaks down. Even an African lion has been seen to protect a baby antelope it found. A Great Dane dog adopted a deer fawn in the USA, and became friends, while a cat in Ireland 'adopted' some ducklings, even when those balls of yellow fur turned into adult ducks twice its size, wandering round the farmyard in a curious procession. Some lions and tigers have become favoured friends of people, such as the famous 'lion man' who owns a wildlife park in New Zealand, and the Hollywood star Tipi Hedren who adopts big cats in America. It shows our perception of normality needs adjusting.

Moving back to the world of different faiths and belief, we can see kindness is the key. This is why Gandhi's practise of non-violence or *ahimsa* was so powerful, because it did not create damage to anyone. The terrible scenes of partition were due to politics and old rivalries, not his policy, which shows there are other ways to act.

We have one last item to solve which requires us to explain why religion has been such a powerful force over the millennia, and used to rationalise actions that are wholly unjustifiable. The essence of the religious aim is to create harmony, which cannot be achieved in a violent way, which is why the old ways of the medieval period are still present to this day. Peace can only be brought about by being peaceful. To attain peace is to attain what some call Nirvana, and this could be the 'region' to which souls travel when they leave the body. It would also make sense that 'souls', as dots of energy, would need to go somewhere at the end of each cycle, and such a region could act as a 'home' of perfect order and peace.

In terms of simple physics, this is a perfectly reasonable thing to suggest, if rather unconventional for physics to be applied to people in this way. In a cyclic world, this would have to be the case if it is true.

We now have to attempt a way of explaining how the universe, particularly the part involving earth as a planet with all of us perched on its surface, could become ordered after the peak of the current period of acute disorder. This would reverse entropy, so while nature would quite naturally be correcting the imbalances we have helped create over the recent centuries, it is impossible in terms of physics that this process could happen entirely by itself.

This could indeed be true for a special reason. In this version of spacetime with a cyclic orbit of events, the prediction is that all events, quite literally, return to a state of complete order, and then begin a new cycle once again. This new cycle would appear to be exactly the same as the last one, and the future one as well, for the simple reason that once Time has been returned to a state of calm and total order, it would then begin the same set of causes and effects. If the instant of this zero state of events is identical to the same moment in time, with the cosmic clock 'hands' at 12 o'clock just as before, then the same set of events would begin to unfold again. If this were correct, as well it may be, then all it lacks in an agent with enough power to re-create the same situation of order once again.

Where could we look to find such an agent? The clue may be in the nature of the self as a quantum dot of power; the human factor. If this is so, then there could be an ascending order of power, if power is equivalent to 'purity of energy'.

Does a cyclic reality suggest a Supreme Being?

Science cannot ask this question. Since science cannot solve the questions of our origins, or those of the cosmos, we do have to. Many already think the answer is 'yes', yet cannot explain how. Many wonder how God may play a role in resolving all these energy issues. Why not? This is where we cross into theology and the history of thought, a realm which science cannot really comment on, except in one respect. There is no actual obstacle within science that prevents this being possible, using logic and reason chiefly. Now that we see science cannot explain the deepest history of reality at all, the spiritual answers using logic and cyclicity become more valid than other claims. The cycle seems able to provide a means for forces to act in unison. This means Big Bang theory is unworkable. Seeing the time problems which the linear version has not solved, the Evolution too hits a wall of belief, with no long time period for it.

Since the errors in the viewpoint and details within science, as explained here, do seem to demonstrate a gap between those theories and actual reality, science no longer appears to have grounds on which it can disagree.

Here is how that may instead work.

In that case, the commonly held spiritual vision of reality remains possible. This is not classical science, yet we are seeing effects science cannot explain. It is possible the cycle of time is 'why' the galaxies lack the mass scientists require for their maths, because they may only have been spinning for a few millennia, not longer.

The evidence of the CMB being 'flat' for no apparent reason, points to this rather unusual conclusion: that the universe did not jump into being by itself, therefore time cannot have had a distant 'start' date, nor derive from another world, as we noted.

To think otherwise would require belief for acceptance, since proof does not exist. We have no grounds for such belief, so we must broaden our vision to see other forces at work. A glance at Munchausen's Trilemma seems to confirm this enigma, since there is no proof at the outset of the 'test', nor for any of the arguments brought forward to challenge it. The conventional science version of reality fails in these three ways or steps.

The three steps are these: 1. Known as 'infinite regress', this illustrates the principal of 'firm proof' being impossible to confirm, since each 'proof' needs earlier proof of that proof, and so on. Theories require both belief [2] and 'circular thinking'[3], in which the mere fact 'life exists' is taken as evidence it came to exist as we claimed. This is why the usual science version may not fairly be called 'scientific'.

Socrates should not have approved of such claims. Here is an example: 'A fish exists, but we should take care in creating a reason to suit us about how it came to be there'. Any philosopher of science can confirm this, as did Sir Karl Popper in several ways, who famously reminded scientists that even theories have to follow some rules of rationale, to avoid 'perishing' with 'our false theories'.

We must therefore face a shocking fact. Science lacks proven facts, and so relies on belief for the big theories of linear time, such as evolution and Big Bang concepts. We therefore have to admit there is no rational way of resolving these problems without faith or circular thinking to support the science view, which may not be quite the outcome science was expecting. The world cannot be explained by using 'chance' events.

Nature has her own version of how reality works, and God could, quite logically, fill that role. Since science has no alternative, it could be so. All the evidence points to an external force that can reverse chaos or entropy, so this is not just an idea, but the only apparent option to explain what we see. There is nothing in science to disagree, other than speculation.

As people in time, even in a cycle, we see a tree of human life expanding. At the very top of this 'tree of life', what might we see? If all of us are 'souls' or stars, might there logically be a top father figure or 'Supreme Soul'? We may in that case see a point of energy or power that is completely pure and kind, and yet a being with conscious power as well...could this be the famous Supreme Being? Most of us in the world apparently think so, in surveys made, and agree that God could be the Being who repairs the cosmos. This can be true, because it cannot be disproved. This may be why every culture remembers a Supreme Being who returns to sort out the mess we make. We may also see this as an answer as to why many see God as the great Father of humanity, because He looks after us all as 'child spirits', so a father in a parental, loving way, not by gender, which could not exist in a purely spiritual context. We all have our own views on this.

It makes sense that there would be a 'Supreme' Being, because we all have such different qualities, skills and virtues, that there must be one being who has the highest degree of such qualities, and so can be supreme in that way. If that Being never lives a normal life as we do, in the human sense, then logically that Being's energy or power would be vast, never being reduced. Some have taken this immense power to be 'in' all things, good and bad, but it may actually be the case that we ourselves do the chaotic actions that cause sadness, and God never does, being the 'Great Parent' of the children.

That would mean God would be entirely altruistic, only carrying out acts of kindness, while never causing sorrow, as some say. This would be logical, so we do the sad things, and God may then 'put it all right' at the close of each cycle, after which we return 'home' as souls or stars, ready to come back in the next cycle. To many people, this is all Life in a sentence, but in a spiritual context. Science cannot assess this, but we can decide.

If so, what might a Supreme Being have actually done that deserved such tremendous praise for 'really kind actions'? It could be just this… the restoration of the cosmos from chaos into order once again, and it may be an action that is repeated forever, each time we mess up the calm of the spacetime continuum. Clearly we lack the power to fix it. This answer could explain why God has over 120 names around the globe in each culture and religion, and may be so much praised for having done something truly important in the past.

As the chaos grows, we can see this cyclic process of action and reaction may exist in real life, and that past era of 'peak chaos' leading to peak calm, can be this period of time we are seeing now.

Again, surveys show this idea is widespread, but it curiously agrees with physics, because the structure of the CMB shows 'an energy' presumably flattened those waves; they are unlikely to have managed that feat on their own. Such microwaves do not resolve themselves into neat flat planes by themselves, without a cause. Could there be an external agency of a spiritual kind that sometimes affects life on earth? The majority would seem to agree. There seems to be no other option on the table, however odd that may be to some. There is no other conceivable answer, since pure physics stops short of a solution. Science cannot comment here, because this is a matter of the spirit, not physics alone. Using linear time, there would seem to be no alternative in science anyway.

Yet it is logical that this could be true, since science cannot offer any other reason why the universe shows signs of the cycle being 'restored to order' at each transition or 'confluence'. Is this why God is the most famous Being in all of human culture and history? It could be so, because no other explanation exists so far. We have to ask: if not this, then what? At least this explains the viewpoints of both science and religion, and the ground they seem to share.

Not many people would disagree. Why else would God receive so much love and praise unless there had been such a momentous set of actions that reversed the chaos? Every past civilization suggested this as real. We can all see how it may be true, that God sets the system in motion, leaves us with the freewill to choose how to act, sees we mess it up royally, and then returns at the chaos peak to sort it out again, wipe away the tears, and take everyone 'home'. Each culture in history had this view, and bearing all the factors in mind, there is no actual obstacle to this answer.

There comes a moment when we have to decide which is real. Did matter create itself and place us on a planet in the middle of nowhere, or is there a family of 'stars', complete with a 'Supreme Star', whose family lives forever in a cycle? History shows this, science with a few adjustments also agrees, and so do our laws of physics. If we allow for a Supreme Being, the circle becomes possible, and the majority appear to have the right idea.

This account works, and is logically valid. We have nowhere else to go, indeed. This appears to be the only way to explain how religion and science have followed such similar paths in explaining Reality, each with their own version of quantum dots of power achieving great deeds of cosmic alteration. By seeing the virtues of both together, we can compose some sense of order between the two, and seek to answer the old questions of how we got here. Do we turn back time, or does it flip back with our help?

A weird idea, but all the signs point to this. As Henry Jones wrote in 1907: 'O God! Put back Thy universe and give me yesterday.' Many have thought that over the years, perhaps because some signs of quality have vanished over time.

CHAPTER 20

Minds Moving Energy

Mere cleverness is not wisdom.
EURIPIDES, 485–406 BC

It is perfectly certain that the soul is immortal and imperishable, and our souls will actually exist in another world.
PLATO, 429–347 BC

I have something more to do than feel.
CHARLES LAMB, 1796

Essence

We sometimes forget we are human beings. We all believe in something, but how did that thinking arise? Science has been created slowly over generations of thinkers. As we now realise, not all this growth has been an advance. Some of our deductions were based on false premises those pioneers took to be true, but were later shown to be figments of our imagination. This is the most serious Achilles heel in Science: to reach a firm decision that may look watertight at the time, for which later and better information reveals to be totally untrue.

The whole of science is aimed at avoiding such situations, yet they happen quite often. All this shows science is not easy. Even Newton was told he had put science back 200 years, when he had advanced it. His peers just did not realise his work was among the most brilliant in history, while looking strange to them. Of course it was strange…it was new. We try to be objective, using our best efforts to derive what 'looks right'. There is always a human element in data selection, and what any experiment is 'supposed to mean'. It may not have any of that meaning at all in real life. Now we can further explore what the evidence seems to point to: the human mind moving the world each second.

Odd as this might seem to some adherents of the old 'material' convention of seeing matter as 'just matter', the truth is that this view could be
the essence of the reality of how Nature works, with ourselves as part
of it all, and minutely and subtly altering the entire mechanism via the
changing state of our minds. A mad idea? Jung thought not in some
ways, as he strove to combine spirit, logic and reason.

The mind does have energy, so there may be an exponential effect
from all of us.

This is the notion of a 'global mind effect' [GME] set within a giant
Cycle of Time, rather as suggested by the term of Carl Jung's *Collective
Unconscious*, but applied to the apparent effects we seem to have on
our total environment, not merely in the gross physical sense, but at a
profoundly subtle level of the sub-atomic, and on even deeper levels
that remain outside the realm of what science can detect at all, let alone
measure.

This may look like going out on a limb, but it offers a new way of
illuminating what many already experience, that science and religion
just use different words to explain similar concepts. Once they were
in disagreement, but now that is no longer true. Those of science and
religion have found a mine of common ground. At their core, the shift
of energy explained in each system is identical. The soul and mind can
be the same.

Some in science may not believe this account, but still they cannot
disprove it could not be working this way. We are told the world of
nature came into being by random effects, yet everything we see in
biology as listed here shows the very opposite to be true, which is the
amazing synchronicity of so many systems that go to make up our
entire terrestrial biosphere. It is the opposite of chance.

So firm was this ancient mental link between stars and people at
that time, that it is valid to look at why this was so, and see how the
idea changed over the succeeding centuries. The ancients saw the effect
some leading 'high energy' people had on earth during their lives, and
reasonably imagined there were other beings or 'souls' who lived
unseen, powerful, and fully sentient lives, only much more so than
mere mortals...so they were named as the gods...deities in effect.

It is easy to dismiss all this as pure fantasy, yet there are things even
scientists do not know, and one of them is how to interpret this ancient

world of God and the gods. This is territory that science cannot test, since such subtlety cannot be measured, prodded with a stick, or fall on the floor, and thus, in science terms, cannot exist.

Not everyone in science realises how deeply quantum physics is changing everything we took to be fact, such as Time, and even what 'life' is. Science as a body is now mounting Mars missions to find life at all costs, feeling certain it must be there. The search will prove fruitless if Time is cyclic, as astrophysics seems equally certain it must be, since there would never have been enough time for life to develop anywhere.

Yet both our ancestors and ourselves maintain a fascination with the stars, since they are the link between we humans on earth, and what lies out there in space. Even people in science feel convinced there are such beings, and that they 'must' come from the stars. These are ideas and wishes and desires from the Stone Age, to meet beings of light and power. The evidence points to an earlier race of people here on earth, who were so pure as to be considered divine by all later eras. Now, only their statues remain to be seen as proof they ever lived, yet their status as 'deities' also survives them in India.

Since Neanderthals are now known to have practised rituals as part of a religious life, it is possible they had similar views of purer beings to whom their rituals were aimed at pleasing, and from whom blessings must consequently flow. This is not different at all to modern science sending rockets to find these beings, or traces of them at the very least. The only problem is that these beings may only have been here on earth, and not have any physical form now, let alone in space where no-one can breathe, in which case we would never find them having tea and cakes on the veranda, waiting for spacemen to arrive in a blaze of exhaust fumes. It is not possible to find alien life in a cyclic cosmos, without enough time to develop, and there is no evidence this ever happened. Our nearest star, Proxima Centauri, is also far away at 4.3 light years, which would take about 25,000 years to reach at space ship speeds. A light second is the time it takes for light to travel in one second, which is the same distance to go round the earth about seven times, so a light year is a long way, and hence used to measure galactic distances.

Many of the leaders or 'stars' in science see the world as a wholly physical place, and remain firm in the belief that is all there is. The Gita even speaks of this material consciousness, held by humans who refuse to accept the spiritual or subtle aspect of human life. They conclude there cannot be any such thing, since it cannot be measured or seen; thus all talk of 'spirit' or hidden forces must be the invention of imaginative minds.

Many do not of course share this extreme view of the material mind, but rarely speak of it until near retirement age, in case it affects their careers. Now the quantum world is showing us that the material world of earth and deep space is not so easy to label in such simple, physical ways.

Enter quantum physics and sub-atomic particles, which do not obey any of those old traditions, and can now be seen in two places at once, which was long considered total fantasy for any particle to achieve. Not any more. The old and apparently simple distinctions of the 1950's are no longer applicable. The worlds of fact and fiction have always been converging, as the Victorians read about, when the author H. G. Wells foresaw the moon landings, even suggesting three days to reach the moon in a rocket.

Our experiences as people show the mind is able to sense parts of reality considered theoretically impossible, and could not happen if science were right.

Since they do happen, even rarely, then science must be incorrect about the nature and abilities of the human mind. It is possible the ancient way of illuminating those lost ancestors as 'stars', special beings of light in point form, or spirits that have changed location, may be an identical way of seeing a different 'world' in each one. It is possible that such concepts have persisted in human thought over all these millennia. If there was an age of 'super humans' well before our own, then it is reasonable they would later be seen and worshipped as deities millennia later. This is not as fantastic as it may sound, since this actually happens in so many of today's religions, such as Hinduism.

The picture of the 'Tree of Life' shows the growth of people from a minimum group of perhaps a million, which then developed into the next cycle of events we have noted, like the seasons of a year. All this could fit into 4,950 as we have seen, and this could be why the ages assigned to the dinosaurs and carbon dates show such extreme inconsistencies. When we add Saturn's F ring eerie youth, it all begins to reveal a new reality. The first part of the tree trunk shows a unity of kindness and harmony, with no conflict, and indeed with so much happiness there is no need for religion. This changes with the descent of Man into chaos, the start of religions when each founder begins their own form of faith, and the inevitable conflict arising from the splitting of each branch.

Now here is a subtle solution to all this that makes logical sense: if time does move cyclically, then our own perception of how this works could depend on what period of that cyclic time we witnessed. An 'older' being would agree, having been alive to see all this in reality. A more recent arrival would make no sense of it.

We have looked into reincarnation in this book, which has a large body of supporting cases to be considered, and we need to take another look at this from the point of view of science. The idea that we change species is not always agreed, because it is possible and likely that people only exist as people, whenever they are born. There are now so many cases, even on TV with dates and time evidence, that a hidden reality may be unfolding here.

Much of the world already agrees, but not all of us. It is too easy to take a 400 year old view about this, throw up one's hands in horror, and dismiss the whole thing, as is our right, but the wealth of case histories about 'another level' more subtle than this one we see, is not something science can dismiss. Having applied the use of logic and reason to these subtle matters, and the evidence of even law courts, there is now a huge mass of detail to work with, and such cases are deeply compelling.

We therefore return, for a moment, to those remarkable cases of the TV documentaries of the *Psychic Detectives* already mentioned. Let's consider this very carefully. These are actual FBI case files of the most serious level of crimes, not some gimmick made for TV theatre. If the FBI can check out the leads generated, with all their resources and vast experience of defining fact and fiction, and find these cases contained accurate and useable facts to solve several cases to the legal standard for convictions, then surely we have to accept they can be real. Many criminals actually confessed.

These real life cases are very impressive in their detail, because they have repeatedly met the highest standards of testing to resolve crimes.

This discovery changes a great deal about what we thought we knew about reality, because it was always thought to be entirely impossible. The Super Grid shows how it can work, as we can see.

Here were top detectives, with no fresh leads to pursue in cases where a killer or major criminal had to be caught, and many a raised eyebrow at the very idea any psychic, however good, could do more than bring doughnuts to these tough investigators. They took a different approach, just to test it. The facts suggested were borne out by actual events that could be checked. This 'fact check' with reality was all real, and led to convictions and even confessions from criminals who asked Police 'how did you find me?' There is no higher level of evidence than this, and it is to their credit that the detectives leading those cases set aside the doubts they all expressed, quite naturally, and pursued the leads all the same, just in case they were real by some strange quirk of fate. They were, and this should persuade the rest of us as 'non-believers', to reassess our thinking about what is possible. The Grid explains how it is possible, with the 'energy' of the actions in those crimes, and even the thoughts used, being tied in to the places they occurred, there to be read later, even years after the event itself. Several cases were not solved at once, yet the best psychics were able to predict the cases would be solved, and often when. One said a case would be solved in exactly a year, and it was, while another said the killer would brag about the murder of a woman; he did, and was caught. All this is only possible if time is cyclically repeating, so even the future can be seen in advance.

The cases of apparent reincarnation and xenoglossy are equally impressive when well documented, as the late psychiatrist Professor Ian Stevenson had so vividly shown[115], and all this enables us to wake up to the 'other world' that seems to exist here on earth. Millions of people have shared the details of such a reality, so we may listen.

At our heart, we are energy. All of matter is energy too, as Einstein famously showed. It would be rather simplistic, and reductionist, to assert the two have no links beyond what we feel comfortable with seeing. It is more logical that the two are closely linked, perhaps so

---

115 Twenty Cases Suggestive of Reincarnation, Ian Stevenson,
     Univ.of Virginia Press, 1980.

much so that each parcel or 'quantum' of energy in one is changing the vibrational order of the other.

There is no evidence that this is impossible, and plenty to suggest it is. Therefore it is a viable view. We therefore have just words to separate science from religion: one calls a particle a deep level of matter that 'exists', the other refers to a spirit. Even scientists admit they do not actually know, which is true.

Now we learn matter is not easy to define. No longer are 'things' solid or not, but there are sub-atomic particles that are not really lumpy particles at all, or as we would usually understand a particulate, but peculiar entities (not meaning alive though) or objects that can exist in two places at once. Now that is weird, but true all the same.

Are there answers to the spiritual questions?

The human mind or spirit may be the key to all this activity. Is it possible there is such an entity that comprises our conscious minds? If the answer is yes, then logically there could also be a Great Spirit as well. Science cannot comment on this, but does so anyway. Some do think of a God or Supreme Being, with about three quarters of the world's people believing in such a powerful being who changes reality.

This feeling alters how we act. If I imagine I am alone in the universe, and that no God of any kind is my spiritual parent after all, then my behaviour will be quite different from that of a person who does have the experiences of a higher being.

One strange enigma we have to solve is this: why is the most enduring memory in all human history of such a Supreme Being who mysteriously hid away, appeared out of nowhere to sort the world out, and then left us to get on with life once again? If that never happened, then we have to ask: how come all of space and time support this suggestion? It is much too easy to dismiss all that as pure invention, but we have to consider this option since science cannot provide a working alternative.

If such scenes never actually took place, then how come the accounts are so identical, and secondly, how come those global accounts existed 'before the fact'? To look at it another way, if Time were not shortly cyclical as suggested here, then where did they get those ideas from, never having met, unless they all went through those scenes, being bound to do so again? This may be why linear time has become a popular idea in science, because it removes the need for a Divinity in the equation of existence. If Time is a cycle after all, then all that changes overnight, because it could be a Supreme Being who remains the only entity who could oversee the changeover of Flash Time by making sure it works. This could explain everything we see, as many already agree.

If there is an extra power needed, we cannot discount that this may be a reality.

Velikovsky wrote a curious book about this memory, and how we tend to forget or ignore it, called 'Mankind in Amnesia'. It is an interesting read. It fits into both science and religion that this cyclic process is the one that unifies all these different and disparate concepts in one possible version of reality. If not this, then what else makes more sense? So far, there is no other contender, because the cyclic nature of all earth's processes really does appear as one vast 'closed' unit, into which we arrive and leave with a degree of accuracy and timing that may be far more striking and exact than we ever thought possible. Why else are kings and queens born as they are, and treated as demigods even when their actions may be less than impressive or humble, if not by a greater degree of spacetime and human influences than the random chaos claimed by Big Bang theory? Each of us may be equally significant in our own way, as we all count.

Here is where that 75% separates from the 'don't knows', and the remaining few who refuse to recognise a God above themselves, and have no experiences on which to base such recognition. This is the way the world is, and that very diversity of opinion can be seen as further evidence that we have free will to act as we see fit, and will then see the results of doing so. This too is why the UN was set up, and every other declaration of human rights since King Ashoka of India, and Magna Carta in 1215, to try and create order and reason where little existed, often caused by the destructive actions of royalty that required help from their own people.

Does ancient history agree?

The Egyptian Book of the Dead is full of hieroglyphs showing references to such events and influences, and the British Museum contains an interesting parchment showing the god Thoth, the divine scribe, standing ready beside the scales of justice, where the soul or departed spirit, shown as a person with the 'ankh' or eye of life, is being judged against the feather of purity on the other scale. A beast, part lion and part alligator, is seated nearby to symbolise justice and show how the process works.

Deeply symbolic of course, but there may be a close fit with quantum mechanics and simple Newtonian physics in all of this, in the sense that if we use our powers and influence to hurt others, the karmic effect of that returns to our society, and the self in particular, while good actions that create harmony and goodwill have the contrasting effect, and create more positivity. This does hold true in physics, combining science and religion to suggest why they are so similar at heart.

Combine the two, and we may just have the total picture, since neither is able to account for everything without the other. This makes sense if we reduce the concepts to energy, since if the self is a star or point, a dot of power, this equates closely to the massless 'particle' discussed, and would allow for the existence of God as the 'Supreme Soul' or Alpha, the Great Point of Energy who may hold the power to restore cyclic time to point Zero, at which second the next cycle begins to unfold once again. The whole understanding could be summed up in these two words 'once again'…a series of events that happened once, as we chose to enact it using our freewill, which is then ready to repeat.

And there we have a possible solution in a practical 'theory of everything'. How this came to be is then the great riddle that may have been solved.

These points of energy are the crucial key. All these points, of both human and physical kinds, may be in a state of permanent connection or 'entanglement', so that any major change in the energy of one directly affects the stability of the other.

Those enigmatic statues on Easter Island may therefore hold a key, since they may represent a race of distant people who were the founders of the human race. Every culture speaks of such beings, and most old cultures worship them as gods with a small 'g', as distinct from a Supreme Being, who would be the Father figure of humanity.

The ancestors have been a focus of worship and reverence since well before history began to be officially recorded, although no one is quite sure when that was exactly. The author used to assume, quite wrongly, that these 'ancestors' were simply local relatives of local families, rather as we have today in every village and town in the world. It slowly became clear that this traditional view did not fit the facts at all. Those ancestors that so many cultures used to worship in the form of statues, sometimes in metal or stone, possibly enhanced with layers of gold leaf, were not local relations, but were instead seen as the 'ancestors of the world', and were considered worthy of worship because they were the same set of ancestors long regarded as deities.

These beings were seen as real special 'stars' of the earth because they were regarded as the original beings who inhabited earth, and were thus the progenitors of the world's population. If they were very special, this may explain why they have always been worshipped as especially pure, hence being seen as 'deities'. Since there are literally billions of people around the globe for whom this has been their worldview, we may take some notice of this vast body of recognition of both an ancient culture of great purity, and a cycle of time in which they will one day return. This is earth's most ancient way of thinking, and it fits.

There is also the science view that only the physical aspect counts, and the invisible version above can have no sway.

'...*experimentalists do bungle sometimes. But if your theory (coun-ters) the* 2nd *Law of Thermodynamics I can give you no hope....*' Sir A. S. Eddington, 1928, astrophysicist.

The evidence here and elsewhere does show the science version appears to fail dramatically, and so it can be possible to counteract entropy. It is possible the human element can alter spacetime, and so this cannot be discounted as a solution. This is where atheism counters the existence of a God, so we can choose. It only remains to say that the physical clues in this book do support the 'spiritual' way of seeing reality, and can do so since no physical way of explaining reality exists.

As Lucretius said in 65 BC: 'Nothing can be created from nothing', so we cannot rely on a line for time. The laws of physics and chemistry very poignantly agree, so the multiverse would appear to fail this test.

Each of us must decide that for ourselves, of course, but it is logical, coherent, consistent, and even fits the few facts we have better than any other. It is therefore put forward as potentially a true alternative. However clever and complex our usual Western worldview may have been all these years, it has never explained all the anomalies raised in this book and elsewhere, so this is the issue we have to face, that the old worldview could have been wrong all these years.

Here is an interesting correlation with so many similar cultures around the globe that share this tradition of worshipping statues of 'deities' in this way, from India and other Asian countries, to the Far East in lands such as Thailand, the Khmer of the former Cambodia, Laos, and right across to Mexico, with Toltecs, Olmecs and others, as well as the famous Easter Island, which share even the Brahmin topknot and long ear lobes from India. It was always thought these huge *moai* heads were also just the ancestors of local people as said, but their appearance in such similar forms all over the globe suggests they may be the same classic depiction of an original 'hero race', who were the first people to populate the earth, and who were very special in their lack of a need for defence or aggression.....unique indeed. Idols were later made, the path of worship began, and as the world descended further into chaos, the reality that they once lived here on earth, drifted into obscurity.

Easter Island is the classic example, but can easily be solved as a mystery when we look at the details of the statues themselves. Enigmatic they certainly are, but they have the topknot of the Indian Brahmanic tradition, the oldest known, as well as the long ear lobes of both old and modern Brahmins, as is the topknot; a direct link as to why so many of these statues on the island also had a large topknot (in place of the usual hair knot) of red scoria rock placed on top of the head. The clash of cultures widely reported to have ended the culture on the island was between the long ears and short ears, which was the single defining feature used to show the difference between the controlling 'priesthood' and the other islanders, who may have been of local or even mainland (perhaps Peruvian) descent. The real secret source of this culture seems to be India, as suggested in 1980.

Similar stories are mirrored across history, as the old gave way to new cultures, and descended into chaos. This same pattern can be seen everywhere, right up to the modern day, when even the cleverest minds are unable to create peace in the world. Sound familiar? It affects everything, as Jeremy Rifkin's famous book '*Entropy: A new world view*' showed so clearly [1980], and we do appear to be witnessing this inevitable cyclic pattern, which Rifkin also mentioned in the ancient Greek thinking.

Here is the crucial link to the ancient cultures: unless the events of time were a cycle, how else can we explain the remarkable coincidence that every ancient culture saw time in this way? They nearly all saw God as the Father figure, often shown using the symbol of the Sun, who repaired all the damage humanity had made, possibly including the disruption to the field of Matter itself, and restored the cyclic process to full power.

It seems this classic ancient concept of how time worked in the form of a continuum may not be such a fanciful one after all. How else could such geographically widely distributed cultures as India, China, Egypt, Peru and Mexico all show the same concept of a fatherly Sun God who corrected the imbalances of the universe, unless the same set of events had happened before?

No one ever asked this question. If time does repeat, then it would have to repeat identically if we are to explain this apparent coincidence. If this is true, then the repetition of time's events could not possibly be a coincidence, but the simple turning of the wheel of Time as a continuum.

The name Ra in Egyptian hieroglyphs is shown by the solar disc, as translated by the pioneering French scholar Jean-Francois Champollion in 1822, using ancient Coptic links and the Rosetta Stone. The very meaning of the Pharaoh's name Ramasses means child of the Sun God. Where did Ramasses himself obtain such an idea, and how come it matches similar concepts and symbols in every part of the world, unless a central continental population once shared this concept at a time before their era?

This idea may contradict current archaeological thinking in some respects, yet it matches history in a way that the earlier concepts do not appear to. Could there have been an awareness in both ancient Egypt and other parts of the world, such as India and China, of the same Supreme Being, often known as Alpha, having done something so special that it was an action worthy of praise or worship to such an extent that it changed the universe and put right all past wrongs? This appears to be why the worship of God or Alpha has been as the most famous Being in history, and if this is so then there should be a reason for such praise.

We are clearly complex beings that have an infinite variety of experiences. It is perhaps time we learn to incorporate more of our own personal experiences in our worldview, and challenge the limited version we learned in our youth at school, which turns out to be somewhat incomplete.[116]

The intense colour and astonishing movement in the flight of a hummingbird are a wonderful expression of Nature's unique variety: a bird with up to 1,200 wing beats per minute that move so fast the human eye cannot see them, drinks nectar like a bee, migrates like a crane over mountains from the same bush to the same exact tree each year, and yet weighs only 3 to 5gms. We couldn't make up such a creature and expect anyone to believe it could exist, and yet it does. Is that random? The intricacy of all such systems acting as one whole unit that works suggest it cannot be chance, but a pre-existing cycle. The science we have seems to confirm this.

At first we thought ants were clever to have a Queen, workers and a complex hierarchy in one complete unit, but now we realise that was only scratching the surface. In Brazil biologists found a colony of nearly 8,000,000 leafcutter ants functioning as if they possessed one mind, with a full air conditioning system to draw in fresh air and expel polluted gases, breeding chambers, agricultural farming of fungus growth systems in their own chambers, conduits with cemented channels that resisted water penetration, and all neatly spread over 100 m³ below ground. Now that is clever.

116 Note Student Warning eg at start of Glossary.

Life is difficult to define, as we saw with the wood frog found in northern latitudes, with the peculiar ability to freeze to death each year, only to recover from having no pulse or heartbeat of any kind, and having frozen solid in 65% of its cells, including its eyes, and then spring into life with a fresh heartbeat as it thaws out. Is that weird? Yes, indeed it is, because technically it had died. The Woolly Bear caterpillar does this too. This shows our old definitions of life are no longer valid, along with quite a few other preconceptions about when something is alive and when it is dead.

Lying at the heart of life is what nature actually does, which trumps all the theories.

CHAPTER 21

Some Conclusions

Everything that happens, happens as it should, and if you observe carefully, you will find it to be so.
MARCUS AURELIUS, Roman Emperor, C165 AD

The scientific attitude implies there is no plan...that there is nointention in the universe.
DR JACQUES MONOD, Nobel Prize winner

I observed the many errors I had accepted as true in my earlier years, and the whole dubious superstructure I had since built on them; and the consequent need of making a fresh start for once in my life, and starting again from the very foundations, if I would establish some stable and lasting result in science.
RENE DESCARTES, 1641

Essence

Perhaps the key to progress in understanding is the fresh evidence suggesting the sub-atomic nature of the self as energy. This changes everything we used to think. It is powerful logic that no one can refuter these aspects of the 21st century, despite the attraction of the 1800's version of reality to some of us.

This idea that people are like stars appears pivotal. It is a very ancient notion, but it is a perception reserved for rather special beings, 'the stars', which is why we reserve this title for the cream of the crop, to mix a metaphor. Having looked earlier at what may constitute the 'self', some may agree that we could literally be 'quantum points' of energy. Science has not yet reached this point, but it may also be the point where discovery begins afresh. We can sum up the next step with a change.

Are minds made of more than neurons and brain matter? It is possible they could be, and we have discussed physical reasons why this appears to be true. Even the way our changing moods so deeply affect our health can be the result of our thought energy level.

What effect might all this thinking have on matter, and where does all that energy go? Using reason, it must go into the 'system'. This is not easy to quantify, because no scientist can measure this, but it could be the key to understanding everything, including Time. From what we can see, there could be a 'total effect' that works to an extreme degree, right up to affecting the level of order in *all matter*. The conscious human mind does affect our bodies, and creates an energy field we can all identify as 'the atmosphere' we feel, rather than what we breathe. The subtle effects of mere thought, be it happy or sad, are clearly apparent in our own bodies, so it is reasonable that there may be an effect of some kind on the rest of matter.

The suggestion made here is that this energy may act as the missing power or 'fifth force' to alter Time itself. This may sound weird to some, but then so did electricity and fusion, and being weird or strange does not discount an option; it is merely different to what we expected. We have inherited a whole vision of reality from our famous ancestors, and it came with more holes than a gruyere cheese. As Sherlock Holmes once noted in an Arthur Conan Doyle novel 'It is a capital mistake to theorize before one has all the evidence. It biases the judgement'. Only fresh evidence can alter a world view, and now we have it, we are not allowing it to change our thinking.

Invisible power does exist, so we can check such effects on what we can see. The body is real enough, and so are the effects of our thoughts on its function. It is therefore logical to suggest that our combined human energy, as a Race of all earth's people, could have a cumulative effect that has vast repercussions across space; and if there is such an effect across space, it cannot avoid affecting Time too. If so, this changes everything.

This is the central issue, because if this suggestion is true, it presents a mechanism for altering the cosmos. If matter is 'spin coupled', this process becomes simple.

Here is how the idea works: matter may be so finely balanced and interconnected that a small but pivotal change could alter the quantum state of every particle, then the right switch at the right moment could switch that process of motion instantly. This can be the Flash Time 'machinery', and it is possible that human minds are that pivotal component that has this periodic, pooled effect.

The combined presence of, or lack of, powers or qualities in each person could be a major factor, and one so subtle it remained beyond our recognition as such a vital influence, being beyond physical measurement.

Kindness and fairness feature near the top, especially in a judge, since without these featuring strongly in a society, it would not be a pleasant place to live, so we all agree fair-mindedness is central. In fact any society with a marked lack of these leadership qualities would be unsustainable, and bound to fail sooner or later, as history shows. From the giving and taking in a culture, we can judge its quality, as well as its honesty, and from this view of fairness we get a view of justice, as well as right and wrong. This is why any court of law requires participants to swear an oath, to reinforce the awareness of this principle as of paramount importance.

We regard these merits to be of 'star quality' in any culture, and the contentment of its members as the key measure of success, no matter where it is, or when it was founded. Why? Perhaps because it matters in a universe in which quality is everything, and affects the future. It makes sense, since good causes have good effects.

All societies need to be in harmony for there to be order on earth in general. Nature is *equalising pressures* to achieve this order, hence why we are concerned to be in harmony with nature. When M.K.Gandhi was asked what he thought of western civilisation, he replied 'It would be a good idea'. Drone attacks, kidnap/rendition and prison without trial are not judicial, and show it is not a full reality. Such actions are illegal because they defy the 800 year old Magna Carta; this failure to uphold basic human rights has helped plunge the world into the chaos we now see.

As Confucius said around 500 BC: 'What you do not want done to yourself, do not do to others'. He also reckoned 'an oppressive government is more to be feared than a tiger'. Executing people without trial may look valid, but it validates the chaos returned. We cannot stoke the war and claim to use law.

This makes sense, but living with such stark realities can be tough.

One answer is simplistic, yet true. By not fighting, there would be peace, and sometimes we need reminding of such simplicity. Some claim that some wars 'have to be fought to create peace', but that is a misconception, because such violence may not be perceived as vital peace-keeping by anyone but the aggressors, so would merely provoke more violence in retaliation, and so on in a vicious cycle.

Is humanity a key influence?

Our notion of goodness is one thing, but our actions are another. A lasting peace cannot be created by violence, because each act of aggression presses the set of 'society scales' further out of equilibrium. The Iraq war never quite ended, and nor has the Afghan war, which are two examples of how not to conduct foreign policy, as many agree. They can look like Imperialism thinly dressed up as a power grab, even if not by intention. One solution is to create a Muslim Force that is alone endorsed to engage with Muslim aggressors. If both follow the teachings of the Koran, then no war could continue on that basis, since the scripture expressly forbids Islamists to kill each other, or in fact anyone else.

Being peaceful is a power, as Gandhi showed. Result: the elusive world peace. As he wisely said in 1926: 'Non-violence is not a garment to be put on and off...it must be an inseparable of our very being'. We have forgotten about the self as energy, even though physical clues show this appears to be entirely correct.

There is logic in the old belief that beings cannot die. Gandhi's words also echo some of the most famous writings in history, the Bhagavad-Gita, which said this in about 200 BC: 'As a man leaves an old garment and puts on a new one, the spirit leaves his mortal body and puts on one that is new...Never born and eternal...he does not die when the body dies...Invisible before birth are all beings, and after death invisible again. They are seen between two unseens. Why find sorrow in this truth?'

It is entirely possible the motion and state of the cosmos could be controlled by this fine balance of harmony within humanity. It may sound left field to some thinkers, but evidence backs it up. The motion of Time itself may depend on such subtle aspects.

Such good actions would then be of 'star quality' because they benefit everyone, and create the Order we need instead of the chaos we see, which leads us to two more star qualities: cooperation and friendship, which form the basis of straight dealing in every town and city on earth, increasing trade and providing the means for education, jobs, food and shelter that secure everyone's contentment.

While this provides a gain, just as obviously there would be a loss if personal greed or selfish motives come into the equation, which is why democracy and parliamentary representation are so vital in guaranteeing each person's rights. It is shocking to see slavery is still a part of human life even in the 21st century, along with human trafficking, and inhuman treatment.

Does it matter? We all know it does, and feel it does very deeply. This may be true for a deeper reason, that all these mental 'distortions' may add up to a distorted quantum state. We already know that experiments are affected by the mere presence of the observer, so this fits in quite well. Our lives may have distorted the order of the Grid suggested, if we are affecting the spin state of matter. Science cannot measure this, and cannot even think it in the present climate of 'certainty' over the brain being the self. We may have made an error in seeing the self as physical, which rules out any of the options discussed here. The answer can be very subtle.

K.Gibran wrote a clever piece 'On Children' in 1923, about the way parents might realise their subtle roles: 'You may house their bodies, but not their souls, for their souls dwell in the house of tomorrow, which you cannot visit, not even in your dreams...for life goes not backward'. As Charles Dickens said in 1843, we create our own influences in our lives, and then make the best of those actions. In *A Christmas Carol*, one ghost says to Scrooge: 'I wear the chain I forged in life...I made it link by link and yard by yard', echoing Plato over 2,200 years before, suggesting we alone are responsible: 'The blame is his who chooses: God is blameless'.

Being free of the negative influences, there can be a positive effect as a result. It may be customary to think of these things as of minor importance, but they could be central to how the quality of everyone's lives is affected, for this key 'star' reason. If there is indeed a 'driver' of the body, rather as a driver controls a car, the potential exists for a better understanding of how we interact with Matter in general, and the two could be much more closely related than we realised, even to this extent of affecting global order at a deeper level. It remains our aim to maintain fair order above all else, yet we are ready to break our greatest laws in a desperate effort to do so. This cannot succeed.

We need a new approach. To find one, first we must accept the old one is at fault, and in particular the concept we hold of the 'self'. The ancient idea of a 'separate entity' being in charge of the body has been rejected by a few, when it may hold the solution. It also affects how we see time, and how we treat each other. No one in the army orders people into battle while showing concern for where those entities go, or how they feel about the fairness of that engagement. It is an act of desperation to engage in war, for all concerned, and often ignores niceties like human rights on both sides. The attacks on civilians are another major error on both sides, as everyone agrees. It makes it all worse, yet we vote in leaders who ignore all these issues.

What we may have missed is the deeper level at which matter functions.

We may therefore ask a question about this factor. The ancients had some interesting ideas about time, which research now validates in many ways. Is this why cyclic time is the most common concept of reality and worldview around the world, as well as the most long-lived, supported, symbolized, described, and respected in world history? This body of recognition may merit our attention for consideration, and points to why we may be seeing signs of such a cycle, but never realised they could produce changes of such immense power.

History has always been a vital way of seeing how the future would unfold, and how to learn from past mistakes, but we could not have guessed that the ancient cultures may hold a secret that only a use of quantum physics could one day confirm.

The secret could be that there is such a process of cause and effect at work in Time as well as Space. The two are so interlinked that they cannot be split in practical terms, because it is usually impossible to have one without the other, except in the mind.

Here we have what may be the secret to understanding the cosmos as a unit. If we have particles and energy flashing around, then we have a timescale in which it happens, which is why astrophysicists and cosmologists use the term 'spacetime' to clarify how they are thus entwined. It is equally plausible that a special 'zero hour' in time may be rapidly reached when all this interaction is no longer sustainable in the way it has been for several millennia, and at that exact second, Time itself flashes instantly into a new configuration. At that moment when space and time 'flash over' into this new state, the old status would be replaced, and the cosmic clock would be reset to Zero, and begin again in a new cycle of the same events, just as before.

In this way, Time may be repeating exactly every few millennia. To us, it would seem to be original, and occurring for the first time, but there would be signs here and there that point to this secret machinery: a simple cause and effect pattern that builds the energy for each cycle to unfold in precisely the same way.

T.S.Eliot wrote of our being profoundly 'At the still point of a turning world', and summed this up in 1930:

And the end of all our exploring
Will be to arrive where we started
And know the place for the first time.

The Ancients seemed to know this, and not a single culture on earth appears to have been unaware of this broad process. That awareness of the Ancients is extraordinary in itself, because it could have been gained from the previous cycle of events. How else did they all think the same way? Maybe they too had a recognition of déjà vu, just as we do. In any case, this is a powerful signal that time could be repeating.

Science has only dismissed this *'déjà vu being real'* interpretation because it had never considered a cyclic universe, let alone all these intricacies.

Sometimes science jumps to the wrong conclusion a little too hastily, and the idea that déjà vu as a human experience that 'cannot be real or true' appears to be one of the most famous such cases in all of human history. Neither is it really the fault of science or its practitioners, because they inherited the linear mind-set, so all they saw with these linear coloured spectacles also had to be linear too. Many still do. A cycle was simply not thought a serious option, so they kept setting it aside each time it sprang into their minds.

Time passed by in thinking that way, and here we are today, with their data, and our own new set.

The only voices that may be raised against this proposal could be from those who regard the cosmos as merely material. That was the popular attitude in some circles, yet not many still hold this firmly materialist view today, and perhaps with good reason. The new world of sub-atomic particles has shown us all how very different Nature can be compared to the way we felt it 'should be'. At least the logic works.

We can sum this up in a paragraph.

It may be true to say that, small as earth is physically, the presence of people on its surface could combine to form such a 'critical mass' of anthropic or human power that has a far-reaching effect. If this is true, then the effect would not logically stop at the edge of our atmosphere, but could have a far-reaching effect on spacetime as a whole. The finding of Cooper Pairs and 'super-atoms' acting as one unit, suggests the larger mechanism of 'all spacetime' could be connected all the time, and so be able to switch instantly to a new state; since all matter could remain subtly 'entangled' as one unit, ready to shift back into the 'original state' the second the conditions dictate they must do so.

The specific discovery of this 'quantum entanglement' of some particles provides a solution as to how such a shift could happen so fast, and faster than light speed indeed.

This may not even disobey General Relativity, if the three directions of time are 'entangled' all the time, and simply revert to the original state (see Fig 23 in 'Now' diagram). The Bose-Einstein Condensate is an example of atoms existing as one entity, and is pivotal.

Although impractical to measure so far, it is predicted we will find ways of making such determinations within 1–2 years, and science will then be able to show that such switches are possible at faster than light speed. If time is truly cyclic as proposed here, then there is no other way that events could 'move back' to position one; therefore it is certain that we will find out one way or another if this can be so.

CHAPTER 22

End Piece: the discussion ... making sense of reality

The truth is on the move, and nothing can stop it now.
EMILE ZOLA, 1898

Lucky is he who has been able to understand the causes of things and
...it is flying, irretrievable time is flying.
VIRGIL, 70–19 BC

Essence

This evidence shows we live in a new and entirely different world to the one science had imagined. It may not be easy for some to accept that old thinking can have been so deeply misunderstood. Yet this is the very aim of progress: making key changes.

Facing reality is often not an easy task. Preparation makes it as easy as possible. A set of clearer facts would help, which is this book's sole purpose.

Our most difficult challenge is not merely to ask the right questions, but to face the answers that emerge. Many of us do not want to accept what may change our lives, if we did not foresee those future scenes.

Seeing all the chaos and conflict, being mentally ready would seem essential. Abraham Lincoln certainly thought so when he wrote a letter in 1861, brief and to the point, with just a single line: 'I think the necessity of being *ready* increases. Look to it.'

It certainly takes courage to face the future. This is the kind of audacity we need most: the personal kind that harms no-one, and improves the world by overseeing improvement in ourselves.

C. S. Lewis saw this as not just a virtue, but the central one at the edge of progress itself, when he reminded us that: '*Courage is not simply one of the virtues, but the form of every virtue at the testing point.*'

Many feel so certain about our own views. The idea of holding a flexible mental approach that warmly welcomes all new ideas is reasonable, but runs counter to human nature. We prefer our own ideas, and all the more if we spent 30 years or more deepening our comprehension of them. We do not lightly let them go.

The top scientists agree it is vital to ask, and try to answer, the very toughest questions we can possibly dream up. The tougher the better, they would say. Their eyes would light up like phosphorus flares in a cave at the mere prospect of trying to answer them. Not only that, but they would take in their stride whatever happened, and be ready for literally any answer that emerged from a fresh analysis. Surely that is science as it is supposed to be. This is why nothing upsets leading experts like Prof. Sir Roger Penrose, Dame Jocelyn Bell Burnell and Prof. Lee Smolin, who look below the surface. They check with care, ever ready for factual changes.

We are in this together, as they say in Terry Gilliam's film Brazil, and these giant decisions affect every single one of us, whether we follow any of the logic of either side, or not. If any of this seems unclear or confusing, simply Google the unfamiliar words. With a science dictionary, such as the superb *Chambers Dictionary of Science & Technology*, anyone can understand anything, and contribute their point of view.

Knowledge leads to a better world.

We need to comment about these issues being played out in our name, and register our interest in our own future. Rather like an imminent war between states, if we don't register a vote against it, they'll claim we're voting for it.

To assess the details of the geology and other earth sciences of this work, then the *Oxford Companion to the Earth* will be the book, as it would have amazed Hutton, Lyell and Darwin. We now have more information at our fingertips than they could have dreamt of, ready to work for us by using it constructively.

On these issues rests our entire worldview, and on that view rests the future of earth, and every one of us standing on it. Therefore, we do need to sort out which of the key views is the one that holds the nearest solution to the strangeness of the way the cosmos actually works.

We need not waste any energy getting even slightly upset about any views we may well not agree with. They will fall away anyway, if they don't fit the facts.

The outcome of this resolution uniquely contains the capacity to solve all kinds of conflict in the world. Sharing entrenched views or long-fixed opinions or beliefs could not be called openness, and will never free us from our past, so finding any remaining mistakes in our logic or science is worth doing. We may even use this method to resolve conflicts between a wide range of combatants, even between religion and science, which would be a prize we can all enjoy.

With so much bad news sweeping the world, it would be good news indeed if each Age of Chaos really is succeeded by an Age of Order. If this mechanism does exist as Nature's method of altering spacetime, then we would be able to use it to gain information ahead of time, which could be our most valuable option. As people from around the world, we are facing the challenges of the future together, since Nature makes no distinction between cultures or creeds. Whatever the 'weather' of the future world, we need to build a new roof well before it rains.

If this version of a cyclic universe is correct, nothing anyone might do would alter the actual outcome of a peaceful world being restored. It matters what we do, and if this study is correct, then the medium of all matter is not only connected, but held in fine balance that we people alter day by day. It makes all the difference if we act calmly. The world will turn in its cyclic path, so it is good to know there are sound reasons for thinking this is a set process, and no one can stop it turning out well each time. The days of violence would then be over, as they should have been long ago.

Being kind is essential. As MK Gandhi once remarked, when asked what he thought of western civilization: *'I think it would be a very good idea'*.

A central figure in 1976 was Prof. Joseph Rotblat, and he expressed the view in a meeting that the task of world peace was often obstructed by the superpowers. One cannot force others to do what we think is 'right', even if we voted for them.

Prof. Umberto Eco was right about why we tend to blame others for what is wrong in the world, thinking *'it would all be ok if those people over there stopped acting that way'*. Blaming others is an error. Our own actions need to change; not waiting for others who may never change. Violence is not an answer, because it is proof of the failure to talk; it fuels chaos and division. This is why the ancient Greeks favoured making as few changes as possible within society, because it would nearly always end in tears, to no-one's benefit.

Cyclic time seems to be Nature's answer, because the world cannot continue in the way it is heading. Seeing how it works, our leaders may then appreciate that helping reduce distress is a priority. This simple aim can be lost in the general confusion, and vast spending on national security generated more fears than it reduced. The great error that fighting terrorism in Afghanistan would protect people in London and elsewhere proved the opposite, and effectively created a slow world war. The London 7/7 July bombings were instant and tragic proof of that, as are recent events.

The linear time idea has removed much of our sense of feeling, wisdom, and concern for others. It has done all this simply by claiming there is no meaning through not seeing any meaning. A cycle explains why we humans are able to sense moral and ethical issues that no machine could ever perceive.

By claiming there is no such meaning to life, we unwittingly remove real meaning that does exist. To this day, many try to ridicule the rise of new ideas, and often with ample justification it has to be said, but hidden amongst the mass of words are some sound ideas we now have to recognise can be valid. When we do, the world will be a better place, to everyone's advantage. The effect for us lies in what role we play in helping.

The ancients wrote about almost all of this, and we can now accept they knew things we have lost amidst the overconfident belief in our own ideas. We now see they were much more aware than we gave them credit for, and wiser than we are, despite all our progress. In doing this we open the door to greater discovery, which would be a good thing if it places people above wealth.

One thing is certain: if we are ever to improve the lives of our fellow human beings around the world, we will need more openness and tolerance than ever before, and more willingness to accept change.

For centuries we have been busy separating the research into ever smaller, more specialised compartments, until few are aware of the others, and fewer still make sense as a whole. Now we have to re-combine them into one coherent picture, if only to check they are still valid within these latest findings.

There is a need for every human being to try to solve the riddle of our existence, and then to be aware of our effect on the future. If this is even close to correct, we have some modernising to do. All these issues affect every person alive, so we may at least discuss them.

Since this cycle has yet to be disproved, the arrival of a new phase of calm in the world could be the best real news we ever hear.

Please register your opinion at the website: www. FTIM.TV
You can register a 'yes' or 'no' vote for Flash Time being possible on the website. Thanks are due to each reader for considering the evidence.

Glossary and Definitions

Words & Meanings

[Student Caution: many of these definitions are agreed in textbooks, yet some points are far too controversial to write in any exam, and many examiners would fail a student who does. Science can take years for new thinking to be accepted, so do not risk a failure; first one must 'pass' an exam before using these new concepts.]

Abiogenesis – old theory that life could form from matter; now outdated.

Abyssal plain – over 2000m deep, part of deepest ocean areas (seaward of bathyal zone), covering over 75% of all ocean area.

Accretion disc – current theory in science that the solar systems in space formed from matter particles or gas joining together to form stars and planets; held to be impossible by some people, and within cyclic time theory of Flash Time.

Albedo – the degree of solar radiation reflected from water, plants (usually 8–27%), snow (up to 90%) or other materials on earth's surface: averages 30%.

Algal growth – growth of algae, a plant type of simple cellular form.

Ankh – Ancient Egyptian symbol of life in hieroglyphs; also of a five part cycle.

Anisotropy – the variations in a medium that exist in different directions, eg plane; opposite to isotropy, which shows uniform properties in all directions. See Flatness.

Anomalocaris – Latin for 'strange prawn', see Index for text details. This oddity has been dated to the pre-Cambrian when fossils were 'meant to be' simple according to Darwinism, yet it is highly complex with eyes showing 16,000 sections: wholly impossible if life on earth had evolved over time as claimed, hence the name. Experts realise this as a serious problem, but never considered a cyclic universe as the reason.

Anomaly – irregular findings that defy explanation in 'linear time' terms.

Anoxic – reducing environment 'without oxygen'; stagnation preserves organic material.

Antarctica – huge 5.4mill.sq mile continent in southern hemisphere of globe which is 1.49 times larger than USA; (Arctic Pole in north has no land, only seasonal ice).

Anthropic effect – the influence of human thought and actions on the order state of the universe; the key factor within cyclic time.

Antikythera – 2000 year old highly advanced mechanism from ancient Greece; pivotal find known as the 'earliest computer'. See Index for details.

Arthropoda – diverse animal group with segmented limb pairs: crabs, millipedes etc.

Assemblage of fossils – group of fossils as found in rock; may show burial details.

Atlantis & Lemuria – Legendary lost continents (see Index).

AU – 1 AU= an Astronomical Unit, or the distance of earth to our sun: 98 mill. miles.

Axial shift – a change in the angle/ tilt of the earth's vertical north-south axis.

Basalt – fine-grained lava covering 70% of earth's surface, can be very fluid.

Basalt, Flood (CFB) – known as Continental Flood Basalt where lava erupts over a huge area such as Columbia River, USA, or Siberia and India's Deccan Plateau.

Bathyal zone – oceanic areas of 200–2000m deep; continental shelf edge and rise.

BCS Theory – see Cooper Pair & Entanglement; quantum linking of electrons.

BGI – British Gemmological Institute; independent science laboratory researching gemmology & cosmology.

Big Bang Theory – a term created by Sir Fred Hoyle to dismiss the idea it represents, namely that the universe 'came into being' in one explosion; the heart of linear time thinking, and now thought to be impossible; see CMB. Since matter cannot be created out of nothing, it has never been explained, and now relies on the invention of other universes as a source of that matter; this theory of a 'multiverse' is now widely seen as ridiculous since each layer relies on another to produce its matter, and so on infinitely, thus never solving the problem. A key error exactly solved by a cycle.

Billion – often as Gy, giga years; one with 9 zeroes or 1000 million or 109

Bioturbation – signs of bio-activity eg burrowing in sediments.

Biozone – total global existence of a family/species in rock; used to date those strata.

Biped – any two-legged species, such as humans; from Latin for 'two feet'.

Black hole – An object of such massive gravity even light cannot escape, ie invisible.

Blake Outer Ridge – 'rapid' clastic deposit that could have been laid down very quickly indeed, in a matter of months, not decades; a 700kms long area of unsorted mud/sand near Bermuda. An axial tilt of Earth remains the only explanation for the formation of this massive anomaly.

Bolide – Large meteor or fireball entering earth's atmosphere from space.

Bose-Einstein Condensate – a group of sub-atomic particles that act in unison as one physical unit when supercooled [Syncytium]. Pivotal evidence Matter can be one unit or system, reacting as one connected body at both atomic and sub-atomic levels; qv Cooper Pairs. A key mechanism that minds could alter the whole universe constantly.

Bottleneck of population – current human population has taken only 4,950 years to reach today's numbers, so theorists have assumed there used to be more people before the initial core populace of about 1million; they failed to consider a time cycle.

Burgess Shale, Canada – unique soft-body fossils with no ancestors, found 1909.

c – Latin; short for circa, ie around or 'about', as in c480 BC.

Calving of icebergs – 'birth' of icebergs where glaciers break off meeting water /sea.

Cambrian Explosion – appearance of life at the start of the Cambrian geological era with 'impossible suddenness'; explained by Flash

Time in that no precursor period is required to form the life species
found, since it always exists.

Chelyabinsk Meteor – Asteroid 20m wide exploded high above
Russia with force of 25 Hiroshima atomic bombs on 15 Feb, 2013
at 9.20am, moving at 60,000kph; 72,000 houses damaged, 1500
people hurt, widely filmed.

Chernobyl – one of the most serious nuclear reactor meltdown
disasters so far, along with Sendai in Japan, with large releases of
fissile material dangerous to health and the ecosystem; claimed no
deaths resulted but this is not true, since cancer-causing effects are
complex, so precise links are difficult to assess, but must definitely
exist.

Chert or Flint – silex: nodules often occur in chalk, formed from silica
that hardens.

Chicxulub Crater – 195km wide sub-sea crater in Gulf of Mexico
from strike by 12km wide asteroid from space, said to have ended
the dinosaur era 65 million yrs ago; Fig 11.

Circular thinking – Using an idea to justify itself; often used in science
when no clear evidence exists; equal to 'invented reason', accepted
as valueless [eg Zonal fossils].

Clastic – sediment derived from pre-existing fragments of rock, eg
sand, gravel.

Coal – compressed and heated plant matter that becomes carbonised;
often confused with diamond since both contain carbon, but they
form wholly separately: coal forms between layers of sediment,
as when a forest is rapidly buried below sand or mud, whereas
diamond forms kilometres below the earth's crust to erupt in
igneous rock. It is certain, though controversial, that coal can only
form in such rapid geological events before the plants and wood
rot away, since coal shows plant cells clearly.

Constant – a value used in maths, created as an invariable; can be
incorrect.

Continental Drift – movement of continental plates;(once thought to
be slow process as at present, but can have moved very rapidly due
to axial shift, requiring plates to move at once to new positions on
the earth's surface [Caution: do not use this answer in colleges].)

Continental Shelf – ocean area from shoreline to continental rise, up to 200m deep.

Cooper Pair – pair of electrons seen to act in harmony as one unit, where each particle of the pair copies the motions of the other instantly; where the spin change of one electron is instantly repeated by the remaining half of the pair at low temperature; suggested here to be evidence of a quantum flux of particles that can instantly alter as one unit, i.e. faster than light. Thought impossible by Einstein, such speed is so far un-measurable in science; ref. Gran Sasso experiment. See **Bose-Einstein Condensate** and **BCS Theory**.

Cosmology – literally the study of the cosmos using theory inventively.

CMB or 'Cosmic Microwave Background' – very weak background 'heat' radiation in space claimed to come from the Big Bang; fits cyclic time version of reality since it shows enough uniformity to have always existed, yet with some anomalies.

Crustacean – species with an exoskeleton eg shrimp. Has no clear fossil ancestor, as with countless species, suggesting short period Flash Time.

Cyclic Time – explained here as part of Flash Time, in which events happen in short and identical periods that continue to repeat in infinity; solves many problems of Big Bang theory such as explaining where the Matter came from to create the cosmos (it always existed).

Cyclothem – cyclic deposition sequence of sediments [e.g. 123–321], separate from rhythmic sequences which repeat again [i.e. 123–123].

Data – information points, plural of 'datum'. Can falsely support assumptions.

Déjà vu – common experience of seeing a scene that had happened before. French for 'already seen'. Evidence of precisely cyclic time in which all events repeat again.

Deuterium – a form or isotope of hydrogen.

Dinosaur – creatures in two groups with separate bone structure: 'bird type' etc. Claimed to have lived for 110 million years/Ma yet only 1450 found; should be trillions if true.

Flash Time

Discontinuity – or unconformity, when a time gap occurs in sediment deposition; Index.

DNA – short for Deoxyribonucleic Acid, which contains our chromosomes etc.

Drake Equation – theory using equation to estimate chances of life in cosmos, assuming linear time allows time for Evolution; invalid if time is cyclic as here; see text.

Ediacaran – Pre-Cambrian rocks with jellyfish, eg in Australia. No clear ancestors.

Entanglement of electrons – where two widely separated Cooper Pair particles can act as one. This crucial finding shows how all matter can be connected at sub-atomic level, and thus may explain how events can be deeply connected via a Grid.

Entropy – principle of thermodynamics where lost energy tends towards chaos.

Epistemology – Study of knowledge; from Greek *episteme*, knowledge + -ology, study.

ESP – extra sensory perception; common daily experience of many, eg telepathy.

Evaporite – sediment formed by evaporation, eg salt, gypsum etc.

Evolution – 1859 theory that life evolved over millions of years from simple forms to more complex types as conceived by Charles Darwin and Alfred Wallace; failed to consider time as cyclic or foresee the problems of radiogenic dating as seen here.

Ex nihil – Latin for 'out of nothing', eg Matter cannot arise from nowhere, *see* Big Bang.

Extrapolation – the artificial extension of a graph line either forwards or back in time.

Flash Time – concept that time moves in repeating cycles of events, so the universe always exists and was never formed in a Big Bang as claimed. Flash Time Zero moment or 'effect' occurs in a cyclical 'instant' in which events begin to happen again as they did before. In that 'zero moment' time begins again. This Flash Time model suggests the universe can 'update itself' faster than light via a Grid, when rotational energy imbalances trigger the 'switch' in Order outlined here, causing the Cycle to continue, as implied by Gödel (c1931) and Bell in 1964. This causal circle of events requires a faster-than-light cosmos thus removing the need for a slower-than-light cosmos using a 'no communication theorem'. These issues appear resolved finally with a triple cycle entangled spacetime state where past, present and future act in unison during any one cycle, in which outcomes must conform to that pattern. Freewill is then maintained, yet depends on what was chosen in the last cycle, while usually being unknown, though not always (déjà vu applies here). Bell realised later a conflict with freewill, yet without the 'non-linear triple cycle' effect of entangled 'triple time' as above, and so decided against a perfectly repeating event sequence, even though one was implied. This Grid enables this to be so, since it appears to allow superluminal update speeds from local realism, and suggests a reform of the Dirac equation's reliance on linear time. See **Relativity** below.

Flatness & Horizon Problems – The cosmic horizons should not be similar if Big Bang theory is correct, since light moves too slowly for them to be linked. Yet they are nearly identical. It means that the universe is oddly 'flat', in the sense of being similar in all directions: unexplained as 'by chance', since Big Bang suggests those horizons are not connected to each other. WMAP 2001 satellite/craft finding that the CMB microwaves appear anisotropic, suggesting an anomaly. Craft ceased working in 2010.

Flint – alternate name for silex; also see **Chert** above; & in text Ch.7 & photos.

Flocculation – particle accretion; as in river delta formation caused by salt water.

Fujita Tornado Intensity Scale – from F-0 for mild damage to F-5 for 'Incredible Damage', with wind speeds classed from 261–318mph; though quite how the term 'incredible' could ever be measured remains unclear.

Ga – Short for a billion or 1000 million; also see Gy.

Geomorphology – the study or nature of surface land-forms or topography.

GISP 2 – short for American-led *Greenland Ice Sheet Project 2*; drilling 3kms ice sheet.

Global Mega-event table – shows how geological timescale is not sequential over long linear time, but one short phase of cyclic time; see Fig 16 for list and explanation.

Globigerina ooze – deep-sea or 'pelagic' fine sediment formed from tiny plankton shells, covers 50% of ocean floor in west Indian, mid-Atlantic and S. Pacific oceans.

Goldilocks zone – Distance of earth from our sun allowing life; any closer and the oceans would boil, while floating further away would freeze the planet.

Gondwana – former supercontinent, containing all land in southern hemisphere.

Gran Sasso experiment – Italian physics laboratory test which appeared to show distant effects transmitted at near light speed; as yet not verifiable either way. See **Flash Time**.

Great Oxidation Event – Theory that oxygen increased on earth c3Billion years ago. In cyclic time thinking, this event has been invented to support evolution.

Grid or Super Grid – idea proposed here for a cosmos-wide 5Dimensional fabric of spacetime which transmits all energy/ gravity between matter and people; it stores actions/ events in one cycle of spacetime, which then repeat precisely. Thoughts affect matter and can also be stored or transmitted. See déjà vu in text, and **Flash Time** above.

GRIP – short for the European-led *Greenland Ice-core Project*, reached bedrock in 2003 at 3084.99m about 30kms from GISP2.

Gy – Gy is short for Giga years, i.e. one billion years or 109 [i.e. 1 with 9 zeroes].

Half-life – time taken for half the quantity of a radioactive material to reach zero activity, carbon 14 being 5730 years ± 30yrs; see text to explain errors.

Haumea – large dwarf planet or TNO located at 45AU with signs of young age.

Helix – spiral in 3D, e.g. in double-helix of DNA as claimed by Watson & Crick.

Horizon Problem – see 'Flatness &' above

Ibid. – same reference source as before, from Latin 'in the same place'.

ICS – *International Commission on Stratigraphy* which last published reports called GTS 2004 and GTS 2012 on the global succession of strata, trying to resolve the many anomalies and misfits that still exist, yet often cannot. Notes 'circular thinking' is an issue. [Began Paris, 1878].

Igneous rocks – red hot volcanic rocks erupted from below earth's crust.

Isotope – various forms of radioactive elements, with different neutron numbers, with 300 natural examples, eg Argon 40 etc.

Isotropic – singly refractive items, ie have the same properties in all directions.

Josephson Effects – Ultra low temperature *Superconduction* used in high-speed circuits or toroidal geometry; by Brian Josephson, Nobel Prize winner.

KT boundary – layer of clay containing iridium derived from meteorite that is said to have struck earth in Gulf of Mexico to end dinosaur era; from German word for Cretaceous Tertiary boundary, hence KT; claimed to be 65mya.

Kuhn, Thomas – author of *The Structure of Scientific Revolutions*, 1962; superbly accurate.

La Brea Tar Pits – famous museum in Los Angeles on Wilshire Blvd; 1000's of preserved bones e.g. from wolves and sabre-toothed tigers in Ice Age era. See Index.

Lake Missoula – famously large ice age era lake said to have formed behind an ice wall near Canada-USA border; on breaking through it caused huge ripple beds and cut cubic miles of rock from 60,000 sq.kms of that area, dumping much of it out at sea. Water released said to have raised global sea level; one of earth history's greatest events.

Late Heavy Bombardment – a mainly theoretical period which appears to have been incorrectly dated by linear inferences, and this 'LHB' refers to the formation of some impressive craters & Earth's oceans, claimed to occur long after its 'formation'.

Laurasia – northern supercontinent with north hemisphere landmasses; see Gondwana.

Lava – mobile form of igneous/ volcanic rock erupting from below crustal layer.

Lenses – different sediment areas within a sequence, due to episodic higher flow rates of water, eg mud within sand; proof of rapid local changes; often eye or lense-shaped.

LHB – see Late Heavy Bombardment above.

Lyell, Charles – Author of *Principles of Geology*, printed from 1830–1875, claiming long age for earth processes in linear time which influenced C. Darwin.

Ma – abbreviation for millions of years, so 12Ma = 12 million years.

Magneto Stratigraphy – dating old igneous rocks by magnetic alignment.

Magma – Liquid rock that erupts from volcanoes.

Mantle – hot molten layer of Earth's sub-surface between crust and core; 2300 kms deep and forming 84% of Earth's volume, 68% of mass.

MAR – short for Mid Atlantic Ridge, a high mountainous region in this area formed from volcanic peaks at the mid-plate zone where the continents split apart; said here to have occurred rapidly hence the lack of sediments in many areas, and the Blake Outer Ridge off the US eastern seaboard, which is also an unsorted rapid-type deposit.

Marl – Fine pelagic open water sediment of mud/silt with up to 70% microfossils, often interbedded with 1.5m calcium or silica oozes (ultra fine particles).

Mass Extinctions – thought to be six 'mega events'* in which over 90% of earlier species on land and in seas died out due to extremes; thought to be spaced out across 500 million years yet which can be explained in millennia; in fact they occur in each 'age'. 'Big 5' are Ordovician, Devonian, Permian, Triassic, Cretaceous; *see diagram.

Megaregolith – lunar highland surface zone where a deep layer of large [i.e. mega] fractured rocks is suggested to be 1–25kms deep, caused by intense early bombardment of moon estimated at 4.44Gy ago; dating errors suggest this age is incorrect.

Mega Cyclic Time – Flash Time concept of a cyclic time process that repeats all events as a Continuum, incorporating all of spacetime in one linked system. qv Flash Time.

Mega-tsunami – giant wave from huge event, eg landslide (Lituya Bay 1958, Alaska: 520m high) or asteroid; qv **Tsunami**.

Metamorphic rock – altered rock, i.e. pre-existing rock from an earlier event changed by recrystallization often due to extreme pressure or temperature changes, such as mudstone changed into slate, sandstone into quartzite; pelite, schist etc.

Meteorite – smaller rock /object perhaps from asteroid belt [zone of debris between Mars and Jupiter, from -1cm to objects 10x30 kms or so] that *lands on earth*; a meteor is the term for the same item while still in space.

Möbius strip – figure of 8 shape used on its 'side' to represent eternity/ infinity: ∞.

Mt – short for 'million tons', thus 65Mt = 65 million tons.

Munchausen Trilemma – 3 problems in study of knowledge showing *proof* is difficult or impossible: i. any proof needs proof of its claims, ad infinitum; ii. circularity, where the proof and the theory rely on each other; iii. a situation requiring acceptance as true for belief (dogmatism). Nearly every theory fails this test, eg Big Bang, Evolution etc. Also called Fries trilemma where infinite regress of proof is needed, dogmatism is invalid on principle, as is subjective perception of 'truth'. Also the 5 tropes or modes of Agrippa in 1st cent. AD and Greek Skeptics: adding Dissent & Progress to above three.

NDE – Near Death Experience, where people report conscious thoughts when the body is reported lifeless at the time, such as in hospital during a general anaesthetic.

Neanderthals – prehistorical 'human' culture first found in Germany, see Index. Many Europeans have 2–4% of their DNA; *only 137 found*, hence solid evidence of short cyclic time, since over the claimed 750k years of their span, *600 billion should exist*.

Nihilist – person who rejects moral or religious principles, or any authority; a person who thinks the meaning of existence is 'nothingness'; from Latin *nihil*. Once a fashionable 'answer', now thought to be impossible since even space contains 'something'.

Occam's razor – 700 year old concept that nature tends to use the simplest systems.

Oort Cloud – theoretical region & source of icy bodies, thought to exist 1 light year from the sun, on the edge of our solar system, from where comets might originate.

Order of magnitude – one Order equals ten times an amount; thus 5 orders would be a 5 with one added zero, ie 50 times or 5000% greater.

Oscillating axial tilt of earth – rapid 'wobbles' in earth's axis that can form 'apparent years' in only weeks; gives the appearance of long linear timespan which has not happened in reality. It can also have produced 21 hour day signs in coral growth from Bermuda and highly significant rapid glacial melt deposits (varves) in Japanese sediments; the ICS has never considered this possibility of such anomalous short cycles.

Ostracoderms – ancient, jawless fish thought of be Ordovician in age, yet have similar modern forms eg lamprey and hagfish.

Outcrop – literally a place where sub-surface rock can be seen above ground.

Paleo- or **palaeo** – prefix for ancient, from Greek *Palaios* meaning 'old'; see Palaeolithic.

Palaeontology – the study of ancient creatures; the fossil division of geology.

Paleoclimatology – study of ancient climates from signs in sedimentary rocks.

Palaeolithic – ancient era, also known as Prehistory, meaning the era before records were kept about which little is known; much has therefore been invented, only to need revising as new finds emerged to show the reality. For example Neanderthals were once thought cultureless primitives, but in fact performed brain surgery and buried their dead with medicinal plants and religious symbols; see Index for details.

Paleometeoric water – ancient water reaching earth from atmosphere; ie above crust.

Pangea – Old supercontinent when all major land areas were one; see map. Split in Triassic into Gondwana + Laurasia.

Pelagic – ocean sediment type, usually, meaning laid down with fine grain size; see Marl.

Piltdown Man – Infamous 1912 trick by serial hoaxer Charles Dawson; see text.

Plate tectonics – where continents behave as rigid 'plates' of stable land, allowing greater volcanic/ quake activity at plate margins, as in Pacific 'Ring of Fire'.

Positive time – a new term to describe how each cycle always returns to order and calm.

Problematica – group of fossils of unknown origin yet considered organic, but which simply do not fit into any known class via taxonomy (the study of such links).

Pyroclastic flow – or ash flow/ nuée ardente: burning cloud of volcanic ash fluidised by gas released as compressed hot material explodes from vent; moves at 100–450kph, eg in Japan, & Vesuvius, Mt Pelée.

Quantum entanglement – particles that have ever interacted at one time will always remain connected in the future as well; appears explainable with the Grid.

Quaternion – a device in maths by which a quantity in real numbers relates to vectors; used to define rotation in the classic x, y and z or 3D dimensions.

qv – 'which may be seen', abbreviation from Latin *quid videt*.

Radioactive rock – with unstable elements that emit particles to become more stable forms or 'isotopes'; some may be created in nuclear reactors, e.g. plutonium etc.

Radiogenic isotope dating method – relies on assumption that decay products of radioactive processes can be used to calculate age of rocks; can fail due to same decay 'daughters' being present at time of original rock formation.

Redshift – shift of the light spectrum to the red end, caused by Doppler Effect of receding light eg from a galaxy or star; used to calculate distance *by assuming time is linear*.

Refractive Index – Measurement of amount light bends entering a denser medium.

Reincarnation – where a human mind or 'self' is said to arrive in a foetus at about 4–5 months of pregnancy; thought to be untrue by some, yet common understanding in many cultures. See *Twenty Cases Suggestive of Reincarnation*, Ian Stevenson, 1980.

Relativity – two theories of relative motion by Einstein: Special Theory in 1905, referred to motion without acceleration, and General Theory in 1915 for accelerated systems. They rely on linear time and appear to be unsupported in various ways by this assumption, by presuming the universe cannot 'update itself' faster than light. Flash Time theory suggests it can.

Ring of Fire – coastal area around Pacific Ocean where plate margins offer weaker tectonic zones for more extreme land movements, as in Japan and western USA; Pacific Ocean floor is sliding under (subducting) the Asian plate off eastern seaboard of Jana islands, causing huge quakes and consequent tsunamis.

Sapropelic coal – with fine plant material or pollen; less coarse than woody or humic.

Sedimentary rock – rock derived from sediments laid down by water or air /Aeolian.

Scotoma – condition in psychology where a person literally *cannot understand* a concept, perhaps being too far beyond their own experience or capacities.

Shock quartz – crystals of shocked quartz deformed by shock waves [speed 10–13km/s] from meteoritic, cometary or asteroidal impacts with earth; see Chicxulub.

Solipsism – theory only 'self' can be shown to exist, via personal experience.

Spacetime – normal 3D space, plus time; modified by gravity and Flash Time effect.

Strata – layers of rock deposits forming a sequence, often horizontally; formed by either water-born or Aeolian [wind-born] sediments.

Stratigraphy – study of strata, esp. used to 'date' fossils by relationship, assuming that strata containing same fossils are the same age.

String Theory – artificial idea about lines in space that is unsupported by evidence; popular currently but relies on linear time, and regarded by many experts as invalid through being pure invention. Relies on 11 dimensional spacetime and forced maths.

Stromatolite – mat of cyanobacteria and said to be pre-Cambrian, yet still growing in Shark Bay, W.Australia, contradicting Darwin's claim no species could remain unchanged over long periods; said to be 3 billion years old; oxygen-producing.

Suess wriggles – changes in $C14$ production [altering accuracy of carbon dating] once thought due to instrument variation but now thought to be 'of uncertain cause'.

Superconduction – supercooled materials where DC current has no resistance.

Super Grid – see Grid above.

Supersymmetry – incomplete theory attempting to link four fundamental forces.

Syncytium – supercooled particles that can act as one 'super-atom'; *see* Grid.

Telepathy – common experience eg knowing the caller before a phone call; defined in tests by Dr Rupert Sheldrake; see text.

Tethys – or Tethyan seaway, is the sea separating Laurasia and Gondwana.

TNO – Trans Neptunian Object, ie one that orbits our sun near Neptune at 45AU.

Toroidal – naming doughnut or disc shape with hole, from torus; used in some nuclear fusion reactors eg JET in UK (*Joint European Torus*); allows fusion reaction in a circle.

Transform Faults – occur at mid-ocean ridges, eg MAR, where rocks split or transform motion laterally after magma erupts at continental margins. See world map.

Trillion – 1000 billion or one with 12 zeroes

Triple Time – evidence shows 3 cycles of Past, Present and Future are always connected at any one moment, allowing only specific outcomes to occur [see Fig 24 & text]; no matter how negative an event, it will always lead to a beneficial final spacetime result.

Tsunami – huge ocean wave from 1–1500metres high, usually 5–15m, caused by various energy shifts near or under water, or asteroid impacts from space (eg **mega-tsunami**).

Unconformity – see Discontinuity: where strata rest 'unconformably' on lower layers.

Uniformitarianism – outdated idea that the present explains processes in the past; set out by Hutton in 1795, assuming today's gradual events were always the case; now realised that events of the past no longer occur today, and thus an oversimplification.

Uranium-Lead decay process – uranium decays into different isotope of lead, theory then suggests quantity of lead can be calculated from their half-lives.

Valley of the Kings – Famous Royal burial area in Ancient Egypt, near Luxor.

Varve – light and dark band layers formed in lakes near ice sheets, the light being coarse and linked to summer, the darker being fine winter silts, it is said; assumed to be seasonal, but 800+ a year is possible due to rapid axial shifts: see Index.

Velikovsky, I. – writer of 20th century books on catastrophism and history, who showed sediments that had been wrongly dated as old when actually young. He also wrote that Egyptian pharaoh Ramasses' time had been incorrectly dated by 600 years; see Index.

Viscosity of lava – degree to which the liquid red hot rock flows easily, or is sticky.

Volatiles – substances that readily become gaseous, eg water, CO_2, SO_2, hydrogen, methane; eg when lava erupts and pressure is reduced.

Widmanstätten lines – structure inside polished and etched iron meteorites discovered by Count Alois von Beckh Widmanstätten of Vienna in 1804, the shape of which describe features that can only form in a space vacuum. These lines thus prove the space origin of meteorites, since they only form beyond gravity.

Xenoglossy – the untrained speaking of a foreign language; many cases are noted globally, often in young people, some suggest where another 'soul' is the speaker.

Zanclean [or Zanclian] – European phase in geology related to the formation of the Mediterranean Sea when land between Gibraltar & Africa was rapidly flooded by Atlantic at rate of several cubic kilometres per day; claimed to be 5.3 million years ago, but likely very recent in terms of cyclic time, eg 3200yrs ago; this old style date has been estimated, and cannot be measured.

Zonal fossils – or Index fossil, whose narrow vertical time range defines that era/rock, ideally nearly global in extent; assumed to have rapidly evolved if narrow range, is an example of circular thinking, where A 'proves' B and vice versa. (See also **Biozone**.)

Useful information and some museums:

– Vitamin C 'flu and cold cure: 1000mg every 40mins with lots of water, derived from work by Dr Linus Pauling in 1954; lower ph increases oxygen in blood.

– Free meditation classes globally given at: www.brahmakumaris.org

– Famously skilled Registered Osteopath & author: Barrie Savory, DO, London.

– Natural History Museum, London: nhm.com and Geological Museum

– National Museums of Scotland

– British Museum, London, Science Museum, London

– Museum of London, City of London

– Ashmolean Museum, Oxford, Fitzwilliam Museum, Oxford

– La Brea Tar Pits Museum, Los Angeles

– Natural History Museum, New York

Bibliography

A History of the Crusades, Steven Runciman, 3 vols, Penguin 1991

A Short History of Nearly Everything, Bill Bryson, Doubleday 2003

A Slice Through Time –Dendrochronology, MGL Baillie, Routledge 2005

Ages In Chaos, I.Velikovsky, 1952

Aladdin's Lamp, J.Freely, Knopf 2009

Amerigo, F.Fernadez-Armesto, W&N 2006

An Analysis of the Egyptian Mythology, JC Prichard, 1819, Forgotten Books 2012

Ancient Philosophy, Sir A Kenny, OUP 2006

Archaeology & Language, Colin Renfrew, Pimlico 1998

Archaeology from the Earth, Sir Mortimer Wheeler, Pelican 1961

Astrophysics is Easy, Mike Inglis, Springer 2007

Atlas of the Universe, Patrick Moore, Chancellor 2001

Bogus Science, J Grant, FF&F 2009

Britain BC, Francis Pryor, Harper 2004

Cambridge Handbook of Earth Science Data, P&G Henderson CUP2009

Carl Sagan & Immanuel Velikovsky, C.Ginenthal, New Falcon 1995

Catastrophes and Lesser Calamities, Tony Hallam, OUP 2005

Celts and Aryans, Myles Dillon, Indian Institute of Advanced Study 1975

Chambers Dictionary of Science & Technology, Chambers 1999

Climate Change in Prehistory, W.Burroughs, CUP 2005

Cycles of Time, R.Penrose, Bodley Head 2010

Daily Life in Ancient India 200BC–700AD, J Auboyer, Phoenix 1965

Discarded Science, J Grant, FF&F 2006

Discontinuity in Greek Civilization, R.Carpenter, CUP 1966

Dorset Coast, GM Davies, 1936, A&C Black 1970 ed.

Early Earth Systems, Hugh Rollinson, Blackwell 2007

Earth In Upheaval, I.Velikovsky, 1955, Abacus 1981

Egypt, K Lange, M Hirmer, Phaidon 1961

Egyptian Book of the Dead, EA Wallis Budge [1895], Dover 1967

Egyptian Gods, A Shorter, 1937, RKP 1979 ed

Einstein, W Isaacson, A Deutsch 2009

Enchiridion Symbolorum, H Denzinger, Ignatius 2012

Entropy – A New World View, J Rifkin, Bantam 1981

Essentials of Oceanography, 8th ed, A Trujillo, H Thurman, Pearson 2005

Europe's Lost World, V Gaffney et al, CBA 2009

Extinction, D.H.Erwin, Princeton Univ. Press 2006

Fabulous Science, J Waller OUP2002

Fashion Faith & Fantasy, R.Penrose, Princeton Univ. Press 2016

Fossils, C.Walker, D.Ward, DK 2000

Geostatistics Explained, S.McKillup, M.Dyar, CUP 2010

Herodotus–The Histories, T.Holland, Penguin 2013

Hesiod (Theogony, Works and Days, Testimonia) G.Most, HUP 2010 Loeb

How the End Begins, R Rosenbaum, Simon & Schuster 2011

How to Read Egyptian Hieroglyphs, M.Collier et al, British Museum 2012

Introducing Greek Philosophy, MR Wright, UCP 2010

Isotope Geology, C Allègre, CUP 2008

Life After Life, RA Moody MD, Bantam 1981 [Reincarnation cases]

Lost Civilisations of the Stone Age, R Rudgley, Arrow 1999

Mankind In Amnesia, I.Velikovsky, 1982

Medieval Philosophy, Sir A Kenny, OUP 2005

Memories, Dreams, Reflections, CG Jung, Fontana 1995

Not Even Wrong, Peter Woit, Vintage 2006

Not From The Apes, B Kurten, Readers Union 1973

Plato & the Upanishads, V Vitsaxis, Arnold Heinemann 1977

Powers and Prospects, Noam Chomsky, Pluto 1996

Prehistory & Earth Models, MA Cook, Parrish 1966

Prehistory, Colin Renfrew, Phoenix 2007

Principles of Geology, Charles Lyell, 1833, J.Secord, Penguin 1997

Principles of Physical Geology, Arthur Holmes, Nelson 1944

Principles of Stable Isotope Geochemistry, Z.Sharp, Pearson 2007

Radiogenic Isotope Geology, AP Dickin, CUP 2005

Ramsses II & His Time, I.Velikovsky, 1978

Roget's Thesaurus (words and phrases), B Kirkpatrick ed, Penguin 1998

Science & Religion 400BC–1550AD, E Grant, Johns Hopkins 2004

Scientists Confront Velikovsky, D Goldsmith et al, Norton 1977

Secrets of the Stone Age, R Rudgley, Century 2000

Seneca, Quaestiones Naturales 4–7, c54BC, T.Corcoran, HUP 2004 Loeb

Some Variations on a Fabulous Florentine, Angus James, Compendium 2006

Submerged Forests, Clement Reid, CUP 1913, Forgotten Books 2012

The Book of Symbols, Taschen 2010

The Collapse of Mechanism and the Rise of Sensibility, S Gaukroger, OUP 2010

The Complete Royal Families of Ancient Egypt, A Dodson, D Hilton, T&H 2004

The Emperor's New Mind: Concerning Computers, Minds, Laws of Physics, OUP 1989

The Essential Chomsky, Noam Chomsky, Bodley Head 2008

The Facts of Life, R Milton, Corgi 1994

The Geological Time Scale, Gradstein et al,2 vols, Elsevier 2004, 2012

The Grand Design, S Hawking et al, Bantam 2010

The Maya, M Coe, S Houston, 9th ed, T&H 2015

The Mind in the Cave, D Lewis-Williams, Thames & Hudson 2008
The Origin of Species, Charles Darwin, Penguin 1985
The Oxford Companion to the Earth, Hancock, Skinner, Dineley, OUP 2000
The Oxford Companion to Cosmology, A Liddle, J Loveday, OUP 2009
The Oxford Concise Dictionary of Archaeology, T Darvill OUP 2008
The Oxford Dictionary of Physics, J Daintinth ed, OUP 2009
The Oxford Dictionary of Geology & Earth Sciences, M Allaby ed, OUP 2013
The Oxford Dictionary of Astronomy, I Ridpath ed, OUP 2012
The Road to Reality, R.Penrose, Vintage 2005
The Routledge Companion to the New Cosmology, P Coles, Routledge 2008
The Sedimentary Record of Sea-Level Change, AL Coe et al, CUP2005
The Structure of Scientific Revolutions, T.S.Kuhn,4thed, Univ. of Chicago 2012
The Trouble with Physics, Lee Smolin, Houghton Mifflin 2006
The Two-Mile Time Machine, R Alley, Princeton 2000
Timaeus, Plato, D.Zeyl, Hackett 2000
Timescales of Magmatic Processes, Dosseto et al, Wiley-Blackwell 2011
Twenty Cases Suggestive of Reincarnation, I Stevenson, Univ. of Virginia 1980
Volcanoes, P Francis, C Oppenheimer, 2nd ed, CUP 2004
Worlds In Collision, I.Velikovsky, Abacus 1980
World's Religions, Lion 1982

Prize

A prize of US$9,000 is offered for an accepted proof that shows time cannot be cyclic as explained here, and that passes the three key tests of the Munchausen trilemma. There appears to be no such evidence-based proof that unequivocally disproves this central proposal of time being cyclic, but if the above level of proof can be shown, the prize will be paid. [The evidence currently shows that no such counter can pass these tests without using presumption or belief, nor may logically be able to do so.]

[Terms: any response to be public & openly published in an academic or book format. The author cannot commit to read any texts nor reply in any format, but any offering must be sure the above criteria are strictly met. No exchange of letters or messages will be entered into and the author's judgement will be reasonable and deemed final in any event.]